W9-ALU-745

HARPER TORCHBOOKS / The Cloister Library

(Continued on next page)

HARPER TORCHBOOKS / The Academy Library

HARPER TORCHBOOKS / The Science Library

ARISTOCRACY IN AMERICA

From the Sketch-Book of a German Nobleman

BY

FRANCIS J. GRUND

with an Introduction by George E. Probst

Why should the poor be flatter'd?
No: let the candied tongue lick absurd pomp,
And crook the pregnant hinges of the knee,
Where thrift may follow fawning.

—*Hamlet,* iii, 2

HARPER TORCHBOOKS / *The Academy Library*

HARPER & BROTHERS · PUBLISHERS
NEW YORK

ARISTOCRACY IN AMERICA
Introduction Copyright © 1959 by Harper & Brothers
Printed in the United States of America

ARISTOCRACY IN AMERICA was first published
in 1839 by Richard Bentley, London.
This is the first American edition.

First HARPER TORCHBOOK edition published 1959

Library of Congress catalog card number: 59–13839

CONTENTS

Part I

CONTAINING THE ADVENTURES OF A DAY SPENT
AMONG THE BLOODS OF NEW YORK

Part II

CONTAINING A SHORT STAY IN BOSTON AND PHILADELPHIA

Part III

CONTAINING A TRIP TO WASHINGTON AND A SHORT STAY
IN THE METROPOLIS

INTRODUCTION

TO THE TORCHBOOK EDITION

AN IMPORTANT part of the foundations of the American commonwealth was established in the Age of Jackson. Unfortunately, this period of American history—1828 to 1840—has been comparatively neglected by historians or recounted by historians with an anti-Jackson bias. Yet it was in the Age of Jackson that the equalitarian character of American democracy received its fullest expression. There was probably never a time in American history when the conditions of life came closer to equality or when the average American felt so confident in his capacity to deal with any problem under the sun.

It was the general condition of equality in America that impressed Alexis de Tocqueville during his visit to the United States in 1831–32, and this formed the theme of his famous two volumes on *Democracy in America.*

Francis Joseph Grund was born near Vienna in 1798. He studied mathematics and philosophy at the University of Vienna before emigrating to the United States about 1827. Grund and Tocqueville shared a deep interest in America. While Tocqueville's famous work was written after a ten-month visit to the United States, Grund lived for more than ten years in the United States before he wrote two treatises about America. Grund in 1837 published *The Americans in Their Moral, Social and Political Relations.* This appeared two years after Tocqueville's first volume on *Democracy in America.*

Aristocracy in America was originally printed in London in 1839. It is now made available for the first time in the United States. The title was undoubtedly selected by Grund with Tocqueville in mind and in it Grund refers to Tocqueville's writings.

Tocqueville thought of American democracy as a portent of the fate which lay ahead for Europe. Grund likes American democracy for its power to destroy self-selected aristocrats and sees it expanding through all of North and South America. Tocqueville admired much in what he saw in America (he even invested money in Western railroad bonds); but he was greatly concerned about the dangers to liberty which seemed to him to lurk behind the drift toward equality. Grund reports the kind of conversations with Americans that Tocqueville must have heard in which they expressed fears of the rabble; but Grund comes to the final view that: "I trust that the good sense of the people, the intelligence pervading the masses, and, above all, the high degree of morality and virtue which distinguishes the American above all other nations in the world, will be proof against the temptations of a handful of political sceptics; and that the country, blessed with Nature's richest gifts, and selected by Providence for the noblest experiment tried by man, will fulfil its mission,—which is not only the civilization of a new world, but the practical establishment of principles which heretofore have only had an ideal existence."

Grund first settled in Boston and taught at Chauncy Hall School. Later he lived in Philadelphia and Washington, mingling in the best society.

Charles Summer mentions him in a letter of July 1837 saying: "Grund is in Boston, fresh from England. I see him every day at Tremont House. He is very able and bold. I am quite struck with his conversation. He talks sledge-hammers." Charles Summer favorably reviewed Grund's *The Americans* in the *North American Review* of January, 1838.

Grund became an American citizen and spent the rest of his life engrossed in American journalism and political activity. He stumped and wrote in support of the Democratic party as a staunch Jacksonian. He took up residence in Philadelphia as a newspaper editor. As the political correspondent of the Philadelphia *Public Ledger,* he spent winters in Washington and was among the first to create the now familiar journalistic style that is full of inside tips and information from behind the scenes. He was a political leader of the German-Americans in Pennsylvania and as a reward for his political efforts at various times was appointed American consul at Antwerp, Bremen, and Le Havre. He died in Philadelphia in September 29, 1863.

Always interested in education, Grund presided in 1837 over the Pittsburgh Convention to establish better schools. He wrote a half-dozen elementary textbooks on mathematics and science. In a notable passage, Grund remarks about what can be learned about a nation by looking at its education:

"There is probably no better place than a schoolroom to judge of the character of a people, or to find an explanation of their national peculiarities. Whatever faults or weaknesses may be entailed upon them, will show themselves there without the hypocrisy of advanced age and whatever virtue they may possess is reflected without admixture of vice and corruption. In so humble a place as a schoolroom may be read the commentaries on the past, and the history of the future development of a nation.

"Who, upon entering an American schoolroom, and witnessing the continual exercises in reading and speaking, or listening to the subject of their discourses, and watching the behaviour of the pupils towards each other and their teacher, could, for a moment, doubt his being amongst a congregation of young republicans? And who, on entering a German academy, would not be struck with the principle of authority and silence, which reflects the history of Germany for the last half dozen centuries? What difficulty has not an American teacher to maintain order amongst a dozen unruly little urchins; while a German rules over two hundred pupils in a class with all the ease and tranquility of an Eastern monarch?"[1]

Like Tocqueville, Grund was very much impressed by the phenomenon that in America the aristocrats cannot escape from the equalitarian nature of American society. Tocqueville had written, ". . . I do not assert that the ostensible purpose or even that the secret aim of American parties is to promote the rule of aristocracy or democracy in the country; but I affirm that aristocratic or democratic passions may easily be detected at the bottom of all parties, and that, although they escape a superficial observation, they are the main point and soul of every faction in the United States."[2]

In the Age of Jackson, nothing is more conspicuous than the resistance to anything which savored of "aristocracy." This took many forms: disapproval of monopolies in every shape and form; the rejection of property qualifications for office; the beginning of the practice of electing judges; giving the vote to propertyless laborers through general adoption of manhood suffrage; the denial that democratic administration needs the services of experts; the growth of political parties and national political conventions; and the exaltation of the Presidential office as the embodiment of the popular will.

Yet Grund finds that nothing indeed is more common than to hear Americans themselves claim that "there is a great deal of aristocracy

[1] F. J. Grund, *The Americans in Their Moral, Social and Political Relations* (London: Longman, Reese, Orme, Brown, Green and Longman, 1837), Vol. 1, pp. 228–229.

[2] Alexis de Tocqueville, *Democracy in America* (New York: Alfred A. Knopf, 1945), Vol. 1, p. 178.

in their country, of which Europeans, generally, are entirely unaware."
He met a variety of fashionable coteries, composed of highly respectable
merchants, literary and professional men, politicians and others, who, it
was evident, considered themselves the nobility and gentry of the land.

This society in America he found characterized by a spirit of exclusiveness and persecution unknown in any other country. He noted, "its
gradations not being regulated according to rank and titles, selfishness
and conceit are its principal elements; and its arbitrary distinctions the
more offensive, as they principally refer to fortune. Our society takes it
upon itself to punish political, moral, and religious dissenters; but most
of its wrath is spent upon the champions of democracy."

Yet, Grund asked, why should the Americans recognize a superior
class of society if that class be neither acknowledged by law nor
possessed of power?

As Perry Miller, Professor of American Literature at Harvard University, has so well put it, "This is the issue which puzzled and disturbed Grund so greatly—the pretensions of a self-appointed upper
class, based only on wealth, trying to act like an old-world aristocracy."

Of course, this issue of aristocracy had been the subject of the great
exchange of letters between Thomas Jefferson and John Adams, who
agreed that it was one of the continuing issues confronting Americans.

But Grund came to America with an acquaintance with European
aristocracy, and he describes his own startled reaction in these words:
"What an extraordinary phenomenon this state of society must be to a
European! And is it a wonder, if under such circumstances the most
paltry scribbler thinks himself justified in caricaturing it? Here is a
free people, voluntarily reducing itself to a state of the most odious
social bondage, for no other object but to maintain an imaginary
superiority over those classes in whom, according to the Constitution
of their country, all real power is vested. And here are the laboring
classes, probably for the first time permitted to legislate for themselves,
worshipping wealth in its most hideous colors."

Like many Europeans, Grund had a contempt for an aristocracy of
money and ironically describes how "We have 'lots' of aristocracy in
our country, cheap, and plenty as bank-bills and credit, and equally
subject to fluctuation. Today it is worth so much,—tomorrow more or
less,—and, in a month, no one will take it on any terms. We have, in
fact, at all times, a *vast deal* of aristocracy; the only difficulty consists in
retaining it. Neither is the position of our aristocrats much to be envied.

Amidst the general happiness and prosperity of our people, their incessant cravings after artificial distinctions are never satisfied."

Grund felt that in order for any kind of aristocracy to be tolerable it should, in some shape or other, either protect the lower classes or never come in contact with them. The aristocracy of the Atlantic cities was unfortunately not a protector of the lower orders, with whom it was continually wrestling for power; nor was it, from its political position and mode of life, capable of avoiding incessant contact with them.

Grund became well acquainted with the general terms on which Americans associate with friends and with strangers. With the advantages of a first-class mind and an accurate ear for the conversations that he heard in the drawing rooms, the oyster bars, the boarding-houses, on the canal boats and the stagecoaches, he supplies in this book one of the most vigorous and refreshing accounts of Jacksonian America.

Tocqueville was careful to delete from his writing on *Democracy in America* almost all specific instances of his conversations with Americans. Grund, on the contrary, presents detailed reconstructions of conversations in Boston, New York, Washington and Baltimore that time after time can be seen as specific elaborations of many of Tocqueville's general propositions about America.

In reporting his many illuminating conversations, Grund carries the reader into the rough and tumble of Jacksonian times. Perceptive biographical sketches of Jackson, Webster, Calhoun and Van Buren offer proof of Grund's astuteness as an observer. Modern historical scholarship has little more to offer on the mysterious question of presidential leadership than does Grund's account of Andrew Jackson's popularity. The popularity of Andrew Jackson is the overwhelming political fact of the time; and Grund pointedly reveals that this popularity has no relationship to education, the power of abstract reasoning, or discussion and analysis of public issues by the President. "General Jackson is popular just because he is General Jackson."

Grund describes the America of the 1830's as a country in which preachers are better paid than actors or musicians. It is a country in which the businessmen have no time for "cooing"; their first object is trade, and the daily routine of a married man in Boston is all work and no leisure time. Grund is most critical of the overbusy way of life and writes:

"I have heard gentlemen in the Northern States boast of having worked sixteen hours a day in a manufactory, or in a store, as if they had actually benefited the world with their manual labour. The thought never struck them that they might have been more useful to society by employing poor men to do the same work for them, and reserving their faculties, if such they had, for some occupation that had some relish of intellect in it. As long as the rich men in America think it more creditable to themselves to compete with the wages of the poor by assuming a part of their labour, than by cultivating the higher branches of knowledge to increase the floating intellect, American society may abound in common sense, but it will prove the grave of talent and genius."

Grund presents a picture of the place women had in American society in the 1830's which emphasizes many of the same characteristics attributed at the present day as being the major defects of the relationship between the sexes. He observes "American ladies are worshipped; but the adoration consists in a species of polytheism, which no particular goddess has a temple or an altar dedicated to herself. Whenever an American gentleman meets a lady, he looks upon her as the representative of her sex; and it is to her sex, not to her peculiar amiable qualities, that she is indebted for his attention."

The social climbing and the instability of fashionable society are to be seen along with the well-known condition of American expatriates railing against American society. The superficiality of American education is entrancingly displayed in such charming vignettes as the fashionable young lady telling of her education and how "Greek and the higher branches of mathematics are only studied by the *tall* girls." Grund's powers as a social satirist are in full action in the account of the New York theater audience reacting to *Othello* as an economic problem and an abolition issue.

Perhaps one of the reasons for the undeserved neglect of Grund's *Aristocracy in America* is its title. Every good historian knows that Tocqueville has the better of the two titles. The movement of American history has been toward an ever-expanding democratic polity. But Grund intends through his work to reveal to the reader the truth that America is steadily becoming more and more democratic by showing that the aristocrats are having a harder and harder time.

A second reason for neglect by historians is the form of Grund's work. Grund has made his observations in entertaining and witty conversations. Much of the conversation is illuminating, sometimes in an exaggerated style—for example, representing regional feelings in the 1830's. The aroma of the Madeira, the rattle of the stagecoach, the apple toddy in the parlor, the calumny and eulogy as the dessert at the end of the public meal, are part of the color of this account of Jacksonian America.

In truth Grund deserves the title, "The Jacksonian Tocqueville." Certainly he is as useful and informative as those other noted travelers to America, Mrs. Trollope, Basil Hall, and Harriet Martineau. Yet Grund's writings have remained little known and are not even listed in the very full bibliography on the Jackson era in Arthur Schlesinger, Jr.'s *The Age of Jackson*. Regrettably, Grund's vivid and perceptive writings have been overlooked as valuable source material for understanding Jacksonian America.

Grund sees that an American does not love his country as a Frenchman loves France, or an Englishman England: "America is to him but the physical means of establishing a moral power the medium through which his mind operates—the local habitation of his political doctrines. His country is in his understanding; he carries it with him wherever he goes, whether he emigrates to the shores of the Pacific or the Gulf of Mexico; his home is wherever he finds minds congenial with his own."[3]

The principles which Americans cherish are those of liberty. Grund believes that Americans will establish a moral empire more durable than human feelings, and less susceptible to change, and says, "the Americans *love* their country, not, indeed, *as it is;* but *as it will be*. They do not love the land of their fathers; but they are sincerely attached to that which their children are destined to inherit. They live in the future, and *make* their country as they go on."[4]

New York University   GEORGE E. PROBST
June 1959

[3] *The Americans, op. cit.,* Vol. II, 263–264.
[4] *Ibid.,* Vol. I, pp. 267–268.

DEDICATION

TO THE AMERICAN PEOPLE

I DEDICATE to you the following pages, written by one of your fellow-citizens, who, though a European by birth, is firmly and devotedly attached to his adopted country.

If their contents should in any way offend you,—if the serious or ironical arguments contained in them should meet with your displeasure,—I entreat you to consider the purity of the Author's intention, who, even where he employs personal satire, wishes but to expose error for the purpose of reform, not of ridicule.

Neither must you look upon them as containing aught against the laws and institutions of your country. Not those glorious monuments of the virtue and wisdom of your fathers, but the men who would turn them to vicious and selfish purposes are justly upheld to derision.

A people like yourselves, great, powerful, and magnanimous, is as much beyond the reach of personal satire as it is proof against the weapons of its foes: not so the men who, claiming for themselves a specific distinction, cannot properly be considered as identified with your principles and character.

Against these then, and against these alone, is the following work—of which I am but the Editor—directed, in the hope of thereby rendering a service to the Public, which, both in the capacity of a writer and a citizen of the United States, I readily acknowledge as my Lord and Sovereign. What other object, indeed, could he have, whose wishes, hopes, and expectations are identified with your own, and who considers no earthly honour equal to that of being

Your humblest servant and
Fellow-citizen,

FRANCIS J. GRUND.

London, May 10th, 1839.

PREFACE

I HEREWITH submit to the British Public a work principally intended for the benefit of the American. Both people, however, are so intimately connected by the ties of friendship and consanguinity, and so many errors and faults of the Americans—as, indeed, most of their virtues—are so clearly and distinctly to be traced to their British origin, that the perusal of the following pages may, perhaps, be not altogether uninteresting to the readers of both countries.

As individuals may study their own character by carefully examining and observing that of their fellow-creatures,—for it is only in comparing ourselves with others that we become acquainted with ourselves,—so may a correct knowledge of one nation, and the tendencies of its institutions, enable another to form a proper estimate of itself, and to set a right value on its own laws and government.

Such is the object of the following publication; the Public must decide whether it has been attained.

THE EDITOR

London, May 10th, 1839.

PART I

CONTAINING THE ADVENTURES OF A DAY SPENT
AMONG THE BLOODS IN NEW YORK

INTRODUCTION

CHARACTER OF THE AUTHOR

THE following sketches of "American Aristocracy" were written in a desultory manner during a journey the Author took some time ago from Boston to Washington, after having sojourned a number of years in the country.

The Author, now *residing in New York,* not having sufficient courage to publish them, I undertook that task for him; not with a view to pecuniary profit, but in order to render a service to truth, which ought to be acceptable at all times, and cannot but benefit a young, aspiring, prosperous country like the United States.

Numerous works have already been published on "American Society;" but its peculiar tendency towards *Aristocracy,* its talents, resources, and prospects, have never been more than generally and superficially dwelt upon, even by the best writers. This is a great fault. The Americans have, as they repeatedly assure Europeans, "a great deal of Aristocracy," and, in general, a very nice taste for artificial distinctions; a circumstance which, as yet, is but little known to the great bulk of the European public, who still imagine them to be a set of savages.

The Author of these pages seems to have made it his study to bring those hidden gems to light, in order to vindicate his adopted country from the reproach of *equality* and *barbarism,* indiscriminately heaped upon it by the Tories of all countries, and especially by the *great* Tories of England.

Before entering on the task assigned me, it is, however, necessary first to acquaint the reader with the personage of the Author, who was once a sporting character; but is now a sedate, moral, religious man, scarcely to be told from a real American. Although of noble extraction, being the seventh son of the Westphalian Baron Von K—pfsch—rtz, whose family dates back to the eighth century, he has, while in the United States, sunk the nobleman in the man of business; in consequence of which he now passes generally for "a sensible man." Had he been *born* and *bred* in America, and inherited or acquired a large fortune, his being descended from a noble family might have added to his other accomplishments; but the pedigree of a poor German nobleman with-

3

out a rent-roll could not possibly do him any good, and might have done him much harm in raising the jealousy of his employers.

For a time he devoted himself to politics, in which he was a great enthusiast, but soon discovered his error; and, finding winds and waves more steady than the favours of the public, became supercargo of an American East Indiaman. He stayed three years in Canton, and on his return married the daughter of the president of an insurance office—the young lady having fallen in love with him at a party,—notwithstanding the remonstrances of the family, who considered the match a poor one. He has since had two children by his wife, and a clerkship by his father-in-law; all which, taken together, has done much to attach him to the country, and will, I doubt not, in due time make him "a patriot."

I must yet observe that the following "sketches" were written during the Author's political career, and shortly after; it being agreed between him and his father-in-law, at the time of his marriage, that he should never again use a pen except for the benefit of the office, or to write a letter to his *beau-père,* provided he be willing to frank it. This promise I understood him to have religiously kept, as indeed every other he made at that time; but, feeling all the while some lurking desire to see himself in print, he thought it no harm to touch up an *old* manuscript, which he was determined secretly to put into my hands, in order that I might select from it what I judged fit for publication. The way in which he accomplished his design, and the charge he gave me, are important items; which, as they are brief, I shall not withhold from the public.

It was in the month of August last year, that, early in the morning of a sultry day, while sauntering along the wide and dirty streets of New York, I was, just at the corner of Chamber Street and Broadway, struck by the singular appearance of a male figure, which I at once recognised as European, though the individual in question had apparently taken the most studied pains to disguise his origin. His stature was straight and erect; his neck, already thin and stiff, was, by the aid of a black cravat, reduced to a still narrower compass; and his hat was sunk down his neck so as to expose half his forehead. His frock-coat, despite the heat of the day, was buttoned up to the chin, and yet of such diminutive dimensions as scarcely to cover any one part of his body. His trowsers were of the same tight fit as his coat, and the heels of his boots added at least an inch and a half to his natural height. His steps were short and quick, deviating neither to the right nor left from a straight line;

and his head, which was thrown back, seemed to act as a rudder in directing his motion. Thus far, his appearance differed in nothing from a genuine New-Yorker, except that his shoulders were very much broader, and his legs much more stout, than one generally meets with on the borders of the Atlantic.

I seldom saw an European imitate exactly the particular business-dress and gait of an American; and in this instance the copy appeared to me so burlesque, that I felt curious to see the full face of a man whose body bore such evident imprints of two worlds. I therefore stepped quickly forward a few paces, and, leaning against the window of a print-shop, endeavoured to take a front view of my hero. He seemed to guess my intention, and, desirous of avoiding observation, turned his head towards the opposite side; which, however, did not prevent me from recognising at once my friend *the Author,* with a large roll of paper in his hand.

"Ah!" exclaimed he, grasping my arm, "I am glad to meet you,—the very man I wanted to see. Whither are you now going?"

"To breakfast."

"Are you invited?"

"Not that I know of."

"Then I shall accompany you. I have to speak to you on a very important subject."

"I am going to the Turkish divan."

"The very place I like,—it's private, snug, genteel; one can be there without meeting a reporter."

It was now seven o'clock. The sun had risen over an infinite canopy of dense vapours, through which his rays of burning light were dissolved into a dark lurid hue which hung like smoke on the red walls of the buildings. The thermometer stood 98° in the shade. After a short walk, which, owing to the excessive sultriness of the air, proved sufficiently fatiguing, we arrived at the coffee-house. The *entrée* was somewhat *dérobée,* for the evident purpose of concealing it from the eyes of the vulgar; and the establishment being on the second floor, and the staircase dark and narrow, none but one initiated into the secret could have found the way to it. We ascended the stairs, opened the folding-doors, and in another moment found ourselves in an elegant apartment, studded with marble tables and stuffed couches, in which a sort of *chiarooscuro*—the window-shutters being but half opened, and the windows concealed by a rich damask drapery,—gave full effect to the numerous oil-paintings that covered the walls. Some of these, we were told by the waiter, were of high value, being *"genuine originals;"* but my friend, who passed for a connoisseur in these matters, merely tossed up his head, and said he knew all about them.

"Have you seen the *invoice?"* demanded the waiter.

"It's no matter," replied my friend; "you had better give us some coffee."

We stretched ourselves each on an ottoman (chairs being entirely banished from the establishment), and "the Author" at once came to the point.

"I wanted to hand you my sketch-book," said he, after heaving a deep sigh, "containing the journal of a tour through the principal Atlantic cities, and a few memorandums of my stay in Washington."

"Ah! have you finally resolved to publish it?"

"Not I. I am a married man, related to one of the most aristocratic families in town, with the prospect of inheriting a fortune. I must not quarrel with my bread and butter."

"Oh! I understand you: you wish me to publish it for you; that's more than I can promise to do without seeing the manuscript."

"But you may omit what you do not like, or soften down what is likely to give offence."

"That you know is useless. The Americans do not like to be spoken of in any way. They are so thin-skinned as not even to bear *praise;* they take it for irony."

"I know it. Our first people are like the Venetian senators, who would not allow the government to be *praised;* because, if one man bestowed praise, another might be guilty of censure. There is no knowing where matters will end when once in the mouth of the people."

"All this ought to put me the more on my guard: yet, out of friendship for you, I will make myself a martyr. If *you* had the courage to *write* the truth, *I* will have the boldness to *publish* it."

"Bravo!" cried my friend, embracing me in a Continental manner, "I see you are a real German; and, if ever I inherit—"

"Pray don't mention it. It will be as much as you can do to pay your wife's mantuamaker. You cannot count your father-in-law's money until after his death. There are bank liabilities, insurance liabilities, and Heaven knows what other mercantile and private liabilities! Just give me the manuscript, and trust the rest to my affection."

"You are too kind—too generous!" cried he; "but I must, nevertheless, give you a few hints. I think you had better omit the account of my *flirtations* entirely. It is not in good taste. All such things are necessarily insipid; and, if Mrs. K—pfsch—rtz should by accident learn—"

"She would never forgive you."

"It is not *that* I am most afraid of; but my father-in-law, and the public—. Besides, my flirtations, as is always the case in the United States, ended in a most *sensible* manner, and on that account are not likely to interest an European reader. The first lady sent me word by her servant not to trouble myself with writing her any more letters, as she was determined to send them back unopened. The second gave me a verbal warning in these terms:—'I am sorry you should be in love with me, because papa and mamma think it all nonsense; I do not say this to hurt your feelings, but merely to prevent you from taking any unnecessary steps in the matter. I shall, nevertheless, be always happy to see you as a *friend*.' And the third ended in the most legitimate manner,—in my marriage. I think my sketches of fashionable parties, and in general of the character and principles of our 'first society,' are much more likely to give satisfaction: only soften them down a little for the sake of Judge Lynch: it would break my heart to see you tarred and feathered. As regards my account of American statesmen and politicians, you must calculate your chances of a duel. A Southerner will fight three times as quick as a Northerner; but the Northerner will never forgive you. Be careful how you repeat what I have said about *parsons;* they have more power in the United States than in any other country. They have the power of breaking any man they please; for they possess the most complete control over the women. I have, in this respect, always been of Jean Paul Richter's opinion, who despised 'the *paternoster globule* of piety,' as much as 'the empty bubbles of worldly prudence.' But you know my religious sentiments, and are best able to judge whether I deserve the name of a Christian. If I have sometimes been severe upon Unitarianism and Dr. Channing, it is because I hate cant in any shape, and would oppose any man that would constitute himself moral pope of the community. The Bostonians, who, according to their own confession, are a 'people full of notions,' are always ready to deify a man that 'captivates their fancy;' and accordingly have within the narrow confines of their city a whole Olympus of gods and goddesses, of which the reverend Socinian is the *Jupiter tonans*. But you will best know how to manage these matters: only one thing,—forgive the vanity of an author!—you must promise me as a *conditio sine quâ non.*"

"And what is that?"

"Not to make such a thing of it as Fanny Kemble's journal;—that is, not to strike out three-fourths of the book, and then publish the rest all dashes and stars."

I gave him my word to leave as few stories untold as possible, and, in general, to stick to my text as far as was consistent with prudence; after which he quietly sneaked off to his office, leaving me to do the best with the manuscript. And now, gentle reader, it is for you to judge whether I have abused the confidence of my friend.

CHAPTER I

> "He cannot be a perfect man,
> Not being try'd and tutor'd in the world:
> Experience is by industry achiev'd,
> And perfected by the swift course of time."
>
> SHAKSPEARE.—*Two Gentlemen of Verona*, Act I. Scene 3.

SOME years ago, early of a fine morning in the month of July, I was sauntering with some Southern friends down Broadway towards the Battery, which forms the eastern extremity of the city of New York. The night had been most uncomfortably hot, the thermometer ranging above 90°, and the sun's lurid glare, produced by a thick heavy mist,— the usual companion of a sultry day in America,—gave to the sleeping city the appearance of a general conflagration.

As long as we were in Broadway, not a breath of air was stirring, and respiration really difficult; but, when we arrived at the Bowling Green, a delicious sea-breeze imparted new vigour to our exhausted frames, and increased gradually as we were approaching the Battery. Arrived at this beautiful spot, the air was quite refreshing, and the view one of the finest I ever beheld. The harbour was covered with sails, a rich verdure overspread the neighbouring hills and islands, and the mingled waters of the ocean and the Hudson, gently rippled by the breeze, tremblingly reflected the burning orb of day.

"What a delicious spot this is!" said I; "there is nothing equal to it in any part of the Union!"

"Certainly not," said one of my companions, who had stopped to survey the beauty of the landscape; "yet how many Americans do you think enjoy it?"

"It is certainly not a very fashionable place," said I.

"How could it be?" replied he: "all the fashionable people have moved to the West-end of the town."

"Where the atmosphere is not half so pure, the breeze not a quarter so refreshing as here; and where, instead of this glorious harbour,—this ocean, the emblem of eternity,—they see nothing but sand,—a barren desert, interspersed here and there by a block of brick buildings," added the other.

"This our people imagine to be a successful imitation of English taste," observed the first. "They forget that the West-end of London contains magnificent squares and public walks; and that it is in the immediate neighbourhood of the Parks."

"And yet," said the other, "if to-morrow the Southwark and all the boroughs east of the Thames were to get into fashion, our New York aristocracy would imitate the example, and inhabit once more this beautiful site."

"It is true," resumed I, "*this* imitation of the English is not a very happy one; and deserves the more to be ridiculed, as it refers merely to forms, and not to the substance of things. I am in a habit of taking a stroll here every evening; but have not, for the space of two months, met with a single individual known in the higher circles. Foreigners are the only persons who enjoy this spot."

"And do you know why?" interrupted one of my friends: "it is because our fashionable Americans do not wish to be seen with the people; they dread that more than the tempest; and it is for this reason all that is really beautiful in the United States is considered *vulgar*. The people follow their inclination, and occupy that which they like; while our exclusives are obliged to content themselves with what is abandoned by the crowd."

"I am not very sorry for that," said the second; "our exclusives deserve no better fate. As long as the aristocracy of a country is willing to associate with the educated classes of the *bourgeoisie*, they set a premium on talent and the example of good breeding. This aristocracy here is itself nothing but a wealthy overgrown *bourgeoisie*, composed of a few families who have been more successful in trade than the rest, and on that account are now cutting their friends and relations in order to be considered fashionable."

Here we heard the ringing of the bell for the departure of the hourly steam-boat for Staten Island. As we intended to join a small party to breakfast at "the Pavilion," we quickly hurried on board, and in less than a minute were floating on the water. A fine brass band was stationed on deck, and the company consisted of a great number of pretty women with their attendant swains, who thus early escaped from the heat of the city in order to return to it at shopping-time,—from twelve till two o'clock. A few lonely "females," only protected by huge baskets filled with provisions, had also come "to enjoy the concord of sweet sounds," and a trip down the harbour for a quarter of a dollar, previous to returning home from the market. The whole company were in excellent spirits, the basket-ladies being arranged on one side,— unfortunately, however, to windward,—and the ladies and gentlemen on the other, the band playing involuntary variations to the tune of "Auld lang syne."

In precisely an hour from the time we had left the wharf we landed on Staten Island, and proceeded at once to the place of *rendezvous*. This was a large public-house fitted up in a most magnificent style by Colonel M***, late keeper of the A*** Hotel, one of the few landlords possessed of the talent of making people comfortable. The building was very spacious; but its wings were a little too long, and the small garden in front almost entirely destitute of trees,—a fault from which no public, and hardly any private, mansion in the United States, can be said to be entirely exempted.

The Americans have, indeed, a singular aversion to trees and shrubs of every description: their highest idea of perfection in a landscape being an extended plain sown with grass. They consider trees as a mark of barbarism, and are, in their zeal for civilization, extirpating them wherever they find them. The hills and islands in the harbour of Boston, which were once studded with the majestic pine and the gnarled oak, are now completely shorn: the city of Albany, built on a gentle declivity once covered with variegated wood, is daily becoming more and more flat and less shady; the fashionable inhabitants paying more for levelling the ground, and felling the trees, than for the erection of their dwellings. The beautiful trees on the shores of the Monongahela and the Ohio are, at an enormous expense, destroyed root and branch, to give the inhabitants of Pittsburgh the benefit of light and air; and even the "old liberty tree" of Boston, with all its historical associations and recollections, stands no more. How singularly this taste of the Americans contrasts with that of the English, who, after burning and sacking the colony of New Jersey, placed a sentinel near the tree under which William Penn had concluded the treaty with the Indians!

The fault of the garden apart, the Pavilion of Staten Island, or "the Brighton Pavilion," as it is sometimes called, offers really a fine and healthy retreat from the noise and dirt of New York; and this the more so, as, from its elevation, it is accessible on all sides to the seabreeze. We ascended a few steps, and found ourselves at once in a capacious bar-room, fitted up in the best American style. Labels of all sorts, and in all languages, stuck on innumerable bottles placed at small distances from one another, and interlined with lemons and oranges, whose bright and pale gold was again relieved by the dark-green hock, and the silver-headed champaign bathed in ice. By the side of these stood the grave and manly Carolina madeira, the fiery sherry, and the sombre port. For the lovers of condensation there were also old French cognac, Irish and Scotch whisky, and an ominous-looking bottle, whose contents portended to be the original beverage of Van Tromp. The favourite drink, however, seemed to be mint-julep; for a huge mass of ice and a forest of mint, together with two large bottles of French and peach brandy, gave, alas! but too positive proofs of the incapability of the landlord to maintain the balance of power among spirits so different in action and principle.

The bar was thronged, even at this early hour, with young men from sixteen to twenty-four years of age, for whom the busy barkeeper was preparing ice-punch, mint-juleps, port and madeira *sangarie,* apple-toddy, gin-sling, &c. with a celerity of motion of which I had heretofore scarcely seen an example. This man evidently understood the value of time, and was fast rising into respectability; for he was making money more quickly than the "smartest" broker in Wall Street.

"Mr. S*** and Mr. P***?" said he, as he saw us enter; and, on being answered in the affirmative, touched a bell, which was instantly answered by a servant. "Show these gentlemen to No. 3."

We were led into a large room, in which from fifteen to twenty persons might have been assembled, exciting their appetite for breakfast by drinking juleps.

"I present you a new friend," said one of my companions. "I hope you will be gratified with making his acquaintance. Monsieur de *** from Germany."

Hereupon all the gentlemen rose, one by one, and shook hands with me; each of them saying, "How d'ye do? Very glad to see you." At last one of them, by way of entering into conversation, told me that he was exceedingly glad to meet with a gentleman from that country. "I have myself," said he, "passed a long time in Germany."

"What part of Germany?" demanded I.

"Oh, no particular part," replied he; "only principally up and down the Rhine. Capital country that!—excellent hock!—fine historical associations!—excellent people the Germans!"

"I am very glad you liked them," said I.

"Yes, indeed, I always did. What noble castles those! How do you call that beautiful ancient castle opposite Coblenz? Erin-bright-insteen?"

"You mean Ehrenbreitenstein," said I; "that is a Prussian fortress."

"No matter what you call it," said he, "it is a splendid specimen of architecture. I wish we had something like it in this country."

"I really do not see the use of it," said I.

"But I do," said he; "we want a little chivalry of that sort,—our people are altogether too prosaic."

"They are too much occupied with politics," observed another gentleman.

"Altogether too much, sir," repeated the admirer of Germany.

"But they say it is all for their own good; it improves their condition."

"I don't want to know their condition. Heaven save me from politics!"

"It is certainly not a flourishing trade in this country," said I.

"Not only that, sir; but it is not a respectable one."

"And why not?"

"Because every blackguard meddles with it."

"But not every blackguard is successful in it."

"Quite the reverse; it is only the blackguard who is successful."

"That's an old one," cried an elderly-looking gentleman.

"But who will talk politics on a hot day without taking a julep? Hollo, John! a dozen fresh juleps, with plenty of ice,—and rather stiff, mind ye."

"It's no use to talk politics to us, sir," observed a Mr. *** of Baltimore, addressing me in a calm, tranquil voice, which had something of the tone of advice and condescension in it; "we are no longer green."

"What do you mean by that?"

"I mean precisely what I say," replied he. "We have all more or less passed the age in which respectable Americans take an interest in politics; and are, thank God! not yet sufficiently old and decrepit to recur to it once more because we are unfit for everything else."

"Yes, yes!" interrupted a highly respectable gentleman, whom I had known in Boston, and who had a high reputation for being fond of cards; "a man never takes to politics in this country unless he is ruined in business. I have seen a hundred instances of it in my own city. Let a man have a falling-out with work, and he is sure to turn patriot."

"Because patriotism is the last refuge of a scoundrel, as Johnson said," remarked a young barrister, visibly contented with having had an opportunity of exhibiting his erudition.

"Happy country this!" observed one of my companions, "in which every scoundrel turns patriot!"

"Say, rather, in which every patriot is a scoundrel," rejoined the lawyer.

"Why, Tom!" exclaimed the Bostonian, "you have broken out in a new place!"

"Why, a man will say a good thing now and then," replied the professional man. "But where the d—l is that nigger with the juleps? I'll be hanged if a person can get waited upon in New York without bribing the servants!"

Here the waiter entered.

"What have you been about, sirrah? It's more than a quarter of an hour since that gentleman" (pointing to the Baltimorian) "asked for some juleps. Can't you move quicker?"

"I goin' as fast as I kin," grinned the negro; "but dere are too many gem'men at de bar."

"I find," observed a grave-looking New-Yorker, who until now had not opened his mouth, except for the purpose of admitting the julep, "that our black servants are getting worse and worse every day ever since that bigoted scoundrel T*** has commenced preaching abolition. Those black devils have always been a nuisance; but now 'a respectable white man' can hardly walk up and down Broadway of a Sunday afternoon without being jostled off the side-walk by one of their desperate gangs."

"And it is still worse in Philadelphia," observed Major ***, "owing to the philanthropy of our quakers. One of those black beasts, not more than a week ago, actually eyed my sister through a quizzing-glass as she was walking in Chestnut-street, accompanied by her younger sister."

"Good God!" cried the New-Yorker, "has it come to this? Must our respectable females be insulted in the streets by a set of dastardly slaves!"

"I can hardly believe it," said a Virginian, who appeared to be displeased with the turn the conversation had taken. "The example must have been set him by some white person. Your Philadelphia dandies have, the whole live-long day, no other amusement but staring women out of countenance."

"Well explained!" ejaculated a young man who had just returned from Paris; "a negro is a mere ape,—he is but a link between man and monkey. *C'est en effet un singe dégénéré.*"

"Witty dog!" said the Philadelphian; "just returned from France!"

"For Heaven's sake!" cried the Virginian, "let us not talk about negroes and abolition. I am resolved never to mention the subject again to friend or foe. If any of those emancipation preachers ever comes to my plantation, I have left the strictest order with my overseer to hang him on the spot. My neighbours are resolved to do the same, and I trust to God the custom will become general throughout the country."

"Bravo!" exclaimed the Philadelphian,—"Virginia for ever!"

"You may well drink to Virginia," exclaimed the gentleman from that state; "it is the pearl of the Union!"

"So it is, so it is!" shouted the company. "It has produced the greatest men in the United States!"

"George Washington!" cried the Virginian.

"George Washington!" echoed the company.

"Thomas Jefferson!" continued the Virginian.

"Don't mention him, for mercy's sake!" bellowed the Philadelphian; "that vile blasphemer!—that infidel scoundrel!—that god-less father of democracy, who has been the ruin of our country."

"In what manner has he ruined it?" demanded I.

"By introducing that vilest of curses, universal suffrage."

"But I see the country prosper more and more every year."

"You do not see far enough, sir," said he. "You do not understand the working of universal suffrage. An example, perhaps, may illustrate the case. You may have heard of Mr. B***, who is one of our first citizens, has always been at the head of the very first society, and is worth, at least, half a million of dollars in bank stock, independent of a very respectable real estate. Well, sir: this same Mr. B***, at our last election, went himself to the ballot-box, and, with his own hand, put in his vote as if he were one of our simplest citizens. Was not that republican? Was there ever a better republican than Mr. B***?"

"Certainly not. But what has that to do with the theory of universal suffrage, except that he was obliged to do so if he wished to vote at all?"

"Hear me out, sir; hear me out!" shouted the Philadelphian. "Scarcely had Mr. B*** deposited his vote, when one of your regular 'whole-hog, hurrah-for-Jackson men,' who, according to every appearance, was not worth five dollars in the world, stepped up, and, right within hearing of our Mr. B***, told the officer with the most impudent sneer that he intended to destroy Mr. B***'s vote. These, sir, are the consequences of universal suffrage."

"And then people wonder if we are not seen at the ballot-boxes," said the New-Yorker. "Who the d—l would scramble up among a parcel of ragamuffins in order to exercise a privilege shared by every pauper! I would as lief do common militia duty."

"What you have told of your friend Mr. B*** in Philadelphia has happened to my friend Mr. H*** in Baltimore," cried the Virginian.

"And to myself," added the Bostonian; "and since that time I am determined never to disgrace myself again by voting at an election, except to oblige a friend."

"Jefferson has ruined the country!" shouted the whole company.

"I only wonder," said one of my friends, "he has left sufficient brandy in the country for you to get drunk on."

"We get that from France," rejoined the witty gentleman; "the Americans produce nothing but whisky and rum, and those only of the most inferior quality. Whenever we want anything decent, we are obliged to send for it from abroad."

"That's a fact," added the Bostonian; "and pay the dealer a hundred per cent. profit on it."

"And, after all, get it adulterated," said the New-Yorker.

"I cannot conceive," remarked the Philadelphian, "how a gentleman of fortune can possibly live in this country."

"He is a great fool if he does," replied the French wit. "England for a rich man, and France for a man of moderate fortune! that's my motto; and as for us,—I mean the higher classes of Americans,—we are everywhere at home—except in the United States. *En Amérique les étrangers sont chez eux, tandis que les Américains ne sont chez eux que quand ils sont à l'étranger.*"

Here the company burst into a horse-laugh.

"Just returned from Paris," whispered the Philadelphian; "capital fellow!"

"Won't you translate it to me?" asked the Bostonian; "I used to know French when I went to school, but I have forgotten it since." (With a significant look.) "You know our girls don't speak it."

" 'Strangers are in America at home, while the Americans themselves are only at home when they are abroad,' said our friend Charles, and he is certainly right; for America, ever since we are overrun by Irish and German paupers, is not fit for a gentleman to live in."

"If I had my own way," observed the Gallicised American, "I would never live in any other place but Paris."

"And I in London," remarked the Bostonian.

"Our tastes are *so* different," rejoined the former; "you like everything that is English,—I love all that is French. Besides, in France one gets so much more easily into society; the English, you know, are ridiculously exclusive."

"But have we not a minister in London? Can we not always be presented at court?"

"Not always; there are too many applicants."

"But it is precisely the same thing in France. One of my acquaintances wrote me from Paris, that the American minister, during the space of one year, received no less than fifteen hundred applications for presentation to their French majesties."

"That may be: but in England one is often obliged to put up with the society of the middle classes, or at best with a sort of respectable gentry; while in France we never associate with anything less than a count or a marquis. My aunt would not speak to a *bourgeois!* She is descended from the Princess of M—y, which, you know, is one of the most ancient families of France; and likes Paris so much, that I don't think she will ever return to the United States. She can't bear America!"

"She would not be wise if she did," observed my friend, half ironically; "she receives a great deal more attention there than she would at home."

"So do all our women," observed the lawyer. "Our people do not know how to treat them, and our women do not know how to take advantage of their position; they are only fit 'to suckle fools and chronicle small beer.' "

"Very well brought in by our professional friend!" cried the Bostonian. "I say, Tom! what did your mother say when you left home to practise law in this city?"

"She gave me her blessing, and told me, 'Go, my son, and improve the talent God has given you, and you cannot fail to make money.' It was very kind in her, poor soul! she little expected I would draw on her regularly every quarter."

"But how do you spend your time," demanded the Bostonian, "if you do not practise law?"

"Literature, literature!" exclaimed the lawyer, emptying his ·glass. "We all dabble, more or less, in that."

"True," rejoined the Bostonian, "I forgot all about literature."

"What o'clock is it?" demanded the child of Paris, stretching himself with the air of an *homme blasé.*"

"Nearly ten," answered my friend.

"Then I wish we might have breakfast, as I have promised to call upon a young lady at one."

"Don't you get yourself into a scrape, Charles."

"Don't you be concerned about me," replied Charles; "I have lived too long in Paris to be easily taken in."

"But our women are not like the French."

"That's one reason why I don't like them. Their everlasting pretensions, their air of superiority, and, above all, that imperious spirit which receives all our *petits soins* as a mere tribute which is due to them, have often completely disgusted me. I like to be at my ease with a woman; it's so much more natural."

"You are not singular in that," remarked the gentleman from New York; "I have had the same taste ever since I was a boy of sixteen."

"What! without having been in Europe?"

"Certainly; but then I was brought up in New York, which, you know, is a little Europe of itself. I have heard Frenchmen say, that, next to Paris, there is nothing like it in the world."

"Pooh!" cried the Bostonian, "I'd rather live in Boston ten times over; and so would you, if you knew it as well as I do; but that, you know, takes time."

"Don't talk to me about Boston," said the Philadelphian; "your women don't even know how to dress."

"And run up bills at the mantua-makers," rejoined the Bostonian.

"The prettiest women in the United States are in Baltimore," observed the Baltimorian.

"Say rather *girls,*" interrupted the Gallo-American; "I have never seen a handsome woman in America yet: if there were one, you would not see her in society; she would stay at home nursing her babies."

"And send her young daughters into company for our boys to dance with."

"And dance they must, because they can't talk."

"What would you have a girl of sixteen talk of, pray?"

"Nothing that I care for. When I was in Paris, I only talked to married women. They alone understand the most delicate allusions, listen with dignity to our affecting tales, and are grateful for the slightest attention, without expecting an immediate proposal and saddling themselves on you for life."

"That would not do in this country," said the Bostonian with great earnestness; "our women are brought up in a different manner."

"Why, upon my word!" exclaimed the Philadelphian with a horse-laugh, "our Boston friend talks to us as gravely as a New England schoolmaster. If you don't leave off some of these ridiculous Yankee notions, you'll never cut a figure in the fashionable world. But you must excuse him, gentlemen; a certain puritanical air always sticks to these 'Boston folks' even after they have turned rakes."

"Oh! he would get over that too, quick enough," cried the lover of France, "if he were to stay a year or two in Paris. But, upon my honour! I cannot stay for breakfast; Miss L*** would never speak to me again."

"I thought you only cared for married women?" remarked the lawyer.

"Neither do I care for anybody else," said the Frenchman; "but you know our girls, who have nothing to do but to walk Broadway in the forenoon, and to go to a party in the evening, govern society; and, if one does not wish to be considered an absolute boor, one must humour them."

"Then you consider your civility a mere act of duty,—a sacrifice brought to society?"

"Precisely so; and in the same light it is viewed by Miss L***."

"The d—l take your attention then! When I want to pay my court to a woman, I do not want to do so in public."

"Miss L***, I assure you, courts nothing but satin velvet and gros de Naples. She will to-day, with her own soft hands, caress every piece of French silk which has passed the Hook for a week past; and I shall have the honour of accompanying her to every fashionable shop in Broadway."

"Delightful occupation this!" exclaimed the lawyer; "I had rather read law."

"Or drink juleps," cried the Philadelphian.

"Or play cards," said the New-Yorker.

"Or go to meeting," added the Bostonian.

"You may do what you like; but Miss L*** is worth a hundred thousand dollars if she is worth a cent; and she has sworn never to marry, except an European or an American who has remained long enough in Europe to become civilized."

"Delightful creature that!" cried the Bostonian: "then I presume I should stand no chance with her at all."

*"C'est selon. Vous êtes beau garçon, appartenez à une bonne famille; vous avez de quoi vivre: mais vous chiquez, et, surtout, vous crachez, et Mademoiselle L*** ne pardonne nullement de pareils forfaits."*

Here the finished Parisian stepped before the looking-glass, tightened his cravat so as to give himself a colour, drew the pale emaciated fingers of his right hand a dozen times through his front hair, studied the most becoming position of his hat, arranged most tastefully two large curls which concealed the cavities of his temples, put on his French kid gloves, exercised himself in balancing a small switch,— which altogether did not take him more than thirty-five minutes,—and then left the room as if he had never known any one of its occupants.

"Clever fellow that!" exclaimed the Philadelphian: "spent all his father's property in learning how to live, and is now marrying one of our richest girls."

"Capital hit!" cried the Bostonian.

"Equal to a profession," ejaculated the lawyer.

"Pray, what may your profession be worth a-year?" asked the New-Yorker.

"The profession is worth a great deal, but I myself get nothing by it," replied the barrister.

"How long is it since you practised law?"

"Five years."

"And how much did you make by it?"

"Twenty-five dollars, or thereabouts."

"How much rent do you pay for your office?"

"One hundred dollars per annum."

"And what do you give to the boy that sweeps it?"

"One dollar a month."

"Why don't you rather take him into partnership?"

"He would scorn the idea."

"And how many lawyers like you are there in New York?" demanded my friend.

"Between three and four hundred, I suppose; most of them sons of our first citizens. All the law business is done by half-a-dozen vulgar upstarts who come here from the country, and whom the public, God knows why, is taking into favour. The profession of physic is a great deal better; the veriest humbug is making money by it."

"Because dead people tell no tales, I presume?"

"Not so much for that, as because a physician often hits where he strikes at random; and because, when a physician is not doing well with his professional practice, he is always sure to make a respectable living by quackery."

"Provided he has money enough to pay for advertising in the newspapers. But then physicians do not rank nearly as high in society as lawyers."

"Neither should they: our profession is, *par excellence,* that of a gentleman."

"And I can assure you," interrupted the New-Yorker, "that, in this city, there is no higher rank in society than that 'of a rich man.' I would rather have the reputation of Mr. A*** than that of our learned chancellor K***."

"So would I," rejoined the lawyer. "Mr. A*** must now be 'pretty considerably' richer than Stephen Gerard ever was; and when a man is once rich, you know, he can do everything."

"I believe myself," said the New-Yorker, "that we are a 'leetle' too much given to money-making."

"And that every person connected with trade is too easily admitted into our first society," added the Philadelphian.

"In what other country," exclaimed the Virginian, "would you see a parcel of drummers or clerks admitted into the company of statesmen and legislators?"

"In none," interrupted my friend, "except where merchants and their agents hold a higher rank than statesmen and legislators; in which it is a disgrace to be a politician, and a reproach to be called a patriot."

At this moment one of the waiters announced breakfast; which agreeable news put us all into the best possible humour, and, amid the hilarity excited by hock and champaign, we soon forgot fashions, politics, professions, and even the riches of this world.

While we had thus been wasting our time, a hundred ships had probably discharged their cargoes; a thousand emigrants from all parts of the globe had landed with big hearts and stout hopes to realise their dreams of the free and happy West. Many of them might have already commenced their peregrination towards the Mississippi, where their friends and relatives who preceded them were already clearing the wilderness, or enjoying the fruits of their labour. Fortunes might have been lost or won, merchants established or ruined, politicians raised or undone. Many an enterprising pioneer might have formed a plan for a new settlement; while hundreds of others were probably employed in transporting the produce of the fertilized West to the seaports of the Atlantic. Wealth and misery had perhaps been expected by thousands with the arrival of the mail or packet. Fathers might have been separated from their children,—husbands from their wives,—in the eager and universal quest of fortune, and many a heart left bleeding with the loss of all it held dear; while others, happier than these, might have greeted the unexpected return of their friends and relatives.

Is it not strange, thought I, before I had drunk the first glass of champaign, that in a country which more than any other convinces one of the vanity of human pursuits,—in which wealth, honour, and distinction are mere bubbles floating on the surface of society,—men should be more eager after aristocratic distinctions, than where these are founded on an historical basis, and in accordance with the customs of the people? Such, however, is the irony of Fate, inseparable from nations as from individuals.

CHAPTER II

Return to the City.—Arrival of the London Packet.—Reception of the
Passengers.—American Speculations on an English Lord.—Introduction
to a Fashionable Boarding-house.—A New England Minerva.—A Belle.
—A Lady from Virginia.—Conduct of Fashionable Young Ladies
towards Gentlemen of an inferior standing.—Confusion produced by
the Dinner-bell.

> *Duke Senior.*—"What fool is this?"
> *Jaques.*—"O worthy fool! One that has been a courtier,
> And says, if ladies be but young and fair,
> They have the gift to know it."
>
> *As You Like It,* Act. II. Scene 7.

On our return to the city, the steam-boat was quite animated. The
packet-ship T*** had arrived from London, and, having reported a
clean bill of health, was permitted to land her passengers. Our boat,
therefore, went alongside of her, and was greeted by loud cheers from
the steerage passengers, who, dressed in their Sunday's best, were
crowding the bow, gangway, and even the rigging of the vessel, eagerly
awaiting their long-hoped-for delivery from imprisonment.

The company on board of our boat, which, besides ourselves,
consisted of a dozen gentlemen and nearly as many ladies, returned the
salute in a dignified manner by a wild stare of amazement; until, turning to the captain of the packet, who had jumped on the bulwarks of
our boat to assist in landing his passengers, a fashionably dressed lady,
accompanied by a gentleman, inquired what sort of *cabin* passengers
he had brought with him?

"Mr. and Mrs. ***," replied the captain, who, from his attention to
the inquirer, appeared to have the honour of her acquaintance.

"Don't know them," said the gentleman; then turning to the lady,
whom I judged to be his wife, "do *you* know them?"

"I am sure I never heard their *names* before," said the lady, tossing
up her head.

"Mrs. *** and two children," continued the captain.

"The wife of that vulgar auctioneer," remarked the lady, "that

23

wanted to outdo everybody. Well, she will find a sad change; her husband has failed since she was gone, and is said not to pay ten cents in a dollar."

"Mr. ***," continued the captain.

"What sort of a person is he?" demanded the gentleman.

"La! don't you know him?" cried the lady: "it's that grocer who made fifty thousand dollars in a coffee speculation, and has ever since been trying to get into the first society; but did not succeed on account of that blubber-faced wife of his. They say that is the reason he went to Europe. Poor wretch! he probably thought people would, in the mean time, forget that he was a grocer."

"Mr. and Mrs. *** of Baltimore," added the captain.

"Ah! our old friends, Mr. and Mrs. ***. What a delightful creature that Mrs. *** is! I used to be quite intimate with her at New Port; she always used to have such a choice set around her."

"Lady *** and her daughter from London," resumed the captain.

"Lady *** from London!" exclaimed the whole company,—"where is she?"

"It's that fine-looking woman there, standing by the side of that young lady dressed in black." (Here the gentlemen applied their glasses.)

"Both equally handsome," cried a young man. "Really English! excellent fall of the shoulders!"

"Only the bust a little too full," remarked the lady, "which is generally the fault of the English women; and, besides, they have such enormously large feet."

"Who is with them?" inquired one of the gentlemen.

"Captain *** of the **th dragoons, who I understand is brother to Sir ***."

"I presume they have brought their servants with them?" observed the lady.

"Two male servants, a lady's-maid, and the governess of the young lady."

"Then they must be rich."

"They have letters to Mr. A***, to Mr. and Mrs. ***, and to many of our first people."

Here the lady whispered something to the gentleman, which, as far as I could understand, sounded like this: "We shall see them at Mrs. A***'s, and you must try to get introduced to them; it will be just the thing for us if we should ever go to England." (Aloud to the captain,) "Have you brought some more English people?"

"Lots of them," replied the captain; "Mr. *** and Mr. *** of Manchester, Mr. *** of Liverpool, Mr. *** and Mr. *** of London,—all in the cotton business."

"We don't want to know *them,*" said the lady; "business people, I presume,—full of pretensions and vulgar English prejudices. Have you brought no other *genteel* persons besides Lady *** and Captain ***?"

"Oh, yes," replied the sailor, who began to be tired of the interrogatory; "a young sprig of nobility, Lord ***, as they call him."

"I am *so* sorry," said the lady with a bewitching smile, "to trouble you *so* much, captain; but really I should be *so* much obliged to you if you were to show me the young lord."

"It's that chap for'ard," said the captain, "talking to the engineer."

"Then I presume he is a Whig lord," remarked the lady.

"I don't care a d—n," muttered the captain as he was going away, "whether he be Whig, Tory, or Radical, so he pays his passage, and behaves himself like a gentleman."

Our deck was now covered with more than a hundred and fifty people, principally English and Irish, among whom there was a great number of women and children. Those that had come over in the steerage confined themselves for a short time to the forward deck; but after they had paid their fare, and ascertained that they were charged as much as those who occupied the chairs and settees that were placed aft the wheels, they gradually came one by one to partake of the same privilege, and, though not without hesitation, took their seats among the better dressed part of the company. This was the signal for a general move; the ladies forming themselves into little sets by themselves, with a portion of the gentlemen standing by their side, and the unencumbered part of the latter walking the opposite side of the deck. But the young progeny of England and Ireland, emboldened by their success, disturbed them a second time by walking the deck in the opposite direction; and one of them, a swaggering youth of about nineteen, actually had the impudence of addressing a gentleman who had been a *cabin* passenger on board of the packet.

The gentleman answered without looking at him, and in so abrupt a manner, that the youth stole away very much like a dog that has been kicked by its master.

"These are the consequences of our glorious institutions!" exclaimed the gentleman, turning towards Lord ***, who had taken his station at a little distance from him, and had evidently observed the reception his poor countryman had met with: "this fellow here would not have dared to speak to *us* while on board of the packet; and now he is scarcely in sight of the American soil before he thinks himself just as good as any body else. Did your lordship observe the insolent manner in which he came up to speak to me?"

His lordship gave a slight nod of assent.

"These people come here with the notion that all men in America are free and equal; and that, provided they pay the same money, they are just as good as our first people."

"Hem!"

"But they soon find out the difference. People think there is no aristocracy in this country; but they are mistaken,—there are just as many grades of society in America as in England."

"Indeed!"

"Yes, my lord, and even more; and the distinctions between them are kept up much more rigidly than in England."

"I dare say they are."

"Yes, my lord: you will never see a gentleman belonging to our first society mix by any chance with the second, or one of the second with the third, and so on."

"So!"

"And if it were not for these intruders, who come here by thousands and outvote us at the elections, our country would be just as refined as England."

"I dare say."

"Your lordship does not seem to believe it; but you will yourself see the progress we have made in the arts and sciences."

"I have heard some of my friends say the same thing."

"Why, my lord, New York is a second London; and, if it goes on increasing in the same manner as it has for the last fifty years, will soon have a million of inhabitants."

"Ay, ay!"

"And Philadelphia is nearly as large."

"Ah!"

"Yes, my lord; and the society of Philadelphia is even more select than that of New York."

Here his lordship yawned.

"But the most literary society is in Boston. Boston is the Athens of the United States."

"Is it a *nice* place?" inquired his lordship.

"Why, I do not exactly know what your lordship means by a nice place; but it is one of the handsomest places in the United States."

"Hem!"

"It has a most beautiful common."

"Ay, ay!"

"And a most magnificent state-house; from the top of which you have a most superb view of the neighbouring country."

"So!"

"And not more than three miles from it is Harvard College, the most ancient and distinguished university in the country."

Here his lordship indulged himself in a very long yawn.

"With a library of more than forty thousand volumes."

"Is that all?"

"Why, my lord, this is a young country; and, considering all circumstances, I think we have done better than perhaps any other nation would have done in our place."

"No doubt of it," replied his lordship.

"Indeed, my lord, I think we can challenge history for a comparison."

"Just so."

"And, if we were only left alone, we would do better still: but we are completely overrun by foreign paupers; they come here in herds, while men of high rank" (here he bowed most gracefully) "are but seldom induced to visit our country."

His lordship gave a slight token of acknowledgment.

"And I trust, my lord, you will not repent of your resolution, and the fatigues of a long and tedious voyage."

The young nobleman nodded.

"You will find the Americans a very hospitable people."

"I have always heard so."

"And, though they cannot entertain you in your own style, they will do their best to please you."

Another nod of his lordship.

"Your lordship must not forget that we are a young country. When we shall be as old as England, we shall perhaps do better."

"I don't doubt it."

"Your lordship is going to put up at the Astor House?"

"I do not know yet."

"Oh! your lordship must put up at the Astor House; it's the only decent public house in New York. I shall myself put up there; and if your lordship will do me the honour—"

"I will see by and by; my servant has taken the list of the best hotels in New York."

———

"Did you ever see such toad-eating?" exclaimed one of my companions, as we landed on the wharf and were walking towards Broadway,—"such a compound of arrogance and submissiveness, haughty insolence to an inferior, and cringing flattery towards a greater person than himself, as this man?"

"He certainly behaved very foolishly," said the second; "the British nobleman did not take the least notice of him."

"And did you see," said the first, "how every eye was fixed upon that lady and her daughter, as if they were the eighth wonder of the world?"

"I saw," replied the other, "that they were embarrassed by attracting so much notice."

"Did you not understand the captain to say that they brought letters to Mr. A*** and to Mrs. S***?"

"I certainly did."

"Then they will be the town-talk for a month, and the subject of conversation for six months after, throughout the Union; and whoever is not introduced to them will be considered as vulgar: in short, they will be the fashion throughout the country, until somebody of a still higher rank shall come and eclipse them. Were you in the country when the Duke of Saxe Weimar was here?"

"Yes; but I was not in the habit of going much into society."

"Then you missed a great deal. You ought to have seen the cringing and fawning of these people, and how prodigal they were of the title of 'Serene Highness,' which, as a younger son, was hardly ever given him in Europe."

"I know," said I, "that he was actually worshipped in the Atlantic cities; and that Mr. W*** and Mr. D*** of Philadelphia were very angry at him for introducing their names and professions in his book, without mentioning that they were gentlemen."

"The same, perhaps, that presided at the dinner given him by the *élite* of the German population?"

"The same, if I mistake not," said I. "I yet remember the witty remark of a German emigrant who was present at the banquet. 'These Germans,' said he, 'behave like so many dogs who do not know what to do for joy at having found their lost master.'"

"And what do you think was the cause of his triumphal entry into every one of our large cities? Nothing in the world but the desire of our exclusives to see a duke,—to shake hands with a duke,—to talk with a duke,—to have a duke to dine with them,—and, above all things, to have a claim on the duke's reciprocal favours in case they should meet him in Europe. I know not what the duke's literary pretensions are; but, if Walter Scott had written a book on America, it could not have made a greater sensation than the duke's."

"You ought to make an allowance for the novelty of the thing," said I. "As yet, but few dukes have visited the United States."

"If their wonderment and toad-eating were confined to dukes and earls," replied he, "I would willingly pardon them; but they worship everything in the shape of a nobleman, until, by continually talking about nobility, they imagine themselves to belong to it. I wish all the poor nobles of the Continent of Europe would come here to get married, and to improve their estates. But they would have to play a difficult part in order to conceal their poverty. A knight without a castle does not excite the imagination of an American damsel."

"I yet remember," observed my other companion, "how they pestered old Lafayette with the title of 'marquis,' as if his birth could enhance the sublimity of his character."

"You ought to have been in ***," remarked the first, "when, a year or two ago, a rumour was spread that Prince Puckler Muskau had arrived in the country. A mustachoed *Russian* actually had the good fortune to be mistaken for him, it being understood that the prince wished to preserve the strictest *incognito*. There was no end to the attention bestowed on him by ladies and gentlemen, and to the particular manœuvres that were made in order to obtain an honourable mention in his book, until the poor fellow, tired of the obsequiousness of his admirers, resolved to inform them that they had been humbugged. There is but one offset to this species of toad-eating, and that is the somewhat too sturdy independence of our lower classes."

"That I willingly grant," said the first. "I know that the Duke of Saxe Weimar narrowly escaped a beating in the western country for presuming to hire a whole stage-coach for himself and his valet. Our country has not been settled long enough, and the conditions of men are too rapidly changing, for any one class to tolerate the peculiar manners and customs of the others."

"Do you know the story about the duke and the New York hackney-coachman?"

"I have heard so many anecdotes about the duke, that I cannot tell to which you refer."

"Why, they say that the duke went one evening in a hackney-coach to a party, and that the next day the coachman—or the driver, as he is here called—came for his money, asking the duke whether he was the *man* he had drove the night before; and, on being answered in the affirmative, informing him that '*he* was the *gentleman* what drove him,' and that he had come for his half-dollar."

"*Se non è vero, è ben trovato.* One thing, however, is certain, that in our attentions to strangers we seldom find the proper medium. If a man of title comes among us, the higher classes will caress and cajole him much beyond what the proudest nobleman could expect in any part of Europe; while, among the lower classes, he will often meet with a spirit of resistance which neither kind words nor money will be entirely able to overcome. Let him take the arithmetical medium between the two, and he will have no right to complain."

"And I can assure you," said I, "that in my own heart I have a much higher respect for the common American, who, in his conduct towards strangers, is solely guided by his own rude notion of dignity, than for the *educated gentleman,* who measures everything, and himself into the bargain, by the standard of another country."

"Agreed! agreed!" cried my two companions; "for the one, however barbarous, has within him the elements of a national character; while the other, however civilized, is but a mutilated European."

We had now come up as far as the Park, and, perceiving by the city-hall clock that it was half-past two, one of my companions, under the plea of an engagement, turned towards Chamber-street; while the other, with whom I had promised to dine, invited me to accompany him to his lodgings.

"Come," said he, "we have but half an hour before dinner;* let me introduce you to the ladies of our boarding-house. It's one of the most agreeable ones in town, and always full of transient people."

* At whatever hour people may breakfast in New York, they are sure to dine at half-past two or three.

"I confess I hate your boarding-houses," replied I. "They are neither private nor public; one is deprived in them of most of the conveniences of regular inns, and yet not sufficiently quiet to be able to say one has got a home."

"Are you married?" demanded my friend.

"Why should you ask me that question?"

"Because you talk like a married man;—they are the best things in the world for bachelors."

"On what account, pray?" demanded I.

"On account of the facilities they afford in becoming acquainted with ladies and gentlemen without an introduction; and because they are the nicest places for hearing the scandal of the town."

"That's precisely the reason why I dislike them."

"If you are married, you are right; because a boarding-house is for a married woman what a boarding-school is for a young lady: one spoils the other by precept and example. Scarcely have the gentlemen left the house after breakfast to follow their respective avocations, before the women form themselves into sets in their several bed-chambers to have a talk."

"That's the most horrible practice I know, especially as young ladies are admitted to them, and the conversation there turns but too frequently on our foibles."

"Your three-dollar boarding-houses," rejoined my friend, "are capital things. One gets plenty to eat for little money; turns in at an early hour in the evening in order to rise early in the morning; and, when the men are about their business, the women attend to their own affairs. Besides, all our cheap boarding-houses are small, accommodating seldom more than two or three families, including that of the landlady; but your fashionable establishments are constructed on the plan of regular barracks. You may quarter in them from ten to fifteen families, belonging to at least two or three different sets, visiting in different societies, and envying each other the very air they breathe. If a card be left for one of them, all the rest will talk of it; if one goes to a party to which the rest are not invited, all the others will be jealous; if one is more indulged by her husband than the rest, she is made the subject of remarks by all her *friends;* if one shows herself smarter than the others, all will turn up their noses, and declare with one voice that she is a forward woman;—in short, I would rather expose my wife to the perils and inconveniences of a voyage by sea, than leave her with half-a-dozen women at a boarding-house. They are the destruction of domestic happiness; break in upon the sanctity of private life; blight a thousand germs of affection, which can only be matured in retirement; make mutual tenderness the subject of ridicule, and publish those foibles to the world which love and forbearance would scarcely have discovered, and certainly never revealed. If I were a man without a fortune, I would a thousand times rather emigrate to the far West, and live with my wife in a log-house, than in one of those palaces constructed for the torture of husbands! But, as I said before, they answer very well for bachelors; I always advise my single acquaintances to go to a boarding-house in preference to a tavern."

On entering the parlour, my friend presented me in due form to the landlady, who, being not altogether displeased with his having brought a friend to dine with him, for which she had the right of imposing a tax of one dollar, received me with becoming graciousness. From her my friend turned to a lady of the olden times, dressed in the true style of the Pilgrims, with a plain, dignified, but a little too austere countenance. She received me with the utmost imperturbability, changing not a muscle of her face or body as she drawlingly uttered the words, "How—do—you—do?" By her side sat her daughter, a lovely maiden of between thirty and forty years of age, dyed in the deepest blue of New England learning, with a sharp aquiline nose, over which the reflection from her sharp grey eyes had diffused a sort of *aurora borealis*. Her upper lip was long, and her mouth unusually large; though her thin compressed lips were strongly indicative of firmness and prudence. She had the good sense to wear a cap; behind which, with becoming bashfulness, she not only concealed her own hair, but also a large portion of that, the continuance of which hung in graceful curls over her waxen cheeks, touching the protuberance of the clavicle.

When my name was mentioned as "from Germany," I thought my New England Minerva gave some slight sign of emotion, which, with more justice than personal vanity, I traced to the recollection of some difficult points in Kant's Metaphysics; and, desirous of avoiding a discussion on a subject on which neither her nor my wisdom could contribute much to enlighten the world, I pressed my friend gently towards the next lady, whose youthful appearance was much better calculated to put a man in good-humour for a dinner party. She was a new-blown rose, scarcely past sixteen, with black eyes and black hair, a straight Grecian nose,—and, to say all, she had dimples in her cheeks.

Her neck, in gracefulness and whiteness, might have challenged that of a swan; and, although her bust was somewhat diminutive, it corresponded well with her slender waist and the extreme delicacy of her hands and feet. In short, she was one of those American beauties one cannot behold without loving and pitying at the same time; for such is the exquisite proportion and symmetry of their limbs, that not an atom of them can suffer the least alteration without completely destroying the harmony of the whole. One might compare their beauty to that of an elegantly-turned period, in which you cannot alter one word without destroying the whole sentence; or, to use a more correct simile, to a finished piece of poetry, which, by the alteration of a single syllable, degenerates into prose. I never could look on any one of those sylphs without feeling an involuntary emotion to place them, like other jewels, in some velvet *écrin,* to protect them from vulgar contact, or the blighting influence of the atmosphere.

On this occasion my usual tenderness for these victims of a rigorous climate was rapidly changing into feelings of a more ardent nature, when the young lady rose, and, throwing her head back and her breast forward, imitated by a sudden jerk of her body one of those ludicrous bows which the Gallo-American dancing-masters have substituted for the slow, graceful, dignified courtesies of old; and which fashionable women in the United States, who are generally in advance of the most grotesque fashions of Paris, are sure to turn into a complete caricature. For a moment or two I took the spasmodic contraction of her body for the effect of some nervous excitement, produced, perhaps, by the sudden appearance of a man who was not yet old enough to be her grandfather; but the undisturbed ease with which she immediately after took her seat, and the perfect indifference with which she asked and answered half-a-dozen complimentary questions, soon convinced me that she must have been "out" ever since she was old enough to spell her name.

Next to the young *belle* sat two ladies, mother and daughter, who, to judge from their appearance, had not yet been long admitted into fashionable society. The mother, whose *mise* sufficiently betokened a woman that had given up every pretension to please, was between thirty-five and forty years of age; the daughter might have been eighteen. She was a *piquante brunette,* with large black eyes, and a profusion of dark auburn hair, which, I dare be sworn, was all her own. Her pouting red lips, according to Lavater, proved her to be capable of sympathising with the feelings of others; and her embarrassment when I was presented to her showed that she had not yet become sophisticated in contact with the world. I told her all the pretty things I could think of; and secretly resolved, *coûte qui coûte,* to take my seat not far from her at the dining-table.

Next in turn was Mrs. ***, a widow-lady of ***, who I understood had been exceedingly handsome in her youth, and had now the singular good-nature of admiring and praising the beauty of others, without the dolorous reflection of many a withered *belle*—

"Sono stata felice anch 'io."

She had buried her pretensions with her love; and her claims on the world were now confined to that respect which even the worst of men, at all times and in all countries, willingly pay to a woman whose countenance serves as a visible index to a virtuous life. Her husband had held a most distinguished rank as a public man in his State; and her son, brought up in the simplicity of country life, and imbued with those principles which in the revolutionary struggle animated the American patriots, was heir to an immense estate left him by his uncle. She received me with that friendly but dignified manner, which, without attracting or repulsing, puts a man at once at his ease, by leaving him in every respect complete master of his conduct.

We exchanged a few complimentary phrases; when my friend, leading me to the other part of the room, introduced me at once to half-a-dozen young ladies, who had formed themselves into a small circle, whispering to each other, and alternately laughing and looking at some of the gentlemen, who, completely separated from the ladies, were filling the background of the scene. My name without the *"de"* being announced to them, one or two just moved their chairs, while the rest continued their conversation without appearing to take the least notice of our intrusion. These I knew were the manners of young ladies belonging to the first society towards gentlemen of an inferior order, or towards those whose rank, for some reason or other, were it but the omission of certain formalities, has not yet been generally established. I therefore observed to my friend, in a voice sufficiently low not to be heard by the company, that it would probably be best to leave these girls to themselves.

"By no means," replied he in a whisper; "I have that with me which shall revenge every impertinence I have thus far suffered from them.

They never knew my connexions here; and are only *cutting* me because they have been invited to two or three parties, where, owing to my short stay in this city, I did not care about being introduced. Besides, I mean to teach them better breeding for the future." Then, turning to one of the young beauties, "Pray, Miss ***," demanded he, "what did you do with yourself during the whole of this beautiful day?"

"That's a secret, sir; we don't tell that to everybody."

Here the young lady endeavoured to cut the conversation short by whispering something to her neighbour.

"But I thought I saw you come out of one of the shops in Broadway?"

"I assure you I did not see *you*," replied the lady, with a remarkably acute accent.

"That I can easily account for," replied my friend; "I was walking on the other side, and there were several carriages in the street."

"Oh! I should not have seen you if I had stumbled over you. I never look at gentlemen."

Here she again whispered to her acquaintance, with her eyes fixed upon us; but my friend was determined to see her out.

"Do you know," said he, "Mrs. *** is going to give a magnificent ball?"

"I am glad to hear it," replied the young lady.

"It is said the first invitations are already given out. I dare say you have received yours?"

The young lady exchanged looks with her friend.

"Are *you* invited, sir?"

"Oh, I am an old friend of the house; I go there whenever I please."

"Even without being invited, I suppose?"

"You know, Miss ***, I never stand upon ceremonies."

"One would suppose so."

"And yet I flatter myself I never give offence."

The lady made no reply.

"I hope," said he to the second girl, "you have got over your cold?"

"I don't 'mind' a cold."

"But it gives me great pain to see you afflicted."

Here the young lady rose, as if she intended to leave the room.

"Pray, Miss ***, don't rise," cried my friend, "before I have delivered to you Mrs. ***'s invitation. I received it only last night, with the request to hand it you as soon as convenient; and I would not incur Mrs. ***'s displeasure for the world."

"You are very kind, Mr. ***; have you got it with you?"

"Here, Miss ***, you see I directed it myself; it will be one of the most brilliant parties given in New York this season."

"Well, I declare you are monstrous good-natured," said the young with a bow; then, turning to her companion, "Dear Fanny, only look at Mrs. ***'s politeness; she invites me ten days *ahead.*"

"Pray, won't you act the post-boy for *me,* Mr. ***?" said Fanny, looking half ironically, half condescendingly, upon my friend.

"Most willingly, if anybody will intrust me with a note to you, which I dare say will be in the course of to-morrow."

"Well, I do admire Mr. ***'s gallantry, I declare!" cried the young lady, relieved from a painful embarrassment: "what would become of us if we had not Southerners and Europeans" (here she deigned to notice me for the first time) "to take care of us? Our New York gentlemen will be devoted to business; you can get no more attention from them than from a stick of wood."

At this moment a stout negro rang the bell for dinner. It was one of those high-toned, shrieking bells, a single note of which would have set a musician crazy; but, to judge of the electrifying effect it produced on the whole company, it was far from being disagreeable even to the most refined American ears. The gentlemen especially smiled with approbation, as it called them once more from helpless idleness to active industry; and, in their eagerness to obey its summons, offered their arms to young and old, in order to have the good fortune of the first *entrée.* It was a scene of complete confusion,—one of those which occur but rarely in America, except just before dinner,—a *mêlée* of ladies and gentlemen. I saw three young men offer their arms to an old lady near the door, and a pretty little creole woman was actually marched off under double escort. I felt my heart bleed as I looked round for my unsophisticated *brunette,* and saw her dragged along by a young broker, who was already smacking his lips in anticipation of the turtle. Her mother was gone long ago: when she heard the bell, she made an instinctive move towards the door, and was immediately snatched off by a young man, who made the most of her in the way of taking precedence of his friends. Even the old widow-lady vanished with a gentleman from Boston. What was to be done? Without a lady there was no seat to be had at the upper part of the table, and, in fact, no certainty of obtaining a seat at all; and there remained yet two Englishmen,—a physician, and an agent of a house in Manchester,—a Spaniard from the island of Cuba, two Portuguese, my friend and myself, to be helped to partners. Fortunately for us, however, the young lady who had just passed such high encomiums on Southern and European gallantry, had already seized my friend's arm, before he had a chance to offer it; and her amiable companion thought herself bound to accept the offer of mine. The remaining girls were equally divided among the representatives of the three nations; but the British Æsculapius, being the stoutest man of the company, was a host by himself, and formed the rear of the train.

CHAPTER III

The Dinner.—Reflections on the Homage paid to American Women.—
Observation of a Fashionable young Lady on American eating.—The
Party after Dinner.—An American descanting on the Fashions.—Parallel
between English and American Women.—Manner of rising in Society.—
Extravagance and Waste of the Middle Classes.—Toad-eating of
Fashionable Americans in Europe.—Their Contempt for the Liberal
Institutions of their Country.—Manner in which the Society of America
may be used as a means of correcting the Notions of European Exaltados.
—The British Constitution in high favour with the Upper Classes.—
Southern and Northern Aristocracy contrasted.—Aristocracy of Literati.
—American Women in Society and at Home.—Pushing in Society the
cause of Failures.—Western Aristocracy.—An Aristocratic Lady in Pitts-
burgh.—Aristocracy in a Printer's Shop.—Philosophical Windings-up of
the Party.

> "To feed, were best at home;
> From thence, the sauce to meat is ceremony;
> Meeting were bare without it."

Macbeth, Act III. Scene 4.

WHEN we entered the dining-room, soup and fish were already removed, and active operation commenced on chickens, ducks, turkeys,
beef, veal, mutton, and pork,—the seven standing dishes in the United
States. We were fortunate enough to obtain seats not far from the landlady, right in the middle of a garden of blooming beauties. The ladies
were all *en grande toilette,* though among the gentlemen not one appeared to be dressed for dinner. The conversation was very loud; but,
notwithstanding, completely drowned in the clatter of knives and
forks. I perceived that the women talked, not only much more, but also
much louder than the men; American gentlemen of the higher classes
being indeed the most bashful creatures, in the presence of ladies of
fashion, I ever saw. They approach women with the most indubitable
consciousness of their own inferiority, and, either from modesty or
prudence, seldom open their lips except to affirm what has been said
by the ladies. One is always reminded of poor Candide's honest prayer,
"Hélas! madame; je répondrai comme vous voudrez." I have seen one

38

of the most distinguished old gentlemen in the United States,—one who held the highest rank in the gift of the American people, and whose learning and knowledge on most subjects rendered him a most pleasing and entertaining companion of men,—betray as little self-possession in the presence of women as if he had been making his *début* in society, and this too in the house of one of his most intimate friends.

This excessive awkwardness in the men, to which even the most distinguished of their race make no exception, must be owing to something radically wrong in the composition of American society, which places men as well as women in a false position. The conviction of this fact must force itself on the mind of every impartial observer who has had an opportunity of making himself familiar with the customs and manners of the higher classes. There appears to be a singular mixture of respect and want of sincerity on the part of the men with regard to the women, produced, I believe, by the unnatural position which the latter hold wherever they are brought into contact with the former.

In the first place, American ladies occupy, from mere courtesy, a rank in society which is not only opposed to that which they hold in private life and in their own families, but which is actually incompatible with the exercise of discretion on the part of the gentlemen. "The ladies must be waited upon;" "the ladies must be helped;" "the ladies must be put into the carriage;" "the ladies must be taken out of the carriage;" "the ladies must have their shoe-strings tied;"* "the ladies must have their India-rubber shoes put on;" "the ladies must be wrapped up in shawls;" "the ladies must be led up stairs and down stairs;" "the ladies must have their candles lit for them when they go to bed." On every occasion they are treated as poor helpless creatures who rather excite the pity than the admiration of men; and as the services they require are numerous, just in proportion to the scarcity of hired servants, the gentlemen are obliged to officiate in their stead.

These continual exigencies cannot but render the society of women often irksome to men who are daily engaged from ten to twelve hours in active business, before they dress to do the agreeable at a party; and hence the retiring of the ladies is but too frequently hailed as the signal for throwing off restraint, or, as I once heard it called, "for letting off the steam," and being again natural and easy. If in any of these matters the men were allowed to use their own discretion in bestowing atten-

* This is generally done by gentlemen in the absence of footmen.

tion on those only whom they like, all would be well enough. The ladies would receive a great deal of voluntary tribute; and the gentlemen, delighted with the privilege of a choice, would be more prodigal of their *petits soins* to those who would have a smile in return for their devotion. But, instead of this, a fashionable American is harassed by an uninterrupted series of exactions, made for no other purpose than for gratifying "the ladies;" while the rules of society are such, that he can scarcely ever find a chance of making himself agreeable to a particular individual. Hence an American *salon* exhibits nothing but generalities of men and women, in which no other merit is recognised but that which belongs to the sex. In this manner American ladies are worshipped; but the adoration consists in a species of polytheism, in which no particular goddess has a temple or an altar dedicated to herself.

Whenever an American gentleman meets a lady, he looks upon her as the representative of her sex; and it is to her sex, not to her peculiar amiable qualities, that she is indebted for his attentions. But look upon the same lady when she returns home from a party, or after the company has been dismissed at her own house! She is indeed honoured and respected, a happy mother, a silent contented wife, and complete mistress at home; but how seldom is she the intimate friend of her husband, the repository of his secrets, his true and faithful counsellor,—in one word, the better half of his existence! And yet what woman would not rather be *that,* than an idol, placed on an artificial elevation in society, in order to be deprived of her true influence on the deliberations and actions of men. I have undoubtedly seen American ladies who were all a woman could wish to be to their husbands; but I scarcely remember one, especially in fashionable life, who was not quoted to me as an exception to the rule.

Such were my reflections as I took my seat next to the fashionable angel who, by doing me the honour of accepting my arm, was actually doing me out of my dinner. There were but six black servants in the room to wait upon more than fifty people; and in South Carolina I had often seen six negroes wait upon one person, without being able to make him comfortable. Under such circumstances, the business of a gentleman is to see that the lady next to him does not leave the table without having had something to eat; and for this purpose no small exertion and ingenuity are required, especially when one does not know the names of those sable attendants, and has no opportunity of slipping half a dollar into their hands.

At first we waited a while with great patience, showing to our greedy neighbours that we were neither as hungry nor as ill-bred as themselves; but when I saw one dish after the other disappear—the tender loin of the beef gone—the oyster sauce dried up by the side of the carcass of a turkey—everything which once had wings reduced to its bare legs—and these legs themselves to mere drumsticks—

"George!" exclaimed I in despair, "come and help this lady."

"Never mind me, sir; I get plenty," whispered the fair.

No answer from the servant.

"John, I say! why won't you come hither?"

"My name is not John, sir," grinned one of the negroes as he passed by to wait upon another person.

"Sam, then!" I cried, "and may the Lord have mercy on you!"

"Wat will you be hept to, massa?" ejaculated a dark, glossy mulatto, whose face looked as if it had just been varnished.

"What will you have, Miss ***?" demanded I of the lady.

"Why, I really don't know. I have not had time to think of it. They all eat so fast."

"Sam!" exclaimed a stentorian voice from the other end of the table.

"Yes, massa," replied Sam, and was seen no more.

"Don't you think, Miss ***," said I, "it would be better for you to make up your mind as to what you intend to eat before you come to dinner? It would, I think, be an easy task, as in every large hotel or boarding-house there appears to be the same daily variety of standing dishes."

"I am not hungry," replied the lady, with a furtive glance on the plate of her *vis-à-vis,* on which the white tender breast of a turkey, hugged in the embrace of a ruddy slice of Virginia ham, was softly reposing on a bed of mashed potatoes, and that delicious vegetable designated by the poetic appellation of "squash." The extreme borders of the plate were garnished with cranberry and apple sauce; and a quarter of a cabbage, placed with the dexterity of an artist in the background, just completed the perspective.

"Neither am I," said I. "Will you allow me to take wine with you?"

A slight convulsion of her body, similar to the one previously described,—and of which no one can form a correct idea who has not witnessed the effect of a galvanic battery on a person touching the two poles,—informed me of her acquiescence. Accordingly I filled both our glasses with champaign; and, looking at her with all the tenderness which the effervescence of that sparkling liquid is capable of inspiring, emptied mine to the very bottom. When I raised my eyes again I found hers dissolved in dew; for, instead of drinking, she had only suffered the spiritous ether to play with the end of her nose, the liquid itself remaining untouched in the vessel. I now began to feel concerned for her; so, seizing the arm of one of the attendants, who was just attempting to make his escape with the remnant of an oyster pie, I made at once a prize of his cargo, and without further ceremony shared it equally with my fastidious companion.

"Now what vegetable will you be helped to?" demanded I.

"To none, if you please, with a *pâté aux huîtres*," was the reply of the young lady.

"But, before you will have done with the *pâté aux huîtres,* the vegetables will be gone."

"I am sorry for that," said she; "but I cannot bear taking so many things on one and the same plate. The very sight of it is sufficient to take away one's appetite."

Here her *vis-à-vis* bestowed upon her a long look of astonishment, resting his left elbow on the table, and reducing the velocity of his right hand, which was armed with a formidable three-pronged fork, almost to zero.

"Indeed," continued she, without appearing to notice his emotion, "our people do not know how to eat."

"Indeed, I think they acquit themselves admirably," said I.

"And do you call *that eating?*" said she. "What must the English think of us when they see us act in this manner? Oh! I wish dinner were over! Are the gentlemen not already leaving the table?"

"Yes, Miss ***; those, probably, whose business will not allow them to stop for pudding."

"Oh, I did not wish to deprive you of your enjoyment; I would merely tax your politeness with the request of accompanying me to the door."

"I know no greater happiness than that of obeying your commands," said I, doing as I was bid. "I shall have the honour of joining you by-and-by in the parlour."

"Pray, don't let me interfere with your favourite amusements. I know you like to take a glass of wine and smoke a cigar after dinner."

"I can assure you," said I, "I do not smoke at all."

"What! you don't smoke? For mercy's sake! I hope you don't *chew?*"

"I do not use tobacco in any shape."

"Well, that is certainly a great recommendation!" exclaimed she. "I wish I could persuade *our* gentlemen to imitate your example; it would perhaps cure them of the disgusting habit of spitting."

All this was said sufficiently loud for every one near her to hear; after which the young lady, having attracted the general attention of the company, vanished through the folding-doors with the same ease and composure as a French actress who has been the favourite of the public for years.

When I regained my place, pudding and pastry had disappeared; and, the cloth being removed, dessert was placed on the table. This was of course the signal for the general departure of ladies and gentlemen; so that in about five minutes my friend and myself, two or three elderly gentlemen, the agent of the Manchester house, and the fat English doctor, were the only persons remaining in the room.

"Let us club together," said the doctor, "and call for an extra bottle of old Carolina madeira."

"I am glad to hear that," cried my friend; "but, above all things, let us get some biscuits and cheese,—I have not had a mouthful of dinner."

"Served you right!" said the doctor; "why will you be prating to those girls? They have had their dinner long ago at a confectioner's shop. I have made it a rule of my life, ever since I came to this country, to take my place at the end of the table, as far as possible removed from everything feminine; and to the observation of this maxim I am indebted for my good figure, in spite of the fogs and the easterly winds."

"Why, you know, doctor," interrupted a thin-looking American, "that your shape would not answer at all for a ladies' man. In the first place, you have the chest and shoulders of an English collier; your face is full and round, as though you had been swilling porter all your life; your legs, especially your thighs, are the very essence of beef; and, above all, sir, you have a paunch!—a paunch which would frighten any of our West-end ladies into hysterics! An American exquisite must not measure more than twenty-four inches round the chest; his face must be pale, thin, and long; and he must be spindle-shanked, or he won't do for a party. There is nothing our women dislike so much as corpulency: weak and refined are synonymous."

"That's a fact," rejoined my friend; "I heard Mrs. ***, of F——a, descant on the vulgarity of English women, because they were accustomed to *walk*."

"And in all sorts of weather, too, without being laid up six weeks with the hoopingcough!" cried the doctor.

"The fact is," rejoined the American gentleman, "your English women *are* of a much coarser make than ours; they are eternally taking exercise for their health; and, as for *physical* strength, I believe there are no women equal to them in the world."

"And it is well for them they are so," observed another American, who, I understood, was a gentleman established in New York; "for they are not treated with nearly the same respect as ours."

"If by respect you mean external attention," rejoined the doctor, "and more especially exemption from labour and personal exertion, you are certainly right as far as regards your *city* women of New York, Boston, Philadelphia, &c. Our London women of the middle and even higher classes can walk alone, stand alone, and, when taking tea or coffee, do not require a gentleman to hold the saucer for them. Whenever they require an attendance of this sort, they hire it; and, until they can afford paying a page, manage to dispense with his services."

"Excellent Englishwomen!" cried the third American, who happened to be a Boston lawyer, and a great admirer of England. "Would to Heaven our Yankee women were like yours! I do not mean to cast a reflection on the high moral qualities of our ladies; for I believe that, in regard to virtue, they can challenge the world for a comparison. I speak of the excessive pretensions and fastidious conduct, not only of our rich fashionable women, but also of the wives and daughters of our men of moderate fortune. No sooner do they find out that their husbands or fathers have laid up a couple of thousand dollars in a bank, than they set up for ladies of the *ton;* and then they want to ride in their own carriages; live in houses for which they pay from eight hundred to a thousand dollars' rent; give parties to which they invite people whom they never met before, and from which they exclude their friends and nearest relations, in order not to be shamed by their presence; rake up a relationship with some colonel in the revolutionary army, or some noble family in Europe,—the latter is by far the most respectable; hang up the portraits of their ancestors in their parlours; make the tour of the springs in the summer; and spend a winter in Washington. Waste becomes now the order of the day; and if, in spite of their scrambling after fashionable society, they do not obtain access to the very first of it, the men are teased and tormented until they leave their native city to seek in one of the numerous 'growing places' of the West an asylum in which they cannot be outdone by the *old families.*"

"Our Yankee moralist is right," exclaimed the New-Yorker; "nothing can be more contemptible than the endless pretensions of our *parvenus.*"

"If you speak in this manner," rejoined the Boston lawyer, bestowing a knowing glance on the New-Yorker, "you pronounce sentence on nine-tenths of our industrious citizens. What great difference, after all, is there between a *parvenu* of ten years' standing, and a *parvenu* who is just making his *début* in society? I have nothing to say against those who by perseverance and success in business have acquired fortunes that enable them to live in a style superior to that of their neighbours; but there is a way of playing the *bourgeois gentilhomme* which exposes a man deservedly to ridicule."

"Like Mr. *** the grocer, who has just turned India merchant, and who will crowd his rooms with the most costly furniture, in such a manner that you cannot pass from one into the other without running against a table, a sofa, or a piano."

"Or like Mrs. ***, the wife of the ironmonger, who has taken it into her head to patronize the arts, and has overhung the nice clean walls of her parlour with all the dirty daubs her husband has bought on his late tour through Italy."

"Or like Mrs. *** of Philadelphia, the wife of the auctioneer, whose *bals costumés* are said to rival those of London and Paris, and whose husband gives to his male friends 'a treat' once a fortnight."

"Or like those poor devils who live 'all in a row' in the West-end of our city without ever seeing one another, each expecting to be in due time admitted into fashionable society on paying the penalty of a party."

"To which none but the gentlemen come."

"And those only at a very late hour, just in time for supper."

"I should not care for all that," resumed the Bostonian, "if one could get away from that sort of society; but this is actually impossible, unless one emigrate to the South or West. The same artificial distinctions exist at the South: but then in the Southern States the distinctions are real, not imaginary; they date from the time of the colonies, and, being in part based on the possession of real estate, do not change with every fluctuation of trade. A man may there visit ten years in the same circle without seeing a single new face, except that of a stranger; while in New York every new quotation of exchange excludes a dozen families from the pale of fashion, and creates a dozen new candidates for its imaginary honours. Every commercial loss or gain," he continued, "exercises a controlling influence on the happiness and prospects of our families. It changes at once their friends, their associates, and often their nearest relations, into strangers. How many ties are thus broken by a single failure in business! and how many failures occur, because the heads of those families dare not retrench,—have not the courage to live within their income,—cannot bring themselves to lead their children out of a higher circle into a lower one,—have not the heart to blight their prospects in life! No! they must play the hypocrite,—live as though they were men of fortune; marry their daughters, who are brought up in the most expensive habits, to young spendthrifts, who expect them to inherit fortunes; and then die, without leaving to their heirs wherewith to procure for them a decent funeral! This, sir, is a picture of our first society, established on the system of credit! And then how much real happiness is lost in the foolish endeavour to get into the first society of our Atlantic cities; which, after all, differs from the second and third, from which it is necessarily daily recruited, in nothing that could strike an European except in the greater display of wealth and waste. The little Miss at school is already panting for the society of 'the higher girls,' and cuts her old playmates the moment her father can dress her well enough for better company. No sooner has she left school than she teases and torments her parents until they allow her to give a party, to which, of course, none but her new acquaintances are invited; and which, with her, is the beginning of a new era,—the commencement of her formal separation for life from all her early friends, relatives, and often her own parents. This, sir, is the first act of a young fascinating creature of seventeen, introducing her to the attractions of fashionable life. At that tender age, when girls in other countries are considered as mere children, she has already learned to check the better impulses of her nature, in order to conform to the customs and usages of the world. But this is not all. The bold, sophisticated girl, who has struck out her independent course of life, is no longer conducted and watched by her parents, whose inferior rank in society does not allow them to accompany her to any of the balls and parties to which she is now invited: her mother ceases to be the repository of her secrets, her guardian, and friend; she is barely asked her consent when

the young heroine is at last going to be married. If, under these circumstances, and despite of the perverse rules of society, the conduct of our
women remains still unexceptionable, it must be ascribed to the force
of religion, to the constant occupation of the men, the practice of early
marriages, and, above all, to that all-embracing power of public opinion,
which in no other country punishes the vicious and guilty with the
same unrelenting severity."

"And a good deal perhaps also to that part of public opinion which
punishes the gentlemen as severely as the ladies," observed the doctor,
finishing his glass.

"You may perhaps object," continued the Bostonian, who appeared
to be bent on a homily, "that a similar sort of toad-eating to the higher
classes exists also in England; the lower order of the English being
even more submissive to those above them than the same classes in
America: but on the Continent you seldom see a man or woman pay
their court to a superior, except for a special object; the mere admission
into fashionable society rarely induces a man to throw away his self-
respect, and to cringe and fawn before titled personages."

"It is for this reason that the manners of certain classes of the English
are less free and natural than those of the same orders on the Continent; the former being only easy and agreeable in the society of their
native town, where their character is known and understood. Go and
visit all the courts of Europe, from Paris to St. Petersburg, and from
Stockholm to Naples, and if you find a toad-eater caressing the feet of
majesty, and exercising his utmost ingenuity to be on good terms with
the most distinguished noble families, you may be sure he is either
English or American. But the American will outdo the Englishman.
He will be twice as humble before ribands and stars, and three times as
insolent to an inferior, as honest John Bull. He will feast six months
on the breakfast of a duke, and then regale his countrymen six months
longer with the recital of its splendours. He will actually beg himself
into society, solicit letters of introduction on the most humiliating
terms, pocket quietly a thousand refusals, and, when finally he succeeds
in being smuggled into the drawing-room of a princess, is the first to
betray her hospitality in publishing her foibles to the world!

"Very few Englishmen will go as far as *that;* and, if there be some
that forget to stand sentinel on their dignity, there are fortunately
enough of those whose rank, title, and fortune, readily prócure them
the distinction others are obliged to *court*. But the Americans who go

to Europe leave their self-assumed rank in society behind; they go thither as plain citizens of a republic, dependent entirely on their letters of introduction, and the civility of those to whom these letters are directed. Their first care, therefore, is to impress all with whom they come in contact with the belief that, though the spirit of the American constitution recognises no nobility, such an order of society nevertheless exists *de facto;* and that they themselves belong to the 'few select' of that 'large Augean stable.' I assure you I quote the very words of Americans, as I have often heard them; for railing against their country constitutes one of the chief amusements of our Yankee exquisites at home and abroad.

"In this manner they hope to ingratiate themselves with the old aristocracy of Europe, whom they flatter and console with repeated assurances that the 'mob government of America' will not last half a century; and that they themselves are so far converted to the ancient and noble doctrines as to be determined to leave their country for the purpose of sojourning amongst civilized men. On the principle, then, that *one* repentant sinner is more acceptable in the eye of *the Lord* than a hundred just men, these Americans are admitted into favour; but, notwithstanding their partial success, few of them understand the art of *se laisser aller*. One can always see that they are not brought up for sociable idleness; and when a bill is presented,—were it even for a patent of nobility,—you would see them wax pale with horror as they thrust their hands into their pockets."

"I often remarked the penuriousness of fashionable Americans in Europe; but I cannot say that this is a fault to which they are much addicted at home," observed my friend, with a sarcastic look on the New-Yorker, who, I understood, had just commenced a wholesale business without capital.

"In the United States," rejoined the Bostonian, "a man will frequently be liberal with the money that is not precisely his own; the credit system allows him to spend more than his income: but in Europe, where he is obliged to pay for everything as he goes along, he soon learns to hold on to the cash."

"That is one reason," said my friend; "and the second is, he does not know how to spend his money. He lays it out on things Europeans value but little, and is most parsimonious where Europeans are most liberal. I knew a Bostonian in Paris who would pay twelve francs a day for his fire, and in the evening drive in a common hackney-coach to a party; another would give his wife a shawl of a thousand francs, but refuse her some Nancy embroidery; and a third would purchase for his wife and daughters pocket-handkerchiefs at a hundred francs a-piece, but object to their being washed. I was present when an American lady, who was told by a French gentleman that at a certain shop on the Boulevards there were very nice embroidered ladies' handkerchiefs to be had at two napoleons a-piece, exclaimed, '*Comment! et vous croyez que je puisse porter des mouchoirs à quarante francs?*'

"'*Et quels mouchoirs portez-vous donc, Madame?*' exclaimed the Frenchman, half embarrassed and half amazed.

"'*Je ne porte que des mouchoirs à six-cents francs.*'

"'*Et comment sont-ils donc faits, ces mouchoirs là?*' demanded the astonished Frenchman.

"'*Comme ce-ci,*' replied the lady, turning up her nose, and throwing a huddled-up, dirty, pocket-handkerchief on the table, which the Frenchman, either from delicacy or fear, did not dare to unravel.

"'*Ah! en vérité,*' cried the gallant Parisian, turning away his head, '*ils sont excessivement jolis.*'

"When the same lady was afterwards told that she could perform the journey from Paris to Nice for less than a thousand francs, she remarked to her husband who had made the inquiry, 'Oh, I dare say *some* people may do it even for less; but we always travel *en grand seigneur.*'"

"Pray," said the Bostonian, "did that woman never claim any relationship to some European prince? They are seldom very extravagant unless they can prove themselves descended from a nobleman."

"To be sure she did," replied my friend; "not indeed to a prince, but to a duke, whose name is preserved in the history of his country. She told her friends and acquaintances that she only came to Europe to assist at the coronation of the Queen of England; which, she being a *dame d'atour,* could not very well be performed without her."

"Oh, yes!" exclaimed the doctor; "I believe anything of your fashionable characters, except that they can live a month without Epsom salt or calomel."

"I dare say she would have been just as humble and cringing in company of a British peer, as she was haughty and insolent with a poor Frenchman," observed my friend. "She would have gone through all the regular stages of toad-eating, in order to procure, as a particular favour, a place in some corner of a room from which she might have peeped at the lovely person of her British Majesty."

"I am sure of that," cried the Bostonian; "that's the way our people do when brought within the sphere of attraction of a court."

"And is it not strange," resumed my friend, "that the Americans, who at home are the most thin-skinned people in the world,—always ready to punish in the most severe, and sometimes in the most atrocious manner, every offence offered to the nation or to individuals,—should, on leaving home, so far lay aside their character and self-respect as to literally creep through the palaces of princes for the sordid satisfaction of being able to say that they have been there?"

"The contempt of our fashionable people for the liberal institutions of their country, and their admiration of everything that is European, are so well known and understood in Europe," observed the Bostonian, "that of all the travellers through France, Germany, and Italy, the Americans suffer the least molestation or inconvenience from passports. Their presence in any country can only serve to chill the ardour of the liberals, as there is indeed no greater punishment for an European demagogue than to pass a year or two in the United States. Our fashionable society is capable of curing the maddest republican of his political distemper. Just send him over here for two months, with plenty of letters to our first people, and he will return home as quiet and loyal a subject as any one born in the sunshine of royal favour."

"And, on the other hand, it is the European emigrants that have been chiefly instrumental in establishing our present mob government," observed the New-Yorker. "Those blackguards—I mean principally the Germans and the Irish,—come here with the most ridiculous notions of liberty and equality. Having been slaves all their lives, they set an exaggerated value on freedom, without knowing the value of property. The British constitution, after all, is the best adapted to the wants of a free people; isn't it?"

"Most assuredly it is," replied the Bostonian; "we all know it, but none of us dare say so aloud, for fear of being mobbed: but murder will out, you know."

"What can a man know about our institutions, if he be not 'raised' among us?" rejoined the New-Yorker. "Our institutions, after all, are but the English, improved or mutilated, just as you please; but, be this as it may, I prefer the English to our own. I cannot bear equality."

"Nor I," said the other American.

"Nor I either," said the Bostonian; "and I know a number of our people who would not stay in Paris, on account of the ridiculous equality which pervades all classes of French society. They have had quarrels with their servants, and have been summoned with those scoundrels before the same tribunal."

"That's the reason I dislike the Irish so much," resumed the New-Yorker. "They are scarcely a year in the country before they pretend to be equal to our *born* citizens. I should have no objection to their coming here, provided they would be contented to remain servants,—the only condition, by the by, they are fit for: but when they come without a cent in their pockets, pretending to enjoy the same privileges as our oldest and most respectable citizens, my blood boils with rage; and I would rather live among the Hottentots at the Cape of Good Hope, than in the United States, where every cart-man is as good as myself."

"I assure you," said my friend, with a significant smile, "no people in the world are better satisfied of their superiority than the higher classes of Americans. If their pretensions were recognised by the people at large, there would be no happier set of men in the world. There is no species of perfection which they do not attribute to one another: so that one is constantly reminded of the fable of the two asses, one of which found the other an excellent singer, while the latter discovered in the first a great talent for public speaking; the rest of the animals seeing neither the singer nor the orator in either of them. I am at once for an aristocracy like the English, with some lasting, real distinctions. Our patriots have ruined the country by abolishing the institution among us. It would have protected us against the vulgarity of our moneyed men, and produced noblemen instead of fashionable dandies, who are talking of the privileges of gentlemen before they are entitled to the distinction."

"You are right," exclaimed the Bostonian, "to ridicule the wooden butterflies that play about our glass-house flowers. No one ever dreamt of mocking the manners of the Dutch merchants. They stick to trade; and, if our merchants were to do the same, they would command the respect of the world, instead of affording amusement by their attempt at aristocratic distinctions. You cannot but esteem Brother Jonathan when you see him on the ocean, or in his workshop; but his affectations in the parlour seldom fail to disgust you. In the *salon* the most fashionable of our race is but an anomaly, with not one-tenth part the liberality, politeness, and affability of an European. His bow, his smile, his constrained ease, his affected carelessness, his very apparel, and, if he venture himelf so far, his conversation, are unnatural; and you are actually moved to compassion when you see him sacrifice himself at a dance. The old people will tell you they give parties for their children; the girls dance because it is the way to get engaged and married; but the young men look upon society as a business they must go through at specified intervals."

"And yet, mean and contemptible as the elements of our first society may be," rejoined my Southern friend, "they produce incalculable mischief. In the first place, they are the means of spoiling our women; not that I mean that they destroy their virtue,—which, thank Heaven! is proof against greater temptation than that of our fashionable men, who, moreover, have so little time for the *petits soins* which the ladies require of them, that they prefer the marrying for good and all to the tedium of a long courtship; but it makes our women indolent, unfit for the performance of domestic duties, and, in many instances, prodigal and sophisticated in the extreme,—and this at an age when Englishwomen scarcely venture out into company. And how small is the number of our fashionable people whose fortunes are at all commensurate with their expensive habits! The country at large is rich, on account of the great ease of our middle and even lower classes; but, in attempting to vie with the splendour of the English nobility, we introduce a reckless system of expenditure, wholly above the means even of our wealthiest people, and undermining the solid basis of our national wealth."

"Society in America," continued my friend, "is characterised by a spirit of exclusiveness and persecution unknown in any other country. Its gradations not being regulated according to rank and titles, selfishness and conceit are its principal elements; and its arbitrary distinctions th more offensive, as they principally refer to fortune. Our society takes it upon itself to punish political, moral, and religious dissenters; but most of its wrath is spent upon the champions of democracy. That society is the means of seducing our unsophisticated country members, making them believe that republicanism is only fit for backwoodsmen, is a fact too notorious to be mentioned. It destroys our independence in words and actions, and makes our duties of citizens subordinate to the exactions of a *coterie*. What man is there in this city that dares to be independent, at the risk of being considered bad company? And who can venture to infringe upon a single rule of society, without being published to the world, and persecuted for the remainder of his life? We take it as an insult offered to our joint judgment when a man stubbornly follows his own mind; for we are accustomed to everything, except seeing a man not influenced by the opinion of his neighbours.

"How often have I envied Englishmen for the privilege of being independent in private life! And how often did I wish myself in England, where I might be permitted to have an opinion of my own, and express it, without suffering in the consideration of my friends and the public! Political liberty is, after all, but an abstract and general good, never felt by individuals, unless it be joined to freedom of intercourse, and that degree of independence which leaves a man in all matters relating to himself sole arbiter of his actions. Intolerance and persecution in private and social intercourse are far more odious, and, perhaps, more destructive to the higher faculties of the mind, than the most systematic political despotism acting from above. And yet I would pardon our society all its faults, if it did not act perniciously on the women."

"Let us hear what complaint our Anglo-maniac has against our women," exclaimed the New-Yorker, who had already looked more than twenty times on his watch as if pressed by urgent business.

"Oh!" cried my friend, "my charge against them is small, and refers principally to our exclusives: I am sorry that they are unfit for anything but society, and that in society they do not fill the place which belongs to them."

"A mere trifle!" said the doctor, filling his glass.

"I do not speak of the great mass of our women," rejoined my friend; "much less of the wives and daughters of our Western settlers, who, Heaven knows, are as busy and industrious as the best German housewives: what I have to say applies merely to our aristocracy, and still more to those who aspire to being considered candidates for that distinction. Our women in general are, as you know, not brought up to work,—the chivalrous spirit of our men spurning such a vulgar abuse of their delicate limbs; they ought, therefore, to be brought up to save, or at least to live within their income. If, for instance, one of our tavern-keepers will not allow his wife and daughters to appear before his guests,—if a shopkeeper will not exhibit his wife before his customers,—I shall certainly respect the feelings and principles of both: but if the tavern or shop keeper's wife insists upon living in Broadway, wearing nothing but satin and gros de Naples, and is constantly emptying her husband's purse for the purpose of 'pushing in society;' if she does not regulate her expenditure according to his means; if she takes no pains to ascertain what these means are; in short, if she be but a useless article of furniture in his parlour,—then I certainly maintain that there is something radically wrong either in her education or in the state of society of which she is a member.

"If we had as many distinct and established orders of society as in England, there would not be that everlasting attempt to go beyond one another which particularly characterises our women, and, joined to the credit system, is the cause of so many failures; a circumstance which, in whatever light merchants and bankers may view it, is nevertheless one of the greatest moral evils with which an honest community can be afflicted.

"A large portion of our matrons," he continued, "would, I am sure, be more happy in wearing muslin or calico, instead of silk; and the men, instead of racking their brains in order to find the means of providing for a thousand unnecessary expenses, would find their homes cheap and comfortable. They would look upon their wives as friends and counsellors, instead of mere companions of their pleasures. Instead of 'boarding out,'—a custom which is the grave of affection and domestic happiness,—young husbands would be enabled to keep house, and to give their wives a home; a thing which is not so much rendered difficult by the badness of the servants,—the usual complaint of the higher classes,—as by the exactions of society. I know many an American that is now living in Europe merely because he does not wish to board, and is not rich enough to keep house according to our expensive fashion.

"If this state of things were confined only to the wealthier classes,—to those who have large estates and expectances,—all would be well enough; the extravagance of the rich furnishes scope for the industry of the poor: but with us, where young men without fortunes marry, at the age of twenty-one, girls of eighteen that have no money either, where the husband relies solely on his wits for supporting his wife and children, but few men can indulge themselves in reckless expenditure without growing indifferent as to the ways and means of paying their debts. I am proud of the enterprising spirit of my countrymen, who are always full of speculation and hope,—who live in the future, and care little about the present; but I regret that our fashionable ladies too should have caught the inspiration. A large portion of these, as has been said before, know little or nothing about their husbands' property; they live in houses built or rented on credit, drive in carriages that are not paid for, wear clothes that are charged by the milliner, sit down to a dinner which stands in the book of the victualler, and finally sink to rest on beds that are settled for by a note of six months. They have no other regulator of their expenses but fashion;—but not the fashions of their own country, grown out of the natural position and the manners and customs of the people; but the fashions of Paris and London, made for a different people,—at least different as regards custom and circumstances;—and are at last as much surprised at the bankruptcies of their husbands as their creditors, who took them for rich men.

"And this evil, as I said before, is not confined to a small class; it extends to all who wish to be considered 'genteel,'—an appellation which is daily working the most incalculable mischief. In order to be 'genteel,' it is necessary, in the first place, to know nobody that is *not* so; and our fashionable women and girls have a peculiar talent for staring their old friends and acquaintances out of countenance, as often as they take a new house. Next, they must live in a particular part of the town, and pay not less than from one to two thousand dollars' rent. Then they must give so many parties a year, and not be seen wearing the same dress more than once in a season. And last, though not least, their husbands, brothers, and cousins must give evidence of their good breeding by abusing the republican institutions of their country.

"After they have been 'genteel' for a number of years, they are permitted to set up for 'exclusives;' for which purpose they must live in the West-end of the town, keep a carriage, claim a relationship with some French duke or British earl,—a colonel in the army or a captain in the navy will no longer answer at that stage,—invite the most distinguished Europeans (by way of hospitality) to their houses, and have their parlours ornamented with pictures in proof of their taste for the fine arts."

"*A-propos!*" exclaimed the doctor; "you remind me of my friend Mr. *** in Boston, who commissioned a gentleman of his acquaintance to purchase in Italy ten thousand dollars' worth of pictures for his parlour. What sort of pictures did he get? I believe you know him, don't you?"

"He did not want 'any good ones,'" replied my friend; "for, when Mr. *** offered to purchase half-a-dozen originals, he was quite out of humour about it, telling him that for that money he expected to have all his rooms full. But let me continue my argument."

"Don't interrupt him!" vociferated the Bostonian; "he is just labouring under a spell of Southern eloquence."

"An American exclusive," resumed my friend, "is not yet a finished 'aristocrat.' There are yet a thousand things about him which betray his low origin, or, as the English have it, 'smell of the shop.' Though extravagant and wasteful, he has not yet learned to spend his money with ease and gracefulness. The women do not know how to speak French or Italian; and the boys, brought up sometimes at a public school, (for there are few families in the Northern States incurring the expense of a private tutor,) would necessarily imbibe some of the *vulgarising* spirit of democracy. As a finish then to the education of father, mother, and children, and perhaps, also, to drown in oblivion the tedious particulars of their rise and progress, our highest and best families emigrate for a short time to Europe, in order, in the society of noblemen, to attain that peculiar high polish and suavity of manners which it is impossible to acquire amidst the bustle of business and the vulgar turmoil of elections.

"How our ladies' hearts beat when they think of Europe and its pleasures!—of the gay and graceful baronets!—the insinuating lords!—the rich, proud earls!—the noble dukes!—and, oh! the kings and princes and their courts! What magic is there in that word 'KING!' to the mind of a *genteel* American! and how far will he stoop for the distinction of being admitted into his presence! What privilege, I heard them say, is it to shake hands with the President of the United States?—every blackguard, dressed in boots, can do the same. What honour is there in being present at a levee at the White House in Washington?—every journeyman mechanic may enjoy the same pleasure without even a decent suit of clothes. But a reception at a King's, or a ball at court, are things to be proud of! They have slandered an American minister at St. Petersburg, by saying that he knelt before the Emperor; but I can assure you that in England Americans have assumed that attitude before the Queen!"

"That's all right!" ejaculated the doctor; "a man cannot be too humble before a woman; but I do not like to see a Yankee humiliate himself before a King."

"And in proportion before every duke or earl," interrupted the Bostonian. "I remember, a year ago, while at Paris, to have called on

an American lady who had been honoured by a visit from a distinguished Tory leader in the House of Lords. She felt, of course, the
raptures of the blessed during his protracted presence; and when he at
last rose to take his leave, and actually vanished through the parlour
door, she observed to a young American, who had just been announced and was now entering the room, that the gentleman whom he
had met in the entry was actually the famous Lord L——t. 'Lord
L——t!' exclaimed the youth, sinking into a chair; 'was it really Lord
L——t?' Here followed a pause of one or two minutes, during which
he in vain struggled to recover his senses. 'And this was Lord L——t!'
cried he, gasping for breath, and running to the window to catch another glimpse of the lord. 'What an extraordinary man that Lord
L——t is! How did you become acquainted with Lord L——t? Won't
you introduce me to Lord L——t?' "

"Such scenes as these are not worth relating," observed my friend.
"They occur every day in every capital of Europe infested by our
Yankee exquisites. What I most regret is, that our women are the
principal actors that flourish in them. I would rather marry a young
Tartar girl, than a fashionable American *belle* after she has made the
tour of Europe. If she was heartless before she left America, she is sure
to return marble-ised to her own country. And as for our striplings,
who are actually worshipping the feudal institutions of Europe, they
come home with signets and coats of arms, and a lordly loathing of
republican equality."

"And this is not only the case with your inexperienced boys and
girls," observed the doctor, sipping his glass; "but applies also to your
men of letters, your distinguished orators and philosophers. However
fiercely they may extol republican institutions in their writings, they
all sink the republican in company with lords and ladies. 'They know
nothing of Berkeley-square, though they *fancy* it to be inhabited by
respectable people;' but give a long account of the routs in the neighbourhood of Grosvenor-square, and are particularly happy in re-
membering the country seats of the most distinguished peers of the
empire."

"I grant you all this," replied my friend; "and yet I would pardon
Cooper all his sins that way for the love he once cherished for his
country. He has suffered severely for the democracy of his earlier days;
for the meanest scribbler for a penny paper in the United States
thought himself justified in pouring out his venom on the author of

'The Pilot.' He is, after all, the only American that ever poetised American history; the nice, gentlemanly, English-looking Washington Irving has, in his 'Knickerbocker's History of New York,' only raised a laugh at the expense of his country."

"And yet," observed the Bostonian, "he might have written the history of every American town, from the famous city of Boston down to the creole habitation of New Orleans, without rising into notice in America, had his works not been endorsed by the British public. No people in the world know better than our first society that they have no taste of their own; and it is for this reason that our poets must first seek a reputation in England, before they can expect one in their own country. Washington Irving had more credit as a merchant than as an author, and succeeded in his writings only after he had failed in business. Without the latter circumstance, which may really be called fortunate, his talents would perhaps never have been developed. But let the Carolinian go on with his aristocracy; he has already kept us over an hour, and, if you continue to interrupt him, he will never finish."

"I have very little more to say," said the Southerner; "because the tour of Europe *finishes* an American aristocrat. He has now been in England, France, and Italy;—he has, with his own eyes, seen the great and mighty upon earth;—he has exchanged visits with some of them, and has perhaps been asked to partake of their hospitality. It is now the business of the women to collect and carefully to preserve the many testimonials of respect which they may have received in the shape of cards, invitations, and letters; in order, on their return to the United States, to *prove* to the incredulous that they have actually been the fashion in *Europe,* and that in consequence they have a right to be it in America. They are now advanced to the rank of 'leading people,' and an invitation to their houses is as much sought after as a letter of introduction to an European nobleman. '*They* know Lord So-and-so!' '*She* was quite intimate with Lady So-and-so!' '*He* stayed a week at the country seat of the Marquis of ***!' '*She* was presented at the Queen's!' '*Both* their names were in Galignani's Messenger!' '*She* is corresponding with the wife of the Honourable Mr. ***!' 'The Duke of *** was quite attentive to *her!*' 'The Prince Royal of *** accompanied her on horseback!' And a hundred other fine and flattering things are told of them in our fashionable *salons;* until Mr. and Mrs.

*** are not only the fashion, but the envy of every family in Broadway.

"Fortunately for the business habits of our people, they cannot make proselytes among our industrious male population: but our fashionable women, one-half of whom live in boarding-houses, and the other half in houses kept by their servants, are wondrously taken by such accounts of the 'success of the Americans abroad;' and exhibit by their unnatural, affected, forced manners, and by the total abjuration of everything American, their solicitude to be governed by the same elevated standard of refinement. On this account many of our women think themselves vastly superior to their husbands; and a certain portion of them actually have a higher standing in society. Hence the thousand incongruities and absurdies you meet with in our fashionable circles; all proving that our people do not act from habit and conviction, but from imitation and precept, and that, consequently, they are always at a loss how to act when they come to a part not contained in their lesson. They will send out invitations to dinner at eight o'clock, merely because this is a good hour in London, deranging thereby not only their own business, but the business of everybody they ask; commence balls and parties at eleven or twelve o'clock, and end them at four in the morning, though at eight they have to be again at their counting-rooms; and visit at an hour when the majority of the people are at dinner. Fashions which are worn in London and Paris in the month of October, are introduced immediately after their arrival here in the beginning of winter. They must have musical *soirées* without music; *thés littéraires* without literature; and they must crowd their staircases with statues, to show that they have a taste for sculpture. One finds in our fashionable society some feeble, and, for the most part, unsuccessful imitation of everything that exists in Europe, but scarcely one original object as a proof of our national existence: so that, if it were possible to transfer a person directly from some fashionable French or English party to one of our stockholders' balls in New York, Boston, or Philadelphia, he would scarcely perceive any visible change; though he might consider himself transported from the West-end to the City, or from the Faubourg St. Germain to the neighbourhood of La Bourse."

"Pass the bottle!" cried the doctor; "I believe he has finished his long speech."

"*I* have a word to say now," interposed the Bostonian; "I must wind up my argument with regard to our women as compared to the English."

"Is he a 'hard' speaker?" inquired the New-Yorker.

"He isn't quite equal to the member from Massachusetts," replied my Southern friend, "who spoke seven hours in succession against time; but, before he continues, I must ask him whether he has seen Mrs. ***'s *tableaux vivants*. I believe she had some highly classical representations the other evening."

"Just so," said the doctor; "in which her daughter made the Sphinx, and Mr. ***, the Wall-street shaver, the Numidian lion."

"Capital!" ejaculated the Bostonian; "but I refer to no individual in particular—I only speak of the absurd tastes of our fashionable women in general. I would ask, by way of finishing the picture which our friend from Carolina so happily commenced, and in order to settle the question of reckless expenditure, on which you all seem to exhaust your eloquence, how many of those that belong to our fashionable society can afford its expenses without impairing their estates?—how many of them would be able to continue them without the assistance of credit? —and how many of them, if their estates were to be settled tomorrow, would be able to pay fifty cents in a dollar? I am accustomed to bring everything down to *figures*. We at the North are a practical people: we like to *calculate*."

Here the New York gentleman took out his watch, and, pretending to be in a great hurry, abruptly left the room.

"Do you think *he* is solvent?" said the doctor drily, emptying his glass.

"Not I," replied the Bostonian. "Out of fifty persons that commence business in Boston, forty-nine are supposed to fail within the first five years; it takes them that long to learn the trade: and *we* boast of doing business on a solid capital in comparison to the New-Yorkers. But they beat us all hollow in the way of credit; our most cunning brokers in State-street are nothing in comparison to a regular Wall-street shaver. But let me come to the point. Our fashionable people are prodigal of other people's money; and, in entertaining their guests, go to the extent to which they are trusted. Take, for instance, the case of one of our pushing retail dealers. He is, of course, a married man, and has one or two partners who are also married. Each of them lives in a house for which he pays not less than six hundred dollars' rent, and the furniture of which costs from three to four thousand dollars. Each of them keeps one male and one or two female servants, and, in short, supports his wife *as a lady*. Each of them must ask people to tea, each must give dinners to his friends, and all 'push to get into society.' Suppose these men to do business on their own capital,—a thing which does not occur once in fifty cases; and let us suppose that their joint stock in trade is worth a hundred thousand dollars; let us take for granted that, deducting losses and bad debts, they realise a clear profit of ten per cent. on their capital; and I can prove to you that, in the ordinary course of things, they must be bankrupts in a few years. What, then, are we to expect of the generality of our young men, who commence business with a borrowed capital, on which they pay from six to eight per cent. interest?"

"Let him figure it out!" cried the doctor,—"let him figure it out! he is a Yankee."

"With all my heart," said the Bostonian, "if you will only promise not to interrupt me."

"Suppose the borrowed capital to consist of one hundred thousand dollars?

	Dollars.
"Then the interest, at six per cent. would amount to . .	6,000
"Store rent, say	1,200
"Two clerks with a salary of 300 dollars per annum . .	600
"Insurance on stock	1,000
"House rent for two partners, each 600 dollars . . .	1,200
"Expenses of housekeeping, interest on furniture, servants, &c. each 2500 dollars	5,000
"Ladies' dresses, parties, carriage hire, and incidental expenses, say each 1000 dollars	2,000
"Gentlemen's dresses, horse hire, newspapers, and tobacco, say each 500 dollars	1,000
"Grand sum total	18,000
"Clear profit on 100,000 dollars' worth of stock (deducting 25 per cent. bad debts), say 10 per cent.	10,000
"Deficit	8,000

"Pray, what ruins these men, but the want of domestic economy in their own households? An English shopkeeper would be content to live in a house for which he would not pay more than from fifty to sixty pounds' rent. His carpets would be Kidderminster, instead of Brussels or Turkey. His wife would require no other servant but a cook or a kitchen-girl; and would no more dream of giving parties, or vieing with the splendour of merchants and bankers, than she would of bringing up her children to match the peers of the empire. This is the advantage a shopkeeper has who marries an *English* girl. He gets, at least, a wife that wears well,—a substantial housekeeper, that administers to his comfort, and assists him in laying up a penny for rainy days. If her husband dies, she is, for the most part, capable of continuing his business, and making an honest living for her children. With all the morality, virtue, and beauty of our women, they are but helpless creatures. The wife of one of our young 'merchants of respectability' requires more waiting than, in proportion to her rank, an English peeress; and, ten chances to one, does not even understand superintending her servants. Her husband, in addition to ten or twelve hours' hard labour at his counting-room, has to take care of his household, in which he is intrusted with the several important and honourable functions of steward, butler, groom, footman, and housemaid; while the education of the children is only at the extreme North and South—in New England and in the Southern States—superintended personally by the mother.

"One of our fashionable young women,—innocent, kind, gay, handsome, beautiful, as she may be,—is after all of no use whatever to a poor man who has to work for his living; except that, by trebling his expenditure, she is a most powerful stimulus to industry and enterprise. If he fail in business, or die without providing for her and her children, she has no other means of saving herself from starvation than that of opening a boarding-house; which is generally so ill managed, that in less than a year she is involved in debt, and sees her furniture brought to the hammer.

"As long as our young merchants get rich by speculations, or have their notes shaved by a Wall-street broker at the rate of one per cent a month, they may be right in marrying those dear little objects of care and caresses; but when, at some future day, wealth will become the reward of labour and frugality, our 'respectable young men' will be obliged to select their wives for the kitchen as well as the parlour. All I can say in favour of our fashionable women is, that they do more for the settlement of the Western country than the soil, climate and the cheapness of land."

"And what is most remarkable," interrupted my friend, "is, that those very women, after they have resided a year or two in the Western States, become, by the strong force of example, and perhaps also from dire necessity, real Dutch housewives."

"That is to say," observed the Bostonian, "they scrub their own floors, clean the door-handles, wash the windows, sweep the rooms, make themselves busy in the kitchen, and walk about with children in their arms; all which, I can assure you, is done by the women of the best society in the Western States without destroying either their health or good looks. Women there are obliged to work, because they cannot find servants to do the work for them; and yet they are infinitely happier than your New York or Philadelphia ladies, who rise at eight or nine, breakfast at ten,—then, as Miss Fanny Kemble would have it, *potter* three or four hours,—then have a chat with three or four women of their set,—then walk Broadway or Chestnut-street, or go shopping,—then sit down to dinner,—then *potter* again until six o'clock,—then take tea,—and finally dress for a party, at which, unless they be very young, they stick up against the wall until supper."

"I certainly wish for a medium between the extreme hardships of American women in the Western country, and their comparative indolence in the seaports," observed my friend; "and yet I am glad that the republican spirit of the West is opposed to servitude of any kind, for it is a great corrective of our vulgar aristocracy of money. If, in the Western States, you could at all times command a sufficient number of hands, the possession of large real estates would soon lay the foundation of an aristocracy much more substantial and durable than that which effervesces on our seaboard. The human heart, after all, is aristocratic—that is, selfish—by nature; so that, if the resistance of the lower classes does not check the aggressions of the higher ones, the latter are sure eventually to get possession of the government. The Western settlers, who are obliged to work, and their wives, who must themselves superintend their households, have not even the time necessary for forming those exclusive coteries which govern society in the Atlantic cities."

"And yet," said the Bostonian, "it is not more than a year ago that I heard the wife of a Pittsburgh lawyer complain of the state of their society, which was 'dreadfully' spoiled by the number of adventurers pouring in from the Eastern States."

"Capital!" cried my friend; "the probability is she herself was but settled a few years."

"That was precisely her case," rejoined the Bostonian; "and, while she was playing the old family of the place, she wiped her children's noses with her apron."

"Now, I like that kind of aristocracy," cried the doctor, "which is obliged to wipe babies' noses, and that kind of family which is considered ancient when it has been three years stationary in a place; for it affords the surest proof that the true elements out of which an aristocracy may be formed are not yet to be found in the country."

"You are out again," cried the Bostonian. "You Englishmen, for some reason or other, never understand the particular genius of our people. We have 'lots' of aristocracy in our country, cheap, and plenty as bank-bills and credit, and equally subject to fluctuation. To-day it is worth so much,—to-morrow more or less,—and, in a month, no one will take it on any terms. We have, in fact, at all times, a *vast deal* of aristocracy; the only difficulty consists in retaining it. Neither is the position of our aristocrats much to be envied. Amidst the general happiness and prosperity of our people, their incessant cravings after artificial distinctions are never satisfied; they are a beggarly set of misers that will not sit down to dinner as long as there is a stranger present whom they are obliged to ask; and, as for the women, their position is truly deplorable. They are neither employed in domestic pursuits, nor does our society furnish them the *agrémens* of Europe. In a country whose population is the most active and industrious in the world, they are troubled with *ennui,* and have the whole livelong day no other companion than a few inquisitive creatures of their own sex. Were our women more engaged in the pursuits of active life,—were our state of society such as to offer them a more extended sphere of influence and usefulness,—did they receive less homage as *women,* and more as rational accountable beings, their aristocratic squeamishness would soon yield to a more sensible appreciation of character, and a patriotic attachment to their country."

"The same aristocratic feeling which pervades our fashionable women, operates also on our girls in the lower walks of life," observed the Southerner; "only that it is there called 'independence.' Now, I like independence in men, but I despise it in women. The dependence of women on men is the proper tie between the sexes, and the strong basis of gallantry and chivalry. I dislike your 'independent factory girls,' though they *did* turn out six hundred strong, all dressed in white, to be reviewed by General Jackson."*

"Since you mention the 'independent factory girls,' you ought not to forget the girls of our independent press," observed the Bostonian.

"What sort of girls are those?" demanded my friend.

"They are employed as compositors and *pressmen* in our printing-offices," replied the Bostonian, "reducing the wages of our journeymen printers, and preparing themselves for housekeeping by composing the works of our best authors. I know two of them who became expert cooks by composing 'The Frugal Housewife,' by Mrs. Child; and a third prepared herself for her approaching marriage by setting up 'The Mother's Book.' These girls, you must know, are distinguished by a highly aristocratic feeling; and would no more condescend to speak to one of our waiting-women, than the wife of a president of an insurance-office would deign to leave a card for the poor consort of a professor in one of our colleges. *They dress and act as ladies;* and, if you do not believe their claims to 'gentility,' they will show them to you in print."

"It is not more than a month ago, that, while in Washington, I had occasion to call at the office of one of my friends who is an editor of a daily paper. Not finding him there, I entered the press-room, where, much to my surprise, I found three pretty girls, dressed as if they had been measured by *Madame Victorine,* and in *bonnets* corresponding to the last fashion of the *Rue Vivienne,* busily engaged in multiplying the speeches of our orators and statesmen. This, however, was done in the most dignified manner; for when I asked for the master of the establishment, where I could find him, when he would be in, &c. one of them, in lieu of an answer, merely pointed to a large placard stuck to one of the columns which supported the ceiling, on which there was the following peremptory request, printed in gigantic letters:—

" '*Gentlemen are requested not to stand and look about,—because the ladies don't like it.*' "

"And did you then immediately leave the room?" inquired the doctor.

"I had no other alternative," replied the Bostonian: "if I had remained one minute longer, there would have been an article against

* When General Jackson, on his tour through the Northern States, visited Lowell, the girls employed in the cotton manufactories of that place turned out, dressed in white, to welcome the American President.

me in next morning's paper. This is a sort of trades' aristocracy formed by the female part of our population; for such seems to be the disgust of our girls for domestic occupation, that they will rather become tailoresses, printers, bookbinders, or work at a manufactory, than degrade themselves by 'living out.'* And yet I am bound to say they maintain their aristocratic dignity better than many a stockholder's wife and daughters; and I have never known a single instance in which they did not completely succeed in keeping their fellow-workmen in subjection and at a proper distance."

"This deserves a sentiment," cried the doctor; "let us call on our friend from Massachusetts to propose one."

"With all my heart, gentlemen," said the Boston lawyer. "I give you 'The Young Ladies' Trades' Union, and their champion Mr. C——y of Philadelphia: may they never reduce the price of labour of their fellow-workmen, but rather succeed in raising their own!'"

"Bravo!" shouted the company; "and worth as much again, coming from such a source. Old C——y himself could not have proposed a nobler sentiment. Pity it won't be published; it would make him immensely popular!"

"Pray, don't pass him the bottle," cried my friend; "he is done up for to-day. I never knew a Bostonian to talk of raising the price of labour except when he was drunk."

"Nor I either," cried the doctor. "I always heard them boast that no Jew could live amongst them, because they cheated him."

"Then let us vote him drunk, and fine him an extra bottle," said the doctor.

"He will never forgive you *that*," observed my friend.

"Call for the wine," cried the Bostonian; "call for it instantly,—we must drink it on the spot."

"We shall not have time for it," observed my friend; "for, if we do not quit this very moment, the negroes will drive us away in order to set the table for tea."

"You touched the bright side of his character," whispered the doctor to my friend as he was slowly rising from the table. "He has the most irresistible aversion to spending money; but, when caught in a trap like this, I don't know a person who can affect so much generosity."

* The usual American appellation for living at service.

CHAPTER IV

Joining the Ladies.—Education of a Fashionable Young Lady in New York—Her Accomplishments.—Tea without Gentlemen.—Commercial Disasters not affecting the Routine of Amusements in the City of New York.—The Theatre.—Forest come back to America.—Opinions of the Americans on Shakspeare and the Drama.—Their Estimation of Forest as an Actor.—Forest and Rice contrasted.

"A maiden never bold;
Of spirit so still and quiet, that her motion
Blush'd at herself. And she—in spite of nature,
Of years, of country, credit, everything,—
To fall in love with what she feared to look on!"

Othello, Act I. Scene 3.

On returning to the parlour, we found the ladies, whose number had considerably increased by the arrival of some "transient people," alone; the gentlemen having "sneaked off" to their respective counting-rooms. They were grouped round the piano, on which one of those little creatures that played the exclusives of the boarding-house was "practising" the "Infernal Waltz" from "Robert the Devil;" the rest were talking, whispering, giggling, or amusing themselves with feeling the quality of each other's dresses.

"What a delightful creature that Miss *** is, I declare!" said an elderly lady, whose *embonpoint* sufficiently proclaimed her Dutch origin,—English women being said to grow rather thin in America; "her mother must be proud of her."

"Yes," replied another lady, who *was* rather thin; "but it is said she has not yet paid the teacher who taught her daughter all those pretty things."

"That is nothing to the purpose; I speak of the young lady," rejoined the good-natured woman.

"Surely," whispered a young creature, who was none other than the young girl I had lost sight of before entering the dining-room, "she knows nothing about music; she has been practising that piece ever so long."

"That is a fact," said her mother, addressing herself to me; "my daughter went to the same school with her, they had the same masters, and, with the exception of trigonometry and astronomy, for which Susan never had any particular taste, she beat her in everything. My daughter can play 'The Storm;' and her music-master tells me, when a young lady can once do *that* she can do anything."

I bowed assent.

"And as for trigonometry," she continued, "I care not how little my daughter knows of that. It's all *arches,* and *angles,* and *compliments,* as she tells me, which are no use to a young lady except in society. But Susan knows a great deal more about *magnetism* and *electricity,*— don't you, my child?"

Here the girl looked very bashful.

I congratulated the mother on possessing such a treasure; and was just thinking of something pretty to say to the girl, when I was interrupted by the old lady.

"Yes," said she, "although I ought not to say it, being my own child, I was present at the last exhibition, when she explained the whole of the electrical machine. And she is doing just as well in history. How far have you got in that, Susan?"

"About *two-thirds* through with the book," said Susan; "but how queer you talk, Ma!"

"And pray, madam, what boarding-school is it your daughter went to?" demanded I.

"It's the *first* in the country, sir—kept by the Misses ***, at T***, three miles from A***."

"And what branches are taught in that school?" demanded I, with an ill-suppressed feeling of curiosity.

"I don't remember all the hard names, sir," replied the old lady, somewhat embarrassed. "Susan, my child, tell the gentleman all you have learnt at the Misses ***."

"We had reading, writing, spelling, arithmetic, grammar, geography, history, maps, the globe, algebra, geometry, trigonometry, astronomy, natural philosophy, chemistry, botany, physiology, mineralogy, geology, and zoology in the morning; and dancing, drawing, painting, French, Italian, Spanish, and German in the afternoon. Greek, and the higher branches of mathematics, were only studied by the *tall* girls."

"And how many masters were there for teaching all that?" demanded I, astonished with the volubility of the young lady's tongue.

"The Misses *** teach *everything,*" replied the girl. "They wouldn't allow a gentleman to enter the house."

"I know this to be a fact," interrupted the mother; "and that's the reason their school is so popular. It is principally on the score of morality I sent Susan there. They have always as many girls as they want, and from the first families too;—isn't it so, my dear?"

"Just so, Ma," replied the young lady. "The first girls in New York are educated there; they don't take everybody."

"I told you so," said the old lady. "It's a great thing to send a girl there; and an expensive one too, I can assure you."

"And what is the usual age of the young ladies?" demanded I.

"They take them from the age of five to the age of eighteen," she replied; "it is only a month ago I left it myself."

"I just wanted to give her a little polish before taking her to Washington, where we are going to spend the next winter," interrupted her mother. "So I took her with me to New York, to let her see European manners. We reside in T***, rather a little out of the way of society."

"I am sure Ma is very kind," said Susan. "I don't know anybody in T***, nor do I *want* to know anybody there. I never associated with any but the New York girls at the Misses ***; I was quite popular, and always belonged to their first sets."

"I am sure of that," said the mother. "Everybody that sees Susan likes her."

I put my hand upon my heart.

"I only trust to Heaven that she will marry a gentleman capable of appreciating her education"—(here the young lady applied her handkerchief to her face, and appeared to be very much embarrassed,)—"and not a man without taste for literature or science, whom she could neither love nor respect, and who would be no *sort* of company to her."

I trusted her amiable daughter would never be so horribly deceived.

"And yet it is *so* difficult to judge of men in these times, especially in New York, where young men keep their knowledge as secret as their cash, and have generally credit for more than they are worth," interrupted my friend sympathisingly.

"Ah me!" sighed the old lady; "it did not use to be so when *my* husband was alive. There was not one girl out of ten of my acquaintance knew a word of Latin and mathematics; and yet they all married respectable men, who were no mathematicians either, and brought up

their children in a right Christian manner. But they say this is the
progress of education; and I do not wish my daughter to be inferior to
other girls. Boys don't cost half so much; they learn everything they
want at the counting-room."

"And what they learn there *sticks* to them as long as they live," added
my friend.

Here mother and daughter were silent; and my friend, seizing the
opportunity, took my arm, and led me to another part of the room,
where my companion of the dinner-table was sitting alone, reading
"The Last Days of Pompeii."

"Ah!" exclaimed he, "always reading. Pray, how do you like
Bulwer?"

"Not at all," replied she.

"Why then do you read him?"

"Everybody does so, and I don't want to be singular."

"But I should think you had independence enough not to read a
book if you did not like it?"

"Why, I am sure it is not for want of independence I took it up; but
Bulwer is popular in England, and I would not give an English person
the advantage of talking about a work I have not read myself."

"And is that the only reason? Do you take no pleasure in his
novels?" demanded my friend with astonishment.

"None whatever, I assure you. I don't like his maudlin sentiments.
And, as for his prison heroes, I am too much of a matter-of-fact person
to think the gallows romantic or poetical. I dare say Bulwer's novels
suit the sentimentality of the Germans; but to me they are a perfect
dose. I dislike his description of passions,—his love-sick girls, dying
with sentiment, and ready to run off with the first bearded biped that
happens to strike their fancy. I think his novels are doing a vast deal
of mischief in this country, *exposed as we are to the continual intrusion
of foreigners.*"

"I am not quite sure," replied my friend, "whether I am to take your
remark as a compliment or a reflection. We Southerners are sometimes
honoured with the title of 'foreigners' in the Northern States."

"I do not speak of our own people," rejoined the lady; "but I know
several instances in which European adventurers have married into
our first families. Our girls seem to have an unaccountable passion for
foreigners, especially if they happen to be noblemen. Have not several

Polish refugees in this city married the daughters of some of our first merchants?"

"And what harm is there in that, if the Poles make good husbands, and prove themselves honourable men?" demanded my friend.

"Why, it's always such an experiment," she replied, "when one of our young ladies marries an European! People from the Old World entertain such different notions about women. Besides, a great many of our girls have been taken in: they expected to marry a prince, or at least a count, when their husbands turned out to have been strolling minstrels or dancing-masters. One of those unfortunate marriages was very nigh taking place the other day, and only prevented by the father of the young lady making a compromise with her admirer in the shape of a handsome sum of money. Another European Don Juan, who was flirting with every young lady in Boston, was considered so dangerous a personage, that the respectable merchants of that city made a very handsome collection to get rid of him by shipping him back to Europe."

"And I heard that, having spent the money, he made them another visit to lay them under a fresh contribution," observed my friend.

"I believe that *was* the case," affirmed the lady; "and every Atlantic city is exposed to the same calamity. *If we could only tell the real nobleman from the impostor,* I should not care. I prefer, myself, the higher society of Europe to the business people of this country; but, lately, *Continental* noblemen have come in droves, and a greater set of beggars was never known in America. By the by, do you know what has become of that handsome Spanish marquis, who last year was so much the fashion in Philadelphia?"

"The Marquis de *** you mean? I lived with him for nearly three weeks without knowing his title: he is one of the most unassuming men I ever knew."

"And yet I can assure you he is a *real* marquis," retorted the young lady. "Some of our people took a great deal of pains to ascertain the truth. He brought letters to Mr. ***, and to the *** Consul in Philadelphia; and they have written to Europe to learn all about his family. If every foreigner coming to this country were equally respectable, there would be no complaints about impostors; but our people are too easily taken in by high-sounding titles."

"But do you know the marquis is poor? that he cannot at this moment realise a dollar from his estate?" demanded my friend.

"Ah, that is very unfortunate! Poverty is *such* a drawback!"

"But he set out to make an honest living in the United States."

"Not by teaching Spanish, I hope. Nothing can be more pitiable than the avocation of an instructor."

"Indeed he was a long time resolved to do that; but, being a very handsome man, I was told no fashionable lady would intrust to him the instruction of her daughter: so he cut the matter short by opening a fashionable boarding-house; just the thing for him, you know; he speaks half-a-dozen languages, and plays the piano equal to some of your first professors."

"O horror!" exclaimed the young lady. "A marquis establishing a boarding-house! If I had known that, I should not have mentioned his name. That must, of course, have thrown him at once out of society."

"I believe he had prudence enough to quit society before the latter had a chance to abandon *him*," observed my friend calmly.

The young lady made no reply, and was fortunately relieved from her embarrassment by another negro summons to tea, equally loud, though less potent in its consequences than that which had called us to dinner. I expected another rush to the dining-room, but was agreeably disappointed. Not a single gentleman made his appearance; so that, with the exception of the two young ladies whom we had before had the honour of escorting, the women were obliged to form into single file, which proceeded with the solemnity and slowness of a funeral procession.*

Arrived near the table, they took their seats in profound silence, and with such evident signs of exhaustion from fatigue, that I felt inclined to believe that they had not yet recovered from the exertion of the dinner. Nothing, indeed, can be more tiresome than a dinner at which one does not eat; it is equal to a ball at which one does not dance, or to a *conversazione* at which one is obliged merely to listen to the nonsense of others. I inquired what had become of the gentlemen? and was told that they had not yet returned from their counting-rooms,— that they hardly ever took tea, but were rarely absent from supper, which was sure to be put on the table at nine o'clock in the evening, in order to remain there till three or four in the morning. The gentlemen, moreover, I was informed, were so much in the habit of eating oyster suppers early in the morning, in some of those innumerable subterranean eating-houses and oyster-rooms which decorate the Park

---

* In the larger boarding-houses in America, tea is not handed round, but served like a regular meal on the dining-table.

and other fashionable avenues of the city, that they did not "particularly care" about taking a cup of tea and a cold piece of meat at seven o'clock with the ladies. Dinner was quite a different concern, for which they were always ready to suffer some inconvenience.

The conversation at tea flagged from the very beginning; and it was easy to perceive that the ladies, being accustomed to make this meal the occasion of their regular confabulations, considered my and my friend's company rather *de trop*. We therefore pleaded an appointment with some gentlemen and, in the words of a French vaudevillist, "did them the pleasure of afflicting them with our departure."

"What are you going to do with yourself this evening?" demanded my friend, as we were going towards the Astor House.

"I shall look into the Park-street theatre," replied I, "and then spend the remainder of the evening at Mrs. ***'s."

"Then I shall have the pleasure of being with you all the evening," rejoined he. "Mrs. ***'s party will be one of the finest given this season."

"Which is perhaps not saying much for it, as the commercial difficulties of this year must necessarily interfere with all amusements of that sort."

"That does not follow," observed my friend; "neither is it actually the case. Public amusements are going on as usual,—our theatres are well attended,—crowds of well-dressed people are nightly listening to good, bad, and indifferent concerts at Niblo's garden,—horse-races are going on in fine style, and are this year surpassing all that is on record by the gentlemen of the turf,—there is the same quantity of champaign drunk as in former years;—in short, people seem to do as well with their 'shin-plasters'* as formerly with redeemable bank-notes. Our merchants are certainly the most extraordinary people in the world; and, if every other resource were to fail them, would not hesitate one moment, instead of payment, to take and offer drafts payable in the moon. That's what I call the genius of a mercantile community."

"And the way of keeping up appearances by credit."

"But the credit system enhances their profits more than in proportion to their liability to losses," remarked my friend; "and, besides, sharpens

* This part of my friend's journal seems to have been written in the summer of the year 1837, when, shortly after the suspension of specie payments, the country was flooded with small notes of 6¼, 12½, and 25 cents, which were termed "shin-plasters."

their wits, by obliging them to inquire into the character of those whom they trust."

"All this may be very well with regard to one merchant and another. Both find their remedy in the enlarged profits of the system; but the consumer is obliged to pay the advanced price of the merchandize. This is taxing the labouring classes for the defalcations of the traders. Besides, when a failure takes place, the merchant, who is more or less prepared for it, loses generally but a part of his profit; but, if the creditor be a mechanic, he loses the whole fruit of his labour."

"But the American merchants say, if it were not for the credit system, the labour of the mechanic would not command nearly so high a price."

"And I can assure you," said I, "that this is altogether an erroneous conclusion. The wages of the journeyman mechanic or the day-labourer, and the prices of the common necessaries of life, are *not* in proportion to the credit of the merchants—but to the actual demand and supply. During all this trouble, and while the banks stopped specie payments, all sorts of provisions were unusually high, and so were all articles of manufacture. All that the credit system of your merchants can do consists in creating, *for a time,* an artificial demand, and thereby raising, for a short period, the price of a peculiar description of labour; but, if you will take the pains of examining the history of American trade, you will find every such extraordinary price of labour soon after followed by a proportional depression, which could not but prove a greater disappointment to the workmen than would have been a regular succession of moderate prices."

"I said that the credit system favoured only *for a time* particular trades and occupations; because it is a well-known fact that the Americans seldom follow the same trade a great number of years. Let it be known that the cotton speculations of one or two individuals have been successful, and immediately half the merchants in the United States will commence speculating in cotton, until the trade is completely run down, and half the speculators reduced to bankruptcy. When, in the course of last year, twenty millions of dollars were to be raised on credit to pay for the purchase of public lands, what influence did *that* have on the industry of our working men, except that the diverting of a large portion of the capital from which they received their emoluments, into a different channel, reduced the demand for, and consequently the value of, their industry? But even granting that the American credit system, which is said to act favourably with regard to the merchants, proves also a benefit to the small trader, the mechanic, and the farmer, would not the prosperity of the latter entirely depend on the former? and would not the extension or restriction of credit, which, with such a system, can always be effected by the rich capitalists, affect the demand and supply, and place the whole community at the mercy of a few individuals?"

"And what is the moral effect of the credit system on the sturdy husbandman or the mechanic? Instead of being sure of the price of his labour,—a surety without which the labouring classes of all countries lack the principal stimulus to exertion,—he sees his success in business reduced to a game of hazard; in which, like other gamblers, he often stakes his whole fortune on a single chance. Hence, instead of adopting a course of rigid economy, he indulges in reckless expenditure, and a degree of luxury which sooner or later may prove the grave of the republican institutions of the country. For why should a man be saving, whose success depends, not on frugality, but on a 'successful hit'? and who, in a single speculation, may lose the savings of years?"

"That is a fact," observed my friend. "How many of the gentlemen that dined with us to-day do you think are possessed of real property? Not one-third of them. And yet they are all 'young, respectable merchants,' as a certain New York paper calls them, doing 'a handsome business' on a borrowed capital. You could see them again at the theatre, and, after that, dashing at some fashionable party, where they will talk of thousands as of mere bagatelles. And yet nothing acts so demoralizingly on a community as the insecurity or instability of property. I would rather see the United States 'progress slowly and steadily,' than, as they have done, by fits and starts, with periods of commercial calamities, such as no European nation has felt under the yoke of the most odious tyrant."

"What's going on this evening?" demanded my friend of the box-keeper at the Park-street theatre. "I understand Forest has come back."

"Yes, sir; fresh from England."

"Is he to play this evening?"

"Here is the bill, sir. He is going to play Othello."

"Pretty full house?"

"I don't believe you will find a seat. There was a great rush for tickets this morning. The best boxes were sold at auction to the highest bidder."

With this piece of information we lost no time in seeking a place, and were fortunate enough to be able to squeeze ourselves into a box on the first tier, filled with little more than eighteen or nineteen people, most of whom seemed to belong to the first society. A stranger always feels agreeably surprised at the neat arrangement of the interior of the Park-street theatre, whose outward appearance resembles much more a Dutch granary than a temple of the Muses. The first tier of boxes displayed, as usual, one of the choicest collections of fine women it had ever been my good fortune to behold in any part of the world: the effect of the second was scarcely inferior to that of the first: while the third, which in America, as in England, is almost exclusively reserved for those unfortunate wretches on whom society wreaks its vengeance for the commission of crimes in which the principal offender escapes but too frequently with impunity,—presented, as yet, nothing but empty benches. In a short time, however, these began to fill with such pale, sad, haggard-looking creatures as seemed to have escaped from Purgatory to seek a few moments' relief from their torments. Immediately above them was the gallery of the gods, which on this occasion, however, bore a much greater resemblance to the infernal regions, being studded with the grinning visages of negroes, the outlines of whose sable countenances so completely intermingled with one another as to present but one huge black mass, from which the white of their eyes and teeth was shooting streaks of light like so many burning tapers from an ocean of darkness. The whole seemed to be a reversion of the unrivalled fiction of Dante,—the *angels* being *below,* and the *damned* occupying the *upper* regions,—as if it were the purpose of the Americans to invert even the order of the universe.

It was now very nearly seven o'clock; and the impatience of the audience began, very differently from that of Boston, to manifest itself by shrill whistles, loud screams and yells, and the beating of hands and canes. At last the orchestra, composed of very little more than twenty musicians, began to play something like an overture; which, however, was completely drowned in the noise from the pit and gallery, who seemed to look upon the musical prelude as an unnecessary delay of the drama. At last the music stopped, and, amid the loud acclamations of the people,

Enter *Roderigo* and *Iago*.

Roderigo.—"Tush! never tell me; I take it much unkindly
    That thou, Iago, who hast had my purse
    As if the strings were thine, shouldst know of this."

"Who plays *Iago?*" demanded a young lady in the box, addressing the gentleman behind her.

"Only one of our *ordinary Americans,*" answered he. "We have not had a decent *Iago* since Kemble left us."

"I thought Kemble made an excellent *Cassio,*" observed the lady.

"That he made indeed," replied the gentleman. "I never saw an actor perform the part of a tippler better than he did. It was perfectly natural to him."

"Yes," rejoined the lady; "he could admirably perform the part of a tipsy *gentleman,* while *our* actors only play the part of a drunken blackguard. I think it ridiculous to go and see one of Shakespeare's plays performed on one of our stages. But they say Forest has much improved while in England, and that the first nobility went to see him."

"That's a fact," ejaculated the gentleman; "I have seen it in the papers, or I should not be here this evening."

Iago.—"And I, of whom his eyes had seen the proof,
    At Rhodes, at Cyprus, and on other grounds,
    Christian and heathen, must be be-lee'd and calm'd
    By debitor and creditor. This counter-caster,
    He, in good time must his lieutenant be;
    And I (God bless the mark!) his moorship's ancient!"

"Is it not singular," observed a gentleman right before us to his neighbour, "that Shakspeare, who with the English passes for the arch-inspector of human nature, should have had so poor and erroneous an estimate of the character of a merchant? If an American author were to bestow the opprobrious epithet of 'counter-caster' on a member of that most respectable part of our community, nothing could save him from being Lynched."

"The character of a merchant," replied his neighbour, "is decidedly one in which Shakspeare was altogether unsuccessful. Take, for instance, his 'Merchant of Venice.' What a ludicrous caricature his Antonio is! On the one hand, the very paragon of prudence,—a man who in 'riskiness' would be outdone by the veriest Yankee shopkeeper;

while, on the other, he stakes his whole credit to aid the foolish adventures of a lover! His merchant has no notion of banking; for

> 'He lends out money gratis, and brings down
> The rate of usance.' "

"And then becomes security for a friend," added the first,—"not
merely by putting his name on the back of a bill, but by pledging his
flesh! How very improbable! And then again consider his insolence to
Shylock, of whom he wants to borrow money; which is about as wise
as if an American who wants credit were to insult Nic'las Biddle!"

"All my sympathies in that play," rejoined the second, "are with the
Jew; who, after all, claiming nothing that was not lawful, and in
every one of his speeches evinces more common sense than the Christian, who suffers his vessels to go to sea without having them insured.

> 'And thrift is blessing, if men steal it not,'

is a very good motto. The Jew is no fool, I tell you."

"Quite a sensible man, that," exclaimed a sharp-featured, long-headed,
grey-eyed, raw-boned male figure who had taken his stand by the side
of us, and had evidently overheard the severe critic: "if it were not for
our *thrifty* merchants, I do not know *what* figure we should make in
the world!"

Here the commentators on Shakespeare looked round and measured
the pedlar (for such he was from his language and appearance), and
then turned back again with a doubtful shrug of their shoulders, which
had the effect of completely silencing the "Down-Easter."

The momentary quiet produced by the cold rebuke of the gentlemen
was soon taken advantage of by the ladies, who, engaging with each
other in loud conversation, notwithstanding the cries of "Hold your
tongues!" from the pit, gave the strongest possible proof of their fashionable indifference with regard to ordinary acting; until, at last, the
appearance of *Othello* silenced every voice with the universal roar of
applause from the pit, boxes, and galleries. *Othello* bowed, the ladies
observing "that he had learned that in England." Fresh acclamations
and plaudits, followed by renewed acknowledgments on the part of the
actor; during which *Iago* finishes his speech, and gives the cue to
Othello.

> *Othello.*—" 'Tis better as it is."

"After all, I do not see what the English people liked in Forest," observed a lady on the front seat. "I think him excessively clumsy."

"He is just the man to play the gladiator," replied her fair neighbour; "but I dare say he is the first English actor now living."

"Unquestionably," resumed the first. "How Macready must have been jealous of him!"

"And, in fact, every other English actor!" added the second. "You know the prejudices of John Bull with regard to America."

> *Othello.*—"For know, Iago,
> But that I love the gentle Desdemona,
> I would not my unhoused free condition
> Put into circumscription, and confine,
> For the sea's worth."

"A fine moral lesson, this, for our young men that want to get married!" exclaimed an elderly lady, turning round to the gentleman behind her.

"You must not forget, ma'am, that he is but a negro," replied the gentleman.

"I don't like this play at all," rejoined the lady. "I think it immoral from beginning to end."

"And most unnatural too!" vociferated the gentleman. "A white woman to fall in love with a black man!"

"And the daughter of a senator too!" exclaimed the lady.

"It's preaching a regular amalgamation doctrine! The play ought not to be allowed to be performed before our negroes."

"But he was not a negro," exclaimed a young lady; "he was a Moor, Ma: there is an immense difference between these two races. I am sure no *lady* would fall in love with a negro."

"Or with anything that is coloured," added the elderly lady with dignity.

"If we stay in this box," observed my friend, "we shall have no chance of listening to the performance. They are sure to make an abolition question of it. Let us seek a place elsewhere."

We accordingly scrambled out of our little prison, and, making the round of the tier, discovered two slips in a box not far from the stage, which was almost wholly occupied by gentlemen.

"It must be allowed after all," said the one; "Forest *is* the greatest actor America ever produced."

"An enthusiast," replied another, "who has encouraged the drama not only with his play, but also with his purse."

"By putting a prize on the best tragedy written in America; which, at any rate, is more than any of his patrons would have done on this side of the Atlantic."

"And then Forest is a self-taught man, who has never had any model to form himself after."

"And, besides," resumed the first, "he is a *modest* man, who seldom undertakes what he is not equal to. It is for this reason he hesitated so long before he ventured to appear in one of Shakespeare's plays in England."

"And he did well to hesitate," replied another; "he appears to much greater advantage in one of our Indian dramas."

"Come," said the first, "none of your English prejudices, Tom! You seem to forget that Forest declined being run for representative in Congress; or, as *I* heard the story, that he *was* run and elected without his consent, and that he refused to take his seat."

"So would I have done in his place," rejoined Tom. "What man of talent would forsake a respectable position in society, in order to earn eight dollars a day in Washington by making or listening to dull speeches?"*

"With such notions about you, you had better go at once to England."

"That's what I am about to do. I shall sail in the next packet."

"How long do you mean to stay in Europe?"

"As long as possible; nothing but absolute necessity shall ever bring me back to this country."

"Then it would be cruel to wish you a speedy return!"

(Tom took his hat, and left the box.)

Iago.—"Thou art sure of me; go, make money."

"*Iago* is no fool," observed a gentleman, who, until now, had attentively listened to the play, struck with so sensible a remark.

"Nor *Othello* either," replied another. "Forest must be worth upwards of a hundred thousand dollars. Do you know whether he has got any money by his wife?"

"I do not," observed the former; "but Forest is a sensible man, and so I rather think he has."

---

* Eight dollars a day is the pay of every member and senator in Congress.

"But he must have made a good deal of money in London. Do you know what his engagements were?"

"I have heard different accounts; but he must have made money in *this* country."

"How much do you think?"

"Fifty thousand dollars at least; and, now that he has succeeded in England, he will make a great deal more."

"How much do you suppose he makes to-night?"

"Let us count the boxes, and I will tell you in an instant. Have you got a piece of paper and a lead pencil?"

"I won't stay here either," said my friend. "Let us see whether we cannot find a place up stairs. When these fellows once begin to talk about money, they are not likely soon to change their conversation: and, besides, I can only stay another act; I have a particular reason for being early at Mrs. ***'s."

I willingly consented to the proposition; and, the first act being over, accompanied my friend to the second tier of boxes. This time we took our seats among a set of people evidently "from the Western country," from the natural sagacity of whose remarks my friend and I anticipated a great deal of amusement. They seemed to be in the best humour; and, though somewhat noisy, (for they looked upon the theatre with little more deference than upon a public-house, and "upon the fun that's going on there" in the light of "an election spree,") enjoyed the play better than the people of fashion who had congregated to endorse the opinion of the British public. I had not, however, much time to listen to them, as I had promised to meet a friend at half-past eight; but the little I heard satisfied me that, much as they liked *Forest,* they loved *Rice* more,—the latter being, after all, *"the* real genuine nigger, the very bringing down of whose foot was worth the price of a ticket."

CHAPTER V

> "Imperial Waltz! imported from the Rhine,
>   (Famed for the growth of pedigrees and wine,)
>   Long be thy import from all duty free,
>   And hock itself be less esteem'd than thee!"
>
> BYRON.

It was half-past ten when I made my appearance at Mrs. ***'s "rout." The rooms were richly decorated, and the company in excellent spirits. My friend had already arrived, and was talking to a young lady in one of the corners of the dancing-room; which was called "a desperate flirtation," inasmuch as the young lady appeared to be past sixteen, and not yet twenty, and the gentleman in circumstances which enabled him to support a wife. Similar flirtations were going on in other parts of the room; the married ladies being seated on benches or settees near the walls, and acting, if not as judges, at least as recorders of the events. The music, consisting chiefly of clarionets, flutes, and horns, was stationed to great advantage in the entry; leaving not only more room for the dancers in the parlour, but softening also the harmony of sounds by the greater distance. The ladies, especially those who danced, were, in point of dress, the exact copies of the patterns issued weekly in the French metropolis; and the gentlemen, though apparently timid in the presence of so many beauties, looked, nevertheless, sufficiently smart and enterprising for men of business.

I looked for a while on the group of dancers, in hopes of perceiving some slight variation, but was not a little annoyed by seeing continually the same figures and the same dancers. I afterwards communicated my surprise to my friend, but was told that I was in a fashionable house, in which none but fashionable young ladies and gentlemen could be expected "to have the floor;" and that if, from courtesy, some other people had been invited, it was expected they would have sufficient good sense not to obtrude themselves on the notice of the company, and least of all to make themselves conspicuous by joining in a qua- drille or a waltz. "There are," added he, "some dozen of young girls here dying to show their 'steps,' but none of the fashionable young men would risk his standing in society by bringing them out; and, as for the young men of neither family nor wealth, who are only asked because they are relations of the house, (a custom which is by no means general in the United States,) they know their place too well to be guilty of such an impropriety.

"Whenever one of our wealthy stock-holders," continued he, "invites a poor devil to his house, the particular relation of entertainer and guest changes nothing in the relative position of the parties: the rich man still continues to assume the peculiar insolent condescension of a patron; while the man without credit will exhibit in his conduct the humiliating consciousness of his 'insufficiency.' If you took notice of the manner in which the lady of the house courtesyed to the gentlemen that were presented to her, you must have been able to distinguish the capitalist from the poor beginner, or unsuccessful speculator, as effectu- ally as if their property had been announced with their names. Every additional thousand produces a new smile; for it is impossible for our people to consider a man independently of his circumstances."

"This," observed I, "is the fault of every practical nation, especially of the English, who are the most purse-proud and exclusive people in Europe."

"I know that," replied he: "but the English reward talent of every description higher than any other nation in the world; so that money is, in a certain sense, the just measure of capacity. In America, on the contrary, there are but few branches of *industry,* and almost none of *learning,* which are sure of meeting with an adequate remuneration in money; so that, if men are merely judged by their wealth, the meanest bank or counting-house clerk, or a common shopkeeper, has a better chance of arriving at respectability than the most successful scholar in the most difficult branches of human learning. Society, in this manner, must become lower and lower every day; there being no entailed estates or large hereditary possessions in the United States, securing to a privileged class the necessary means and leisure for the gratuitous pursuit of arts and sciences. And, as for the English being exclusive, you forget that, when English people assume that character, they possess generally the tact and *à-plomb* necessary for carrying it off; whereas, here you often meet the same spirit among people whose wealth is *credit* and *expectancy,* and whose manners and education are identified solely with the desk and ledger. Thus the terms 'patron' and 'client' are in New York, for instance, synonymous with 'creditor' and 'debtor;' and as the banks, according to the prevalent system of credit, must inevitably be the creditors of nine-tenths of the community, every person connected with them—and, above all, a stock-holder, cashier, or president—must necessarily be a patrician. The whole composition of our society is arithmetical; each gentleman ranking according to the numerical index of his property. You need only watch the conduct of the society in this room, and you will satisfy yourself of the truth of my assertion.

"Do you know that lady in pink satin," he continued, "who is talking to the lady dressed in white, across that modest-looking woman with the pale face, who is evidently embarrassed by this rudeness?"

I replied in the negative.

"The first," he said, "is the daughter of an honest shoemaker, who has become very rich by his industry, and is bitterly grieved by the aristocratic haughtiness of his daughter. I have heard it asserted that he often threatened her to hang up a last in his parlour, instead of a coat of arms, to punish the ridiculous pretensions of his family."

"Such a character," said I, "would have done credit to a Dutch burgomaster in the best times of the republic. But who is the lady thus planted between two of her sex, who are determined to take no more notice of her than if her chair were empty?"

"She is the wife of an American commodore," replied he; "one of the most gallant officers in the navy, who has shed his blood in his country's service. What further comment does this require?—what greater proof would you have of the insufferable arrogance of our moneyed aristocracy?"

"Let us follow that young lady, whose face I have never seen before in society," observed my friend after a short pause: "she looks as though she had never been used to company, and will probably become the butt of the aristocratic misses who keep possession of the floor."

The unfortunate girl, led by a young man, who, to judge from his manners, was a stranger in the city, had scarcely entered the dancing-room before every eye was turned upon her, and the most insolent, half-loud inquiry instituted as to "who she was," and "where she came from?"

"Do you know that girl?" demanded a young lady, who had just stopped dancing, loud enough for her to hear.

"I never saw her before in my life, *I* am sure," replied the *ballerina* who had been addressed, with a toss of her head; "do *you* know her?"

"Indeed I don't; I wonder how she got here!" resumed the first.

Here a third lady walked up, and examined the dress of the stranger; then, joining a small circle, "I am sure," said she, in an audible whisper, "it's not worth seventy-five cents a yard."

"And who is that unlicked cub that's with her?" demanded another lady.

"Heaven alone knows!" answered a voice; "I dare say, just come from the woods!"

"With his mouth full of tobacco!"

"I hope she isn't going to dance; if she does, I shall leave the room."

"I sha'n't stay either."

One half of this conversation the poor girl must have heard, as she was standing close to the speakers, and could not even escape from the sting of their remarks through the crowd that obstructed the passage; for it is the custom in America, as in England, for people who give parties to invite as many persons as possible, in order to have the satisfaction of a full room. She was on the point of bursting into tears; and yet the young, fashionable tigresses, of from sixteen to twenty years of age, had not feeling enough to take pity on her. I am aware that, in describing that of which I was an eye-witness, I shall scarcely be believed by my English or German readers, because it is almost impossible for an educated European to conceive the degree of rudeness, insolence, and effrontery, and the total want of consideration for the feelings of others, which I have often seen practised in what is called the "first society" of the United States. I have seen in Boston, or rather in Nahant, a small watering-place in the neighbourhood of that city, two girls,—one the daughter of a president of an insurance-office, and the other the child of a merchant,—supporting their heads with their elbows, and in this position staring at each other for several minutes across a public table; each believing that her standing in society entitled her to the longest stare, and that the other, being the daughter of a man of less consideration and property, should have modesty enough to cast down her eyes.

The same kind of feelings the Americans carry even across the Atlantic. In Paris, Florence, Rome, and other places on the Continent, (in England they have no particular practice of their own, but merely follow in the wake of the nobility,) they form as many distinct sets and coteries as at home; imitating, by degrees, every ridiculous fashion of France and Italy, and endeavouring by their wealth to pave the road to the highest society, and to keep from it the less fortunate part of their countrymen. Two instances of this kind came to my personal knowledge.

About three years ago, while a friend of mine happened to be in Vienna, he met at Mr. S***'s, the United States' consul, a party of Americans, composed of a number of gentlemen and ladies from Boston, Baltimore, and South Carolina. The conversation ran on different topics, until one of the company introduced in his remarks the names of some fashionable people of Boston with whom he professed to be acquainted. Upon this, Mr. ***, descended from one of the wealthiest and most vulgar aristocratic families of that place, and who pretended to know "everybody," whispered something into the consul's ear, and requested him to step with him into the next room. There, as my friend afterwards learned, he assumed at once the rank and office of grand inquisitor; cross-examining the poor consul as to "where he had picked up that man?" and declaring finally that he must be an impostor, as *he* did not know him, nor *ever heard his name mentioned before,* (this is the usual phrase employed by "respectable" Americans when they wish to repudiate a person as not belonging to their set). After he had thus discharged the duties of a high-born citizen, he resumed his seat at a little distance from "the impostor," and remained silent for the rest of the evening. Poor Mr. ***, who was really a gentleman of slender means, could not but perceive the prejudice which his fellow-townsman had excited in the mind of his hospitable entertainer, and soon afterwards left the company.

Another instance of this kind occurred at Munich between two

Americans; one a regular resident of the place for many years, and the other a traveller, who imagined he had held a higher rank in America than his compatriot. The latter, of course, immediately set out to communicate his scruple to the consul, and the *attachés* of the *** legation; assuring them that the gentleman they had taken into favour was neither a scholar nor a man of high standing, and was consequently not entitled to their attention. All this was done while the other person was absent from town, and for no other purpose than impressing the society of Munich with the fact "that there is a great deal of aristocracy in America, and that he himself was one of its noblest representatives." The American ministers in London, Paris, Berlin, and St. Petersburgh, and the consuls in the different commercial cities of Europe, are usually made the repositories of all the slander which one set or *coterie* may have in store against the other; and, as no peculiar discretion is exercised by Americans in the treatment of high public functionaries, the latter themselves do not often escape uninjured, the public press furnishing the meanest scribbler with the means of wreaking his vengeance.

The fact is, the *soi-disant* higher classes of Americans, in quitting the simple, manly, moral, industrious habits of the great mass of the people,—habits which alone have won them the respect of the world,—have no fixed standard by which to govern their actions, either with regard to themselves or their fellow beings; no manners, customs, modes of thinking, &c. of their own; no community of feelings; nothing which could mark them as a distinct class, except their contempt for the lower classes, and their dislike of their own country. How should such an order of beings agree amongst themselves? How should they be able to make themselves, or those around them, comfortable? There is more courtesy in the apparent rudeness of the Western settler than in the assumed politeness of the city stockholder,—more true hospitality in the log-house of the backwoodsman, than in any of the mansions of the presidents and directors of banks with whom it has been my good fortune to become acquainted.

I remember, some years ago, when travelling with a distant relative on the borders of the Mississippi, to have been approaching the habitation of a farmer, whom, in company with his wife, we found on horseback, ready to set out on a journey to the next market town for the purpose of buying stores for his family. There was no tavern or resting-place within seven miles of us; but, not wishing to intrude upon their domestic arrangements, we passed the house and doubled our speed, in order to be in time for dinner at the next village. The farmer, however, did not suffer us to continue our journey without having refreshed ourselves at his house; and, persuading us to come back, he and his wife dismounted, and assisted in preparing and ordering everything necessary for dinner. We of course protested against their putting themselves to so much trouble for the sake of strangers, who, in an hour or so, might have reached a place where they could have procured a dinner for money. "Oh, I assure you, gentlemen," replied our entertainer, "I never suffer myself or my wife to be *troubled* either by strangers or friends; we merely discharge our duty, without either inconvenience to ourselves, or putting others under any sort of obligation. Lucy!" said he to a buxom girl that was playing with one of the prettiest children I ever beheld, "you will see that the gentlemen want nothing. Eliza! we must be off, or we shall not get thither till dark. Good morning, gentlemen!"—"Good-b'ye, gentlemen!" added his wife; both mounting their horses, and leaving us to enjoy ourselves and our dinner as best we might.

What a picture of sincerity, honesty, confidence, frankness, and unostentatious hospitality is this, compared to the formal invitations to dinner, or a party, of one of the nabobs in the Atlantic cities! Take, for instance, the case of a rich man in New York. He prepares a week beforehand, and racks his brains as to what people he shall invite that will do credit to his house, and what persons he may safely exclude without injury to himself, and without offending them past reparation. He has one dinner-party for one set of acquaintance, and another for another. At the one he will act as host, at the other as patron; the expense being in both cases proportionate to the rank of his guests. Who under these circumstances would not rather prefer the hospitality of the honest Kentuckian, whose Western friends averred that he was truly kind, "for, when he had company, he simply went to the sideboard, poured out his glass, and then turned his back upon them, not wishing to see how *they filled?*"

The fashionable people of the Atlantic cities, who give dinner and evening parties either for the purpose of maintaining or acquiring a high rank in society, have themselves little or no disposition for company. With them society does not offer an agreeable and necessary respite from toil; but is merely a means of acquiring influence, &c. For this purpose it is not necessary to treat all persons with equal sincerity and politeness. *"La politesse nous tient lieu du cœur,"* say the French; but the fashionable people of the United States manage to get on without either. There is nothing in the composition of a fashionable American to compensate for the loss of natural affections,—nothing in his manner to soften the egotism which manifests itself in every motion, every gesture, every word which drops from his lips. And the worst of it is, that he imagines all this to be a successful imitation of English manners! He forgets entirely that, in imitating the manners of the higher classes in England, he is very much in the position of a sailor on horseback; showing by his whole carriage that he is out of his element, and, though straining every nerve to maintain his place, ready to tumble off at the first motion for which he is not previously prepared.

As regards the exclusiveness of the higher classes, and especially of the women, the instance before me was certainly one calculated to excite my indignation, had I not known fashionable young ladies that refused to walk in the streets of Philadelphia until the dinner-hour of "the common people," when they would be sure of having the sidewalk to themselves.

But what is all this, compared to the artificial distinctions introduced into their churches? It has always been the pride of the Catholic church in Europe to offer a place of worship to every man, without distinction of rank, title, or wealth. The utmost a man pays for a chair in any of the churches of France or Italy is one *sou;* the fashionable American Catholics, however, imitate the practice of those gentlemanly followers of Christ who choose to worship God in good company. Thus the respectable Catholics of New York, "who do not wish to be annoyed by the presence of an Irish mob," being for the most part composed of their own servants, have built a church for their own specific use,—a snug little concern, just large enough for a *genteel* audience to hear the Lord *en famille.*

In order to exclude effectually everything that might be disagreeable, no one is allowed to stand in the aisles; so that those poor devils who cannot afford to pay for a pew must be content to seek the Lord elsewhere *among their equals.* On the whole, the principles which govern the aristocracy of the Northern States of America are the very counterpart of the sound maxims of Shylock with regard to the vulgar herd of Christians. "I will buy with you, sell with you, talk with you, walk with you," (here might be added, *electioneer* with you,) "and so following; but I will not eat with you, drink with you, or pray with you."

"Come!" said my friend, "what are you reflecting about? Do not look any longer on this tender victim of fashionable society. She is now but serving her apprenticeship; but will soon rise to the rank of 'an ancient' in the clique, and then treat every new-comer in precisely the same manner she is treated now. Let me rather make you acquainted with some of the lions that grace Mrs. ***'s party. Do you know that gentleman with grey hair standing in the corner? It is Mr. ***, originally of German extraction, who has changed his name in order to warrant the supposition of his being descended from a Norman family. He is a great public speaker,—that is, he speaks on all occasions; and has assured his party, who of course look upon democracy as the greatest curse of the country, that his father was a respectable man long before Tammany Hall* was built. This declaration, no doubt, secures to him the *entrée* of the first society; and, if he do not fail in business, the consideration of one of the oldest aristocrats of the city.

"A little further from him, on the right," continued he, "you will notice a gentleman with a white cravat. He has always a little *clientelle* around him, for he is a *millionnaire*, descended from a *millionnaire!* I know very little of him or his father, except that the latter has made his money by successful speculations and great saving,—two poetical circumstances worthy of being immortalized by Washington Irving. Behind him is stationed Mr. ***, a gentleman of great business tact, who writes his letters on the backs of those which he receives; and is always particular in advising his friends with whom he has dealings to get his name on a piece of paper. He is a silent partner in half-a-dozen different concerns, and has the reputation of obstinately refusing in all cases to receive less than a hundred cents on a dollar.

"In the other corner of the room you will observe two gentlemen engaged in conversation with a lady, who is evidently tired of their attention. They are, as you might guess from this circumstance, nothing but ordinary professional men, whose daily earnings are just sufficient to keep them above water. They are merely invited from charity, being distant relations of the lady of the house, who, by showing them up, expects to improve their chance of success in business. One is a lawyer with a small practice; and the other a physician, who, as he cannot

---

* The great rendezvous and headquarters of the democrats of the city of New York.

afford to keep a horse and gig, has as yet but little to do, but will undoubtedly succeed in obtaining a large practice if he should be successful in his attentions to Miss ***, a nice young girl of thirty-two, with plenty of money to set up a carriage."

"But," said I, more than dissatisfied with my friend's satirical remarks, "how do you explain the generosity which some of the wealthiest citizens in this country manifest towards the poor, and especially to all charitable institutions?"

"There is," replied he, "a sort of *public* generosity among the rich men in our Atlantic cities which delights in making donations to public institutions of all kinds; but woe to those who have private transactions with them!

"The public in America is always courted, even by the mushroom aristocracy of New York. Stephen Gerard, who by the moneyed men of the United States was considered as the quintessence of science and virtue, so that a salutation 'Go and do as Stephen Gerard!' would at any time have been equivalent to the *'Vaya Usted con Dios!'* of the Spaniards,—Stephen Gerard himself, I say, was obliged to give away money to the poor, even during his lifetime!

"Besides, there is a good deal of satisfaction in giving away money to the public, in a public way, in a country in which the public is sovereign. It is a way of ingratiating one's-self with one's master, and of acquiring notoriety and credit for wealth, and thereby an indisputable claim to the highest respectability. When, in one of our Atlantic cities, it is once known that a man is rich, that 'he is very rich,' that he is 'amazingly rich,' that he is 'one of the richest men in the country,' that he is 'worth a million of dollars,' that he is 'as rich as Stephen Gerard, or John Jacob ***,' the whole vocabulary of praise is exhausted; and the individual in question is as effectually canonized as the best Catholic saint.

"I often alluded to this species of money-worship, when alone with my Northern friends; but they seemed to be surprised with the simplicity of my remarks. They saw nothing in it that was not perfectly commendable by common sense. 'We imitate the English in that respect, as in every other,' was their excuse; 'and, as is usual with us, *improve* upon them. We do not think John Bull understands the value of money as well as ourselves; at least, he does not turn it to so good an account. All that can be said against us is, that we do not value *other things* as highly as we ought to do;' and with this species of logic they seemed to be satisfied. But let us continue our tour.

"Do you observe that gentleman in tights, with large black whiskers? He is one of the most fashionable and aristocratic gentlemen in the city. I believe he served his apprenticeship in a baker's shop, then went into an auction-room, then became a partner in the firm, and lastly took a house in Broadway, set up a carriage, and declared himself a gentleman. Nine-tenths of all the people that are called 'fashionable' in New York have had a similar beginning; and yet, if you listen to their conversation, you would swear they are descended in a direct line from William the Conqueror.

"No people on earth are more proud of their ancestors than those fashionable Americans who can prove themselves descended from respectable fathers and grandfathers. Take, for instance, the case of one of my young friends, who was sent to Europe by his family for the sole purpose of discovering his ancestors; or that of an acquaintance of mine in Boston, who has found a signet among the rubbish of his household, and now swears that it belonged to his great-grandfather, there being no other person to claim it; or that of Mr. ***, seated yonder by the side of that elderly lady, who has bought a lot of Dutch portraits in Europe,—all knights in armour,—in order to form a whole gallery of ancestors; or that of Mr. ***, who has discovered some faint analogy between *his* name and that of a certain animal, which he now uses as a coat of arms; and a hundred other examples I could quote."

"The same ridiculous folly," interrupted I, "you will find in England, and especially in Scotland, among the gentlefolks."

"But then," interrupted my friend, "the English do not pretend to be *republicans;* they never formally banished nobility and royalty from their country in order to rake them up again from the rubbish of another world; and the particular genius of their institutions is not opposed to any real distinction in the way of family. Our people, on the contrary, are obliged publicly to repudiate what they are most anxiously striving to assert in private; and thus to add hypocrisy to pretensions for which there is not the least apology in the history of their country. But I must direct your attention to that portly-looking gentleman in blue pantaloons, who, in my opinion, is by far the most remarkable personage of the whole company. He wears boots; and his hat and gloves, neither of which can be said to be entirely new, are carefully deposited in the entry. Thus unencumbered, he will play one of the best knives and forks at supper; although the lady of the house herself will take his arm, and put him to his utmost good breeding. She completely monopolises his conversation, and distinguishes him from the crowd by the most studied politeness."

"But what can be the cause of her attention?" demanded I; "is he so very rich?"

"Not exactly," replied he; "he is *barely respectable."*

"What do you mean by that?"

"I mean, in the language of New York, he is a man of moderate property."

"Then I do not see the object of her civility to him."

"She has indeed a different object from what you or any other stranger would suspect. The gentleman is a country representative of considerable talent; of whom the lady, who, like most of the nice women in this city, is in the opposition, wishes to make a convert. A good many unsuspecting 'members of the assembly' are spoiled by our fashionable women; for the spirit of gallantry is stronger in our yeomanry than among our aristocratic gentlemen of the town. Our country representatives can argue for years, and argue well, against the attempted usurpations of certain coteries of gentlemen; but they cannot take up the cudgel against the ladies. It is in the best society where our members learn to listen to the grossest abuse of the institutions of their country without glowing with indignation or resentment; it is there where they study patience in hearing the people's favourites traduced as 'scoundrels,' 'villains,' 'pickpockets,' 'idiots,' 'fools,' &c.; and it is in company of fashionable ladies that they learn to consider patriotism as unbecoming a gentleman,—as a vice which ought never to infect but the lowest orders of society.

"And it is principally because their patriotism cannot be translated into an attachment to some 'great and glorious personage' that these poor devils of representatives, who would have remained honest if they had not been admitted into good society, become, by degrees, ashamed of everything which is their own, from their heads down to the very soles of their feet. At first they are made aware that they are not so refined as some of the New York people, especially those who have been in Europe; and that, in order to get rid of some of their boorish manners, they must needs try to get into good society. Some neutral friend procures them an introduction, and the women do the rest.

"One of the principal things they learn in good society is, to consider politics as wholly uninteresting except to tavern-keepers on election days; as a subject unworthy of the pursuit of a gentleman, and a thing banished from people of fashion and good taste. When they speak of it, or allude to it, accidentally in conversation, the good-natured condescending smiles of the company convince them, without argument, that they have been guilty of some impropriety. When they grow warm at the mention of their country, the calmness of all around them teaches them the absurdity of betraying emotion on so ordinary an occasion; and, if they should ever by chance make use of the words 'liberty,' 'right,' 'independence,' or forget themselves so far as to introduce 'the people,' they are left alone to enjoy these things by themselves.

"When, by this course of instruction, they have amended their manners so far as no longer to be guilty of similar *gaucheries,* they are made to improve their language, to smooth down the roughness of terms by the substitution of more agreeable and palatable synonyms, and to set a right value on certain expressions altogether unintelligible to the great mass of the people.

"Thus the word 'patriotism,' as I told you before, is entirely proscribed by the higher classes; they designate that virtue by 'political zeal,' and the patriot himself by 'a successful politician.' 'A popular candidate for office' is equivalent to 'a vagabond who has no business of his own;' 'popularity' means 'the approbation of the mob;' and 'popular distinction,' 'notoriety in vulgar pursuits.' 'A public man' is 'an individual lost to society and to all its virtues;' the term 'liberty' is synonymous with 'licence of the mob;' and 'universal suffrage' stands for 'universal blackguardism.'

"It is to be observed, however, that all these significations apply only to the members of the *democratic* party; there never having been a single man of fortune, in any of the Northern States, whose patriotic intentions have once been made the subject of doubt or inquiry: for it is easily understood why *a man of property* should be attached to his country; but the poor man has *no right* to be so, and is therefore to be justly suspected whenever he takes an interest in politics.

"Under these circumstances, you cannot wonder at our aspiring people—and where is the man in this country that is *not* so?—deprecating the idea of being called 'democrats,' and the influence which 'good breeding and fashionable society' exercise on our professional politicians. The gentleman I pointed out to you is just serving his apprenticeship in the fashionable *salons* of New York; and there are already heavy bets making on his being brought over to the opposition in less than a year. I have heard it said that he was a 'rank' democrat when he first came to New York, but that the ladies have already tamed him so far as to make him less *positive* in his opinions; and they hope, by the time they will teach him to wear white gloves and 'behave himself like a gentleman,' to make him altogether 'harmless.'

"When once come to that, it takes but very little to make him *ashamed* of serving the 'riff-raff,' and declare in favour of those dignified opinions which are handed down to the Americans by the ablest writers of Great Britain, and which the commercial aristocracy of the United States apply to themselves in precisely the same manner as the nobility of England. He is then likely to perceive 'the *beauty* of those British institutions' which ensure the complete submission of the lower classes to the *superior* orders,—'which assign to every man his proper place,'—which 'teach the servants to be respectful to their masters,' &c. The admiration of England and of the British government naturally begets a wish to establish, in America, a government after the British model; for, in the same manner as the honest Boston baker wished his native town to be raised to the rank of a city, in order that at some future day it might rival 'the ancient and famous city of London,' do our stock-holders and stock-jobbers expect to become 'ancient and far-famed families' in 'the great American empire,' and to outshine the brightest stars in the galaxy of the British nobility."

"And yet," observed I, "there are very few aristocratic Americans who think America capable of national elevation. 'We have gained nothing by our independence of Great Britain,' said a fashionable and learned Bostonian, when the subject was started in the way of a national boast; "on the contrary, we have lost in personal consideration."

"And I have not the least doubt he spoke the truth, as far as *related to himself,*" replied my friend. "Nothing can better prove the corrupting influence of our fashions," he continued, "than the fact that most of the celebrated leaders of the present opposition have commenced their career by advocating democracy, and finished by betraying it. This is the price they have to pay for admission into good society, from which democrats are naturally excluded."

Here my friend was interrupted by the approach of the gentleman of the house, who, in the most polite manner possible, inquired whether we were entertained with the party.

"How could that be otherwise?" replied my friend; "I have never before seen such a collection of pretty girls; I wish I could see them all dance."

"The room is not large enough for that," said our entertainer, little suspecting the meaning of my friend; "but next year I shall take another house, and then there will be no more complaints of that sort."

"With a little forbearance, a good many of those beautiful sylphs could dance in *this* room."

"Quite a gallant speech that!" exclaimed the old gentleman: "one can see that you come from the South."

"There is nothing gives me more pleasure than to see young ladies amuse themselves."

"Just so, sir,—just so! only I cannot get reconciled to the *walse.*"

"And I," observed my friend, "think the *waltz* the finest dance in the world."

"Why, it may do tol—er—ably well for *some* folks; but I have strong doubts of its being an appropriate dance in this country."

"And why that?"

"I shall tell you that in a moment," said the old gentleman.

"You see, sir, that our young ladies are very fond of dancing; and that, when once commencing, they are sure to go on the whole evening. Well, sir, they take a partner,—a young fellow who is quite as fond of dancing as they are,—and then they dance, or *waltz,* as you call it, round and round, until they both get as warm as possible; and then, sir—"

"And then, sir—"

"Why, then they go into a cold room, or into the open air, and catch cold; that's all. 'Tis but a week ago that my daughter recovered from a severe cough. These, sir, are the fatal consequences of that dance amongst us; and that's the reason I don't like it. It is not adapted to our climate. Am I not right, sir?"

"Perfectly," replied my friend.

"Health before everything; that's my motto. But there is no use in preaching to those girls; they *will* have their own way in everything."

"But you seem to forget that waltzing is becoming more and more the fashion in England."

"Is that really the case?" demanded the old gentleman; "then it cannot be so bad after all,—the English have pretty good notions on all such subjects,—if our girls would only take care of their health."

Here the conversation was interrupted by a sudden rush of the company, occasioned by the announcement of supper. At this important summons, ladies and gentlemen, the wife of our entertainer with the pantalooned country representative at their head, were pairing off in great haste, to shape their course down to a large room on the ground-floor, which during the first part of the evening had been kept carefully closed, but was now thrown open for the more substantial amusement of the party. This, however, is too important a subject to be treated as a mere episode: it deserves a separate chapter.

CHAPTER VI

A German Dissertation on Eating.—Application of Eating to Scientific, Moral, and Political Purposes.—Democrats in America not in the Habit of entertaining People.—Consequences of this Mistake.—The Supper.— Dialogue between a Country Representative and a Fashionable Lady.— Mode of winning Country Members.—Hatred of the Higher Classes of everything belonging to Democracy.—Attachment of the Old Families to England.—Hatred of the "Vulgar English."—The French, and even the English, not sufficiently aristocratic for the Americans.—Generosity of the Americans towards England.—A Fashionable Young Lady.—An American Exquisite.—Middle-aged Gentlemen and Ladies.—Americans not understanding how to amuse themselves, because they do not know how to laugh.—Negroes the happiest People in the United States.—Breaking-up of the Party.—Gallantry of the Gentlemen.

> *Silence.*—"Ah, sirrah! quoth-a, we shall
>   Do nothing but eat and make good cheer,
>   And praise Heaven for the merry year."
>
> *Second Part of King Henry IV*. Act V. Scene 3.

GERMANS are by English writers accused of heaviness of style and laborious dulness; produced partly by their predilection for metaphysics, and partly by their inclination towards mysticism. *Martinus Scriblerus* was born at Munster; and, although a German* has since actually discovered the *materia subtilis* ridiculed by Pope, the prejudices of the practical philosophers of England, and in later days of America, remain still as strong against them as ever. Every one, I believe, is willing to concede to them the greatest quantity of abstract learning; very few will give them credit for practical knowledge, and a nice appreciation of the good things of this life. I remember being once told by an Englishman that he did not think it possible for a German to tell the difference between mutton and lamb, inasmuch as both were served up in little bits at the best private tables in Germany. Such a remark offered to a Frenchman would have made his blood boil with rage, and probably have ended in a duel; but *I* resolved upon taking a German vengeance, and proposed writing a small dissertation on the

---

* Mr. Encke of Berlin.

origin, progress, and various applications of eating to scientific, sociable, and political purposes.

Eating, according to the oldest and best records, was invented in Paradise,—where we have strong reasons to suppose it constituted the principal amusement of the first man. From this we may safely infer that it was necessary to *primitive* happiness; although, from a singular perversity of taste, dinners then consisted merely of desserts,—that is, of a choice variety of raw fruit: the chemical process of cooking, the scientific arrangement by which thinking man assimilates and subjects the universe to his own body, was reserved for subsequent periods. The first sin was an *appetite* for knowledge,—the latter being communicated by the simple process of eating; which fact is still commemorated, in the shape of regular anniversary dinners, by most of the learned societies in England and on the Continent.

But eating was not long confined to learning; it extended itself gradually to all other human pursuits, and, in course of time, associated itself with politics, morals, and even religion. The Christian Protestant religion is the only one which does not prescribe a particular diet; and I have heard it asserted in Frankfort-on-the-Maine, (a place where Jews are better known than anywhere else,) that an Israelite may be considered as converted from the moment he has tasted roast pork. With regard to morality, every one knows the influence of a man's diet on his passions, and how often mildness and amiability of disposition are chiefly the result of a particular regimen.

With regard to the fine arts, it has been observed by a celebrated French professor of gastronomy, and with great justice too, that we borrow the whole nomenclature from the taste,—that is, from the palate. What would be tragedy or comedy without the words "bitter," "sour," "sweet," "mild," &c.?—where would be your "sweet-hearts, your sweet faces, sweet voices, and sweet dispositions?" And again, what would become of your "sour dispositions," your "bitter disappointments," and "galling vexations?" The strongest and most lasting impressions are produced by the palate,—that is, by eating; and hence poets and common people refer to them more frequently than to the sensations conveyed by the other senses. "The pleasures of the palate," says the French philosopher, "are the most lasting, and compensate us in our old age for the loss of nearly every other enjoyment."

But the most important influence of eating is exhibited in politics. Here we observe, in the first place, the fact that a substantial diet in a people is, with scarcely one exception inseparable from a certain degree of rational freedom. It is for this reason principally that the nations of the North are with great difficulty reduced to slavery; while the South, more abstemious in eating, has always been more easily conquered and subdued. This rule, however, I can assure my readers, does not apply to the Southern States of America, whose gallant inhabitants are as much used to turtle as any alderman of the city of London, and as loyal as any British subject whenever they are called upon to fire a "royal salute," or, in other words, "empty twenty-seven bumpers of madeira," in honour of any of their celebrated public characters. As a general rule, however, it may be remarked that beef and mutton countries are the most difficult to be governed, or rather that the people of those countries are more capable of governing *themselves* than any other; and that a nation becomes fit for a democratic or *self*-government in exactly the same proportion as its diet consists principally of meat.

With the knowledge of these facts, I would direct the attention of travellers in the United States to the *stereotype* bills of fare they will find in nearly all the principal public houses; which, in my opinion, will best enable them to form a correct estimate of the republican sentiments of the Americans. As far as my experience goes, they all run thus:—

"Roast beef, roast mutton, roast lamb, roast veal, roast pork, roast pig, roast turkey, roast goose, roast chickens, roast pigeons, roast ducks," &c. To which, merely by way of appendix, are added the comparatively insignificant items of "pudding, pastry, and dessert."

For these, however, nobody cares; but the roasts generally go off well, constituting both the pith and luxury of an American table. A few aristocratic innovations on this rule have, indeed, been attempted by the keepers of some of the crack boarding-houses and hotels; but they were soon obliged to come back to the old standard of beef and mutton. Even at private parties the roasts form the principal ornament of the table; though, of late, some fashionable people, preceded by the *** minister in Washington, have attempted, though in vain, to popularize the taste for *"pâtés au foie gras"* and *"aux truffes."*

The Americans eat *cold* roast meat four times a day, viz. at breakfast, lunch, tea, and supper; and *hot* roast beef or mutton twice, at breakfast and dinner:—hence, in spite of all the manœuvres of the Whig and Bank party in the United States to overthrow the democratic principles established by Jefferson, Jackson, and Van Buren, the latter have always prevailed, in the same manner as the quantity of beef consumed exceeded that of all other roast and boiled meats taken together. This correspondence between a man's food and political principles was beautifully illustrated by the late Dr. Johnson, when, in his reply to the American ditty,—

"Who rules o'er freemen must himself be free," he sensibly remarked,—

"Who drives fat oxen must himself be fat." That *impromptu* alone was worth three hundred a-year.

The use of *public dinners* in a free country I need not dwell upon; every one knows that they are the most powerful *stimulus* to patriotism and virtue. It is only after dinner that gentlemen can be supposed to listen patiently to a long political argument, intended to prove their antagonists to be arrant knaves, and their partisans men of sound public principles. Calumny and eulogy are the necessary dessert of a public meal,—a sort of *confiture* taken after the appetite for solid food has been appeased in a more satisfactory manner.

Dinners and suppers are also made use of for the purposes of *diplomacy;* or, as is the case in the United States and in England, for making political proselytes. Napoleon, used to conquest, knew yet the value of good dinners. Instead of repeating the rules and maxims laid down by Machiavelli for a young prince,—instead of echoing the vile saying of Richelieu, *"Dissimuler, c'est regner,"*—he gave to his parting ministers no other injunctions than *"Tenez bonne table, et soignez les femmes."*

A whole world lies in this injunction! *"Tenez bonne table"* precedes the command *"Soignez les femmes;"* a proof that he considered the latter, if not impossible, at least useless, without the former.

Talleyrand added to his political sagacity the most perfect appreciation of good eating; both qualities being absolutely indispensable to an ambassador. The compliment he paid to the English, "that he never knew what French cooking was until he came to England," may be considered at once as a proof of his diplomatic wisdom and taste. Count A—y, who keeps the diplomatic crack house in Paris, maintains his influence with all parties by the most tasteful entertainments; and it is generally believed that Count P——o di B——o's cook has as much contributed to the widespread reputation of his master, as the consummate talents with which the latter has managed the interests of his sovereign. Lord P——, as we are assured by a most able writer in one

of the best periodicals of the present day, has a winning way of conciliating Tory ladies with Whig dinners: and if Lord M——ne is less
successful in this most important art of a minister, it is, I am quite sure,
because he prefers dining out to entertaining his friends at home; a
practice for which no public man was ever pardoned in any country.

In a similar manner is eating made a means of making political
converts in the United States; but with the exception of two or three
wealthy families in Philadelphia, and half-a-dozen of the same kind in
New York and Baltimore, the *democrats* are not in the habit of entertaining people; (in England, according to the most respectable testimony, the Whig lords entertain more than the Tories;) and it is on this
account, principally, that their case seems to be hopeless—in good
society. In the Western States there is a great deal of "treating" among
the "republicans;" but the honour of giving regular dinner-parties and
hot suppers belongs almost exclusively to "the aristocracy."

These dinners and suppers are given to public men as a sort of
"douceur" for their honourable conduct; but, once accused of democracy, it's "no song, no supper." The higher classes of Americans apply
the same method by which beasts are tamed and tutored, to the representatives of the people; they feed them when they behave well, and
kick at them when they show themselves self-willed and disobedient. In
a few instances some of the government officers in Boston and Philadelphia gave parties, at which there was a profusion of iced champaign
and chicken-salad; and the thing went off well enough: the Whigs,
alias Tories, *alias* National Republicans, *alias* Federalists, came, as they
always do when they are invited to a supper, drank the wine, emptied
the dishes, and went off saying, "It's no use for these people to imitate
us; you cannot make a gentleman out of a democrat."

If it were not for the excellent dinners given by the President, and
the delightful circles at Mr. Secretary W***'s, the democratic senators
and members of Congress would never quit their messes, or would be
obliged to content themselves with a steak or a chop at one of the two
mulatto *restaurants* in the Capitol. General Jackson, who was great in
everything, had also an excellent French cook; his dinners, as Miss
Martineau can testify, were in the best style, and his wines of the most
superior quality. "Oh, he is a delightful old gentleman!" exclaimed a
truly aristocratic lady of Baltimore,—"how amiable in his private intercourse!—no one can be with him without loving him! I wish he *were*
ambitious, and met with a better fate than Cæsar!"

The worst objection to democracy is, that, except taverns and coffee-houses, both of which are in exceeding bad repute in the United States, its followers have no regular *rendezvous,* no *réunions,* no *petits comités* amongst themselves, where its zealots might mutually inspire one another with patriotic sentiments, after the example of the Whigs, who, from time to time, refresh their dying love of liberty with the best West India madeira, furnished by their own cellars. And yet man is a gregarious animal, and, as we all know, woman still more so; both like company, or, as the Americans express it, "love cómpany," "admire company," "dote upon company." "They cannot always stick at home;" the young ladies want to dance and to get married,—the young gentle-men want to have an opportunity of addressing an heiress, and of appearing to advantage in society. And of what use, after all, *are* their good manners if they cannot show them? All these things operate against democracy, and tend, in a considerable degree, to swell the ranks of the opposition. The people, assuredly, are in possession of all political power; but a very small number of individuals take it upon themselves to fix the conventional standard.

"With whom are you going to dine to-day?" said a gentleman from Philadelphia to one of his friends in Washington.

"With Mr. W***," was the answer.

"Whom will you meet there?"

"Only General F——s, Mr. C***, and Mr. B***."

"None of the *corps diplomatique?*"

"None that I know of."

"No senator?"

"Only Mr. B*** and Dr. L***."

"No Whig senator?"

"I believe not."

"Why, then, do you go? You will neither dine well, nor will you be amused; and, as for the wine, I never knew a democrat to be a good judge of that article."

This was the death-blow to the young man's democracy. He was a Virginian, and, as such, knew that it was impossible to be a gentleman without being a good judge of wine and horse-flesh. He at first blushed, but soon recovered from his embarrassment by sending "a regret" to his democratic acquaintance. The day following he dined *en petit comité* with Mr. G***, where the ridicule thrown on popular institutions undermined his principles still further; and in the evening the ladies converted him fully to the principles of the opposition.

With the knowledge of all these facts, I could not but tremble for the fate of my pantalooned country representative, who, standing by the side of one of the most enchanting Whig ladies of New York, was now tucking up his cuffs in order to prepare himself for a valiant attack on a goose. This substantial bird, so unjustly ridiculed by the most odious comparisons with the more aristocratic but infinitely less useful swan, is in America—where swans are fabulous animals—the king of bipeds; capons being, either from natural charity to animals, or from want of the higher refinements, seldom to be met with at an American table. Admiral C——n, it is true, came to the United States to teach the Americans the science of preparing fowl in that manner; but, as he was himself but indifferently skilled in it, (his victims usually crowed the third day after the operation,) the thing was given up, as a practice too cruel to be indulged in "by an enlightened, intellectual, and moral community," and the admiral obliged to return to England without the slightest hope of securing to himself that enduring fame which future generations award to the lights and benefactors of their race.

The attack now began simultaneously on all sides, the square-built tribune still keeping his position near the lady of the house, and looking upon her more and more tenderly as he was cutting away at the goose. There was a mixture of gratitude and benevolence in his smile which seemed to tell her that she had not been mistaken; that there was still some hope of winning him,—some slight chance of teaching him refinement and good taste. Accordingly, when he had done eating,— that is, when he could eat no more,—and had rinsed his mouth, in the only way he ever went through that process, by swallowing, in rapid succession, something like half-a-dozen glasses of madeira,—the lady took his arm, whispering, in one of her softest accents, that she disliked a crowd, and that they had better have some chat in the parlour.

"With all my heart," said the tribune, wiping his mouth with a checkered pocket-handkerchief; "I really do not see what business people have here after they have supped."

"At my house, sir," replied the lady, "every one is at liberty to do as he pleases."

"Quite a *clever* party, ma'am," rejoined he, turning down the cuffs of his coat.

"I am glad you amuse yourself."

"Oh that I do! I always amuse myself at a party."

Here the lady made a confused sign of acknowledgment.

"But when we give a party in *our* place," continued the unabashed man of the people, "we don't give such suppers: I have heard the gentleman next to me say that the table, just as it was, must have cost three hundred dollars."

"Why," stammered the lady, "it's impossible for me to say."

"I dare say it cost a great deal more," continued the tribune; "I should not like to father the bill."

"How old is your eldest daughter, sir?" demanded the lady, by way of changing the conversation.

"Pretty nearly sixteen; she is quite a woman, ma'am."

"Why don't you bring her to town? I should be happy to make her acquaintance."

"Very much obliged to you for your kindness, ma'am; but it won't do. New York is too expensive a place; I should not be able to keep my daughter in the fashions, and, without that, she would not find much pleasure in a stay in this city."

"Come, come, that's an old-fashioned notion of yours; you would not bring up your daughter as a country girl, would you?"

"Not exactly that; but still I like her to know something about housekeeping. Your fine city ladies do not seem to trouble themselves much about that."

"Why, they have other things to do," said the lady, almost impatiently.

"I know that," said the imperturbable representative; "and those things are precisely the ones I do not like my girl to learn."

"But how are you off for society in your village, or rather *town?*—isn't it a *town?*"

"Yes, ma'am, it *is* a town, and quite a flourishing one too. We have this year built a new school-house and a tavern."

"Very fine buildings, I dare say."

"Oh no, ma'am! only of wood. We can only afford to build our school-houses of wood; there is no stone building in our place, *except the bank*. We are not as rich as the people of New York, and have not as much credit either; but, if things go on well, we shall build another school-house in the course of a year or two, and add a new wing or story to the tavern. We have raised the schoolmaster's *wages* already a dollar a month; and, if the place goes on increasing, we shall have to look out for an usher."

"I am glad you are doing so well."

"Thank you, ma'am. We have had more than a hundred new people settling among us during the last two years; some of them quite respectable. Mr. Smith, an Englishman, is a very good blacksmith, and understands breaking colts; a young man of the name of Biddle—no relation to the great Nic'las Biddle though—is a good tanner; then we had a new accession of carpenters and day-labourers from Ireland, 'as many as you can shake a stick at.' "

"But, in a growing place, it must be difficult to find agreeable people to visit."

"We don't think of visiting; we have other things to do."

This was the cue for the lady.

"Oh! you are probably taken up with *politics*," said the lady; "a'n't you?"

"Why, we are a pretty patriotic set, ma'am; all republicans to the back-bone."

"I am glad to hear that," replied the lady; "I am myself a republican."

"That's right, ma'am; it's of no use to be anything else in *this* country. I can't, for my life, see how people *can* be anything else."

"Nor I either," replied the lady. "I am sure I am as proud of my country as any one else."

"And good reasons you have to be so," added the tribune; "it's the first country in the world for an industrious man, such as I know your husband to be."

"I don't mean in that way," observed the lady, somewhat embarrassed; "I am proud of its republican institutions."

"It's the only free country in the world, you may depend upon it."

"Besides *England*. I think our people go too far in their liberty."

"I don't think people *can* go too far in that; the freer the better, is my motto."

"That's a very dangerous principle, sir; it leads necessarily to anarchy."

"I have often heard it said, but I never believed it. In our town, for instance, we are all democrats, and yet I never knew a row there ever since I was born; while your nice people of New York run riot on the most trifling occasion."

"That's owing to the great number of foreigners we have among us;

people who have been slaves at home, and on that account have the most extravagant notion of liberty."*

"Why, ma'am, our town consists almost wholly of foreigners, and is as quiet as possible. I think that people who have been oppressed before, may be as much attached to liberty as those who, from its daily enjoyment, have grown indifferent towards it."

"Why, what singular notions you have, Mr. ***!" exclaimed the lady; "I hope you are not an advocate of the *rabble?*"

"Certainly not; I represent the *people* of my township."

"You do not understand me. When I speak of 'the rabble,' I mean those who have no interest whatever in maintaining our institutions,—foreign paupers and adventurers, and particularly the Irish. I have no objection to liberty in the abstract. I think all men, with the exception of our negroes, ought to be free; but I cannot bear the ridiculous notion of equality which seems to have taken hold of our people, and which, if it be not counteracted by persons who have the power to do so," (here she bestowed a significant look upon the tribune), "must eventually prove the ruin of our country."

"I have heard this before," replied he, "and I saw it in print too; but I never believed a word of it. It's all got up for party purposes; you may depend upon it, ma'am."

"Ah, sir! but I see the truth of it every day of my life."

"In what manner, pray?"

"Good gracious! do you ask me that question? Is it not a matter of fact? Can there be the least doubt about a thing which is known to all? Why, it seems you live somewhat out of the world. Do you ever read the newspapers?"

"Indeed I do. There are two of them published in our town,—an administration and an opposition paper."

"Which of the two do you subscribe to?"

"To the administration paper of course. I have always been a democrat."

"Oh! you are a dem—o—crat, are you?"

"My friends call me one at least."

"Ah, then you are a democrat for a particular purpose. *That* I can understand. A man may have a particular object in calling himself a democrat, especially in this country; but no well-informed gentleman, I

* This is an argument I have constantly heard used against Europeans.

am sure, would be so mad as to seriously advocate a doctrine which administers to the passions of the mob, at the expense of the rights and privileges of the better classes. You would not intrust the government to paupers, would you?"

"I believe we have very few paupers in this country, except those who are unwilling to work," replied the representative.

"But if you saw the number of Irish and Germans that are landing here every day—"

"The country is large enough to furnish work for all."

"But they come sometimes five thousand in a week."

"The more the better."

"But would you make citizens of them? Would you allow them to vote?"

"Why not, if they have become naturalized according to law?"

"Do you think those wretches can ever feel what *we* do,—*whose fathers fought and bled for liberty?*"

"But, by granting the privilege of voting only to those that are *born* in the country, you necessarily make citizenship an hereditary distinction, contrary to the spirit of the American constitution."

"But are not hereditary distinctions necessary to a certain degree of greatness? Look at the English, at their literature, their refinement, their manners; and compare them with ours!"

"I know very little about the English, and care less," replied the tribune. "I do not think that the institutions of Europe would answer for this country. We are a young people. Our wants are few, and easily satisfied; and, as we had in the outset no other interests to protect but those of the masses, I do not see of what use hereditary privileges could be to us, except to make the proud prouder, and the rich more influential, than they already are, much to the dissatisfaction of our party; and, as for manners and refinement, I think we are doing very well, considering that our fashionable people have *to import* them from Europe. We are essentially an industrious people," added he; "and nothing promotes industry so much as to let all men start fair and even, the foreigner himself not excepted. When there will be no more land to be disposed of to new settlers, then there will come the time for making laws for the *preservation* of property; at present our chief duty is to facilitate its *acquisition.*"

"And would you make no allowances for superior education and learning?"

"To be sure I would; for such learning as may be applied to some useful purpose,—'not for the fiddle-stick accomplishments of your capering young boys.'"

"But don't you think democracy has a natural tendency towards vulgarity and bad manners?"

"Certainly not, ma'am! certainly not! I am a great advocate of politeness,—good manners, I say,—give me good manners by all means!"

"But how do you reconcile good manners with the everlasting hurrahing for General Jackson and Martin Van Buren?"

"That has nothing to do with good manners; that's what we call *enthusiasm.*"

"*We,* sir, call it madness—downright madness! Jackson has ruined the country."

"I see some folks are doing pretty well, for all that."

"The country went on prosperously until Jackson took it into his head to quarrel with the Bank. He has set the poor against the rich."

"Why, ma'am, when I went last up the river to Albany, and then down again to Philadelphia, I found there was quite as much travelling going on this season as in former years,—just as much wine drunk, just as much eaten; and, compared to last year, rather a little more brandy used than might be thought consistent with the reports of our temperance societies. And, as for setting the poor against the rich, that is a mere matter of opinion. The question of the Bank is a party question. We have attacked it on constitutional grounds, and the opposition have defended it from mercantile policy. We think the constitution of greater importance than anything which is done under it."

"I see, sir, you are wholly taken up with those doctrines which will eventually prove the destruction of the country. For my own part, I want no better proof of the justice or injustice of either principle *than the comparative respectability of the men who advocate it.*"

Here the lady drew herself back, and cast a side glance at the tribune, who, keeping his eyes fixed upon the points of his boots, appeared for the first time disconcerted by the argument of his fair antagonist. He attempted a reply, stammered a few words which were inaudible, and then looked again at his boots. The lady, perceiving his embarrassment, and the effect of applying the argument *ad hominem,* came to his aid by assuring him that she had, in her time, known a great many "smart democrats" who had all gradually become "respectable Whigs." "Democracy," said she, "is a very good beginning,—a sort of political breakfast, prepared in haste, which sits very well on an empty stomach; but it is not the thing a man can dine on, it is altogether too common for that.

"In a little time," added she, "you will be convinced of your error, as many an honest man has been before you. Colonel W***, for instance, has become quite respectable since he gave up General Jackson. Mr. O*** H*** came round in due time; and the list of converts is expected to swell from day to day, in proportion as the people become more and more civilized. It is only in *that* way that politicians can expect to have a standing in society; which democrats seldom have, owing to the peculiarity of their doctrines."

These words, pronounced with a strong emphasis, and with all the aristocratic dignity she could summon to her aid, were not entirely lost upon the tribune, who now looked the lady full in the face, without proffering a single syllable. He probably reflected on his children, on the impossibility of ever introducing them into society as long as he professed to be an advocate of the people: his experience as a public man had probably shown him that he could leave to his children no worse inheritance than the remembrance of his being "a regular democrat;" that his sons would be avoided, and his daughters remain unnoticed, if he did not change his political doctrines. He knew, or might have known, that the inquisition in Spain never exercised so direct and deadening an influence on the minds of the Spaniards, as the intolerance of the higher classes in the United States on the minds of aspiring politicians; and that, in general, the despots of Europe are more willing to make allowances for youth, inexperience, enthusiasm, and political conviction, than the wealthy aristocrats of the American republic. Yet his honesty and fortitude triumphed; he remained imperturbable. But he felt the sting of her satire; and perceiving that he had mistaken his place, and that it was best for him to associate with his *equals,* he "sneaked off," if possible, with a stronger hatred and contempt for the haughty aristocracy of New York than he had entertained before he had tasted of its hospitality.

"Shall I not see you to-morrow at my counting-room?" whispered the master of the house into his ears when he saw him ready to leave the room.

"I don't know whether I shall have time," replied the country representative sulkily.

"Why, what's the matter, sir? I shall not let you go until you have tasted my old sherry; come, Mr. ***, let us have a glass of wine together."

"Thank you, sir! I a'n't dry. *I have had quite as much as I could wish for.* Good night!"

The gentleman looked for an explanation of this extraordinary conduct to his wife, and in an instant all was clear.

"How can you trouble yourself with such a bore?" whispered he; "that's not the way to win him. If you cannot effect your purpose by flattery,—censure, I am sure, will not do it. These proud, stupid, stubborn country fellows require more management than you are aware of. You must puff them up; impress them with the notion of their own importance; show them how their talents might be employed in a nobler cause, &c. If that won't answer, you must endeavour to alienate their wives and children by instilling into them a taste for fashionable society, and, if possible, run them in debt. When their habits have become extravagant, when they are once in debt, then we talk to them differently,—one *accommodation* requires another."

"That man," observed my friend, "understands his business well; but his wife is a mere tyro in the art of converting people to her own persuasion. That representative may yet be won. I have seen better men corrupted, and with less means than will be employed against him; but, should he hold out, nothing will equal the abuse which will be heaped upon him.

"It is indeed strange," continued he, "to see how these two parties hate one another; how there is not the least communion or good fellowship amongst them; how they avoid each other on all occasions; and what a complete system of proscription is practised by the higher classes with regard to the unfortunate democrats! Prince Metternich cannot hold the Radicals in greater abhorrence than they are held by the wealthy merchants, lawyers, and bankers in the United States. And, as regards our Whig politicians, they might go to Europe to learn *moderation* and *tolerance* at the courts of absolute sovereigns.

"And is it not strange, that, in a country in which the *passion* of love is probably less felt than anywhere else, *hatred* should form so great an ingredient in the national composition? And what hatred too! the most constant,—the most steady,—the most unceasing that has ever been known to separate individuals or nations!

" 'Hatred,' says Goethe, 'like love, dies when it ceases to increase;' but he had no idea of the cool, calm, collected, slow hatred of certain classes of Americans. They are not like the French, who, when offended, cannot rest until they are revenged; not like the Germans, who are not easily offended; but being 'wrought, perplexed in the extreme,' they can wait for years until a *convenient* opportunity offers itself for paying off an insult or destroying an enemy.

"I remember, a short time ago, when a public man in Philadelphia had acted a double part towards me, to have called upon an acquaintance and expressed my indignation at what I thought ungentlemanly and villainous conduct. 'What is the use of your saying so now?' said he with great calmness; 'why don't you keep cool, and wait for an opportunity of paying him off in his own coin with interest?'

"Nor is it always possible to tell when they *are* offended. They have too much self-respect to show that they are wrought, but calmly wait for the proper time of seizing upon their victim. The hatred of most men dies when the object of their dislike is removed,—when they are revenged,—when their victim is passed to another world. Not so with the educated Americans. They hate even the *memory* of those that have thwarted their designs. Robespierre is not more detested in France, than Jefferson and Jackson are among the higher classes of Americans. I have seen fashionable women in Boston and Philadelphia almost thrown into convulsions at the very mention of their names. And what appears most strange is, that this hatred is hereditary; for it is a fact, no less interesting than instructive, that the higher classes in the United States have no political conviction at all. Their professions that way are the result of mere bias, produced by the opinions and sentiments of their early friends and associates. Democracy is in bad odour among the fashionable circles, which is quite sufficient for every coxcomb to despise it, and to affect an abhorrence of its 'vulgar and profligate' champions. There exists, in America, the same feeling with regard to republicanism which characterized the French shortly after the publication of the works of Voltaire and Rousseau with regard to religion: every one wants to escape from the lash of satire, and therefore shows in words and actions that he is one of those to whom it does not apply.

"It is quite common for educated and travelled Americans to *apologize* to Englishmen for the extraordinary degree of freedom enjoyed by the lower orders. Their usual excuse is, 'that the constitution of the United States was the work of momentary enthusiasm, which, when the people shall have cooled down, must necessarily undergo such wholesome alterations and modifications as reason and experience shall dictate.' In the mean while they must go on as well as they can, until the influence of wealth and the gradual return to the sound doctrines of English statesmanship, or, perhaps, also 'the evils incidental to a popular government,' shall have prepared the people for a different administration of their affairs, more suitable to the tranquil enjoyment of life. If it were not for the hue and cry raised by Jefferson and Jackson, the thing might have been done long ago; but, unfortunately for the peace and prosperity of the country, there will always be vagabonds enough—people who have everything to gain, and nothing to lose,— ready to follow such leaders!"

"As a proof of the attachment of certain old families to England," said I to my friend, "and the ludicrous notions of their own importance, I must repeat to you the speech of a gentleman from the Eastern States, with whom I had the honour of dining three or four years ago. Dinner went off prosperously; and, the company being small, the bottle came round faster than some of us could wish, until, as a finish, one of the gentlemen present proposed that each of us should give a toast. When it came to my turn, I, as a loyal German, could not but propose the health of the Archduke Charles of Austria. 'Bravo!' shouted the master of the house, 'a good old toast that! drunk many a time at my father's house with three times three and all the honours! I shall not do worse by the duke than my parent.' And hereupon the health of the archduke was drunk in a bumper.

" 'But,' said I, 'in 1809, the Archduke of Austria was an ally of England; and at that time matters in America were assuming a serious aspect, the war with Britain being considered as unavoidable.'

" 'I know that,' rejoined mine host: 'but what would have become of England if *we* had forsaken her at that time?'

"What a debt of gratitude does England owe to America! and yet what an ill-natured, peevish, ungenerous return do the English make for so much kindness bestowed upon them by their friends across the Atlantic!"

"But do you not think," demanded I of my friend, "that this English aristocratic feeling—this going in mourning for monarchy of the old Federalists,—is gradually dying away?"

"To be sure it is," replied he; "but another, much more arrogant in its nature, is taking the place of it. 'The old Federalists,' as you are pleased to call them, who, if not attached to England, at least openly avowed their admiration of the British constitution, were, in spite of their predilection in favour of English manners, infinitely less exclusive and intolerant, and much less addicted to the spirit of castes, than our 'aristocratic Whigs' of the present day, who would rather shut themselves up in hermetically sealed houses than share the light of heaven with a mechanic. The former acknowledged at least some power at home or abroad, to which they considered themselves responsible; the latter aim at the absolute government of the country.

" 'England,' say our *first people,* 'is the freest country in the world,' (which I, for one, am not disposed to deny, inasmuch as a man may speak his opinion there, without setting the whole nation against him, running the risk of being tarred and feathered,) 'and yet in England,' they say, 'there exists the least equality of conditions. Do we wish to be wiser than the English? Shall we shake hands with every one? associate with every one, and treat every one as our equal, because, forsooth, his *vote* is as good as ours?'

"Some years ago," continued my friend, "I remember being told very seriously by a red-nosed friend of mine,—who, by the by, was a great advocate of tea-totalism, but had lived rather freely in his youth,—that most Europeans, but especially the vulgar English, have a notion that in America there is no rank or distinction of castes. 'Here,' said he, 'is a letter I just received from an English music-master, to whom I was obliged to send a note in consequence of his want of punctuality in paying his rent. The note, of course, was written in a plain *business style,* reminding him merely of the fact that the money would fall due on the 15th instant. Now what do you think *the fellow* did? He wrote me back a note couched in precisely the same terms, and, if possible, more cavalierly than my own; as if the whole were a transaction between two individuals of the same standing.' Here he read me the note, which, as far as I am able to recollect, ran thus:

" 'Mr. *** has received Mr. ***'s note of this morning, and, in reply to it, assures Mr. *** that his rent will be ready *when due,* and that it would equally have been so without Mr. *** reminding him of it.'

" 'Such,' said he, 'are the notions of the low English that come to this country!'

" 'Did you take any further steps in the matter?' demanded I.

" 'Oh, no, sir; I thought it best to take no notice of him.'

"Now, where was the impudence of the man, who was dunned before he became a debtor? and what English landlord would have been more shocked with the insolence of his tenant, under similar circumstances?

"Another species of tyranny," continued my friend, "exercised by the higher classes of Americans consists in the proscription of all people belonging, or rather attempting to belong, to different sets. If you belong to the first society, you must not by any chance accept an invitation to the second, or shake hands in a friendly manner with people who are supposed to be of an inferior standing, except it be on election day for a political purpose. If you belong to the second, you may; of course, try with all your might 'to push for the first;' but, if you are once seen with the third, you have done even with the second: and so on.

"The French had, even under Charles X, too much democracy in their composition to be taken for safe models by the enlightened Americans; and, now, even the English are becoming too far liberalised to serve as a proper standard for our aristocracy.

"If the manners of the English are, in general, stiff and reserved, those of our fashionable people are rude and repulsive; for we have the peculiar faculty of improving on everything we borrow from Europe, commencing with the cut of our clothes, and ending with our language and manners.

"It is for this reason the dress of our young ladies—and especially the *costume de bal*—is less becoming than that of the French; their *air dégagé* is apt to be mistaken for forwardness; and their conversation, where the thing is at all attempted, is fraught with the slang—or, what is worse, the *learning*—of the boarding-school. Whenever one of our girls 'gets an European education,' an attempt is made to make her a walking encyclopædia of arts and sciences; and this, not so much for the sake of developing her mind, as to make her 'superior to other girls,' whom she is to outshine in society. I once heard a gentleman recommend an instructor to teach his daughter 'a little of everything.' 'I want her,' said he, 'to know a *little* of Latin and Greek, a little of mathematics, a little of astronomy, and a little of everything else; in short, I never want her to be embarrassed in society, let the conversation turn on what it may.' There is a young lady of that description here. She has just done spouting Virgil to one man, and Euclid to another, and now she is playing a waltz on the piano. She has a whole circle of admirers, fresh from the counting-room, around her, who, I dare be sworn, look upon her as the eighth wonder of the world; only an Englishman was impudent enough to observe that her acquirements tasted, one and all, of 'Murray's Elements.'

"As a *pendant* to the fashionable lady, you may notice, opposite the looking-glass, one of our American exquisites. His dress was made in London, but his manners are those of the most accomplished French coxcomb. His air, gait, and voice are affected, the latter being almost screwed to a childish treble; his conversation is copiously sprinkled with foreign idioms, and he has the vanity of inviting the young ladies of his acquaintance to smell his hair, which he assures them is *scented with real Persian perfume!* Could you expect such a man to be in favour of a less rigid distinction of castes? Could you imagine him to associate with people whose hair is only greased with pomatum, or, as is but too frequently the case in this country, with nothing but natural grease?

"And now look, for one moment, on our *middle-aged* gentlemen and ladies. Among the first we reckon those who are settled down in some respectable business; the latter term comprises all the married women in the country. At a party you can always distinguish them, even if they should happen to be *young,* by their greater sobriety; the men being satisfied with talking about business, and the women, if they do not belong to the very tip-top of fashion, being quietly seated near the wall, or in some corner of the room, talking, at times, very loud amongst themselves, but modestly answering the embarrassing variety of questions addressed to them by the gentlemen, of which unfortunately I was never able to remember more than two, viz. 'How do you do, ma'am?' and then, in the course of a quarter of an hour, with a pathetic emphasis and a sigh, 'How do you do again?'

"It has been asserted that, notwithstanding our many social deficiencies, there is yet a vast deal of *intelligence* in many of our small evening circles. This, in general, may be true; but I do not think our people understand the art of amusing themselves. We have little of the *laisser aller* of the French, and still less of *la bagatelle*. Moreover, we do not trust one another sufficiently, even at our parties. We always are, or imagine ourselves to be, in public, where we may meet with the eye of a reporter, and, perchance, see ourselves in print. Some of our first people went to Europe for the express purpose of learning how to live; but, on their return, never did more than go through the regular exercises of entertaining people,—a thing which proved to be as great a source of annoyance to themselves, as it was one of cheerless dissipation to their friends.

"Our people, in fact, will continue to remain tyros in the art of living, until they will have learned how to *laugh*. The occasional shaking of the diaphragm—absolutely necessary to the health of people not in a habit of taking active exercise—is a practice only popular among the negroes in the Southern States, who, to judge from appearances, are the happiest people in the Union. In New England I have only, now and then, remarked a spasmodic contraction of the muscles of the face approaching a smile or a grin; and in Boston, a city of more than eighty thousand inhabitants, there were but two gentlemen—one of English and the other of German extraction—who were known to have ever burst out in a horse-laugh. The much-praised intelligence of the higher classes of that 'learned' city resembles truly a December sun;—it gives you enough light to see by, but you require a fire to be comfortable."

Hardly had he spoken these words before a new general move betokened the breaking-up of the party. The married ladies and gentlemen had, in fact, been ready to go home ever since supper was over; but remained, either to oblige their children, or out of politeness to their entertainers, who were particularly anxious of the honour of keeping *late* hours. Sundry gapes and heavy eyelids had, indeed, long ago indicated their disposition to go to rest; but they were not taken notice of by the dancers, who appeared to be as fresh as ever, and prepared for the by no means unusual thing of a second supper. The good sense of the elderly portion, however, prevailed; and in a few moments every young *gallant* was on his knees—to assist his fair partner to put on her India rubber overshoes, (for in the United States no servant is permitted to touch the foot of a lady,) and the company separated, after saluting the lady of the house, and shaking the hand of the gentleman.

CHAPTER VII

Late Hours kept in New York.—The Oyster-shops of New York compared to those of Philadelphia.—Important Schism on that Subject.—The Café de l'Indépendance.—A French Character.—Description of a Fashionable Oyster-shop.—A Sensible American just returned from Paris.—His Account of American Aristocracy abroad.—Mr. L*** and Mr. Thistle.—A shrewd Yankee Tailor in Paris.—His Advice to his Countrymen.—An American Senator scorning to become the fee'd Advocate of the Mob, after the manner of O'Connell.

Mons. Jourdain.—"Et comme l'on parle, qu'est-ce que c'est donc que cela?"
Le maître de philosophie.—"De la prose."
Mons. Jourdain.—"Quoi! quand je dis, 'Nicole, apportezmoi mes pantoufles, et me donnez mon bonnet de nuit,' c'est de la prose?"
Le maître de philosophie.—"Oui, monsieur."
Mons. Jourdain.—"Par ma foi! il y a plus de quarante ans que je dis de la prose sans que j'en susse rien; et je vous suis le plus obligé du monde de m'avoir appris cela."

MOLIERE's *Bourgeois Gentilhomme*, Act ii. Scene 5.

THOSE of my readers who are not aware of the fact that New York is an excellent place for shell-fish, know in all probability little or nothing of the many elegant subterraneous establishments called "oyster-cellars" which adorn the principal avenues and public places of the great American Persepolis. The good people of New York swear that their oysters are the best in the world; and though I, for my own part, greatly prefer the delicate little "natives" of Colchester, or the still more savoury "green oysters of Ostend," I never before now dared to express my opinion on so delicate a subject, for fear of becoming unpopular, and being eventually excluded from society. One thing, however, I can testify; which is, that the Americans display, in the different modes of *cooking* and *dressing* them, a degree of refinement altogether incommensurate with the little progress they have thus far made in other equally useful and important branches of the culinary art.

The New-Yorkers alone have, I believe, twenty different ways of cooking oysters; the Philadelphians, who will not suffer themselves to be in anything outdone by their neighbours, twenty-one; and the Baltimorians boast of a still greater variety of dishes prepared of that most excellent shell-fish. This, in a country in which there is but one way of dressing meat, and precisely the same number of sorts of gravy, is certainly a most extraordinary phenomenon, and betokens an aristocratic predilection in favour of that slippery *friandise,* sufficient to establish its vast superiority over roast beef, the standing dish of the great mass of the American people. Oysters, in fact, have acquired a patrician reputation; though, like most of the distinctions lately introduced into the United States, they are only to be found along the seacoast, and for the most part bedded *in sand*. Some of them occasionally find their way to the "Western Country;" but they seldom remain there long in *good odour*. I could tell a number of crack stories on this subject; but, my diary having already grown longer than I at first anticipated, I am obliged to omit them, and content myself with mentioning the important schism, which, ever since the quakers established themselves in Philadelphia, separated the respectable inhabitants of that city from the enterprising descendants of the great Knickerbocker.

The Philadelphians maintain that *their* oyster-cellars are by far the most elegant, the most costly, and the most select in point of company, of any in the United States; which, they say, must strike any one who will take the trouble of spending the hours from ten in the evening till one in the morning in one of the splendid subterraneous vaults of that sort in Chestnut-street. "Not only," say the Philadephians, "would he be astonished at the taste and splendour of all the arrangements,—at the vastness, and even magnificence of the rooms, the excellence of the wines, &c.—but also at the number of respectable young men, sons of the first families, who, by their nightly presence, give a high *ton* to these establishments. An oyster-cellar may, indeed, be considered as a school for good breeding; and is, in a singularly felicitous manner, emblematic of the happiness, quiet, and self-sufficiency of the peaceable inhabitants of the city 'of brotherly love.' Besides, the oyster-cellars in Philadelphia are mostly kept by *white* men; which fact would of itself be sufficient to establish their superiority over the negro and mulatto establishments of that kind in the comparatively dirty city of New York."

Hereupon the New-Yorkers remark "that the company which frequent *their* oyster-cellars, though perhaps not quite so respectable and numerous in the *evening,* is nevertheless a great deal more so in *day-time;* that the Philadelphia company is often *mixed,* and in some instances absolutely *vulgar,* owing to the low price of oysters; whereas in New York, where good oysters cannot be procured for less than 37½ cents (equal to about 1s. 6d.) a dozen, *loafers* (this is the American term for black-guards) are completely excluded, and sent to the more plebeian beef-shops. As regards the stigma of having their oyster-shops kept by negroes and mulattoes, it is to be observed that of late a number of 'clever white men' have taken that lucrative business out of the hands of the Africans, by whom it has been too long degraded, and introduced a series of improvements in every respect worthy of the high reputation which distinguishes New York among her sister cities."

But there is one point in which the New-Yorkers have an immeasurable advantage over the Philadelphians,—an advantage which proves their city as much superior to Philadelphia as Paris is to a country town of France, or London to a rotten borough; viz. the New York oyster-cellars remain open until three or four in the morning, whereas the Philadelphians close theirs very soon after one: a custom which is vulgar and provincial in the extreme; and prevents many a gentleman, who has made but an indifferent supper at a party, from procuring himself the gratification of the nightmare.

These preliminaries, I think, will be sufficient to introduce the gentle reader to the sort of establishment towards which my friend and I were now wending our way. The city hall clock had long ago struck the hour of one; the crowd, which till late in the evening renders Broadway a scene of busy activity, had dispersed to their respective homes; and the inhabitants of the great commercial emporium of the New World actually appeared to have gone to rest for the night; when, on approaching the *Café de l'Indépendance,* the mingled sound of voices and instruments convinced us that a certain portion of the Americans at least were in the habit of keeping later hours than even the Parisians.*

"Let us look in," proposed my friend. "It's quite a nice establishment. The furniture alone cost more than fifty thousand dollars."

"Is it not too late?" demanded I. "I thought I heard you say you wanted some oysters: will they not shut up in the mean time?"

"No danger of that," replied he: "the oyster-cellars of this city are on

---

* It is well known that, except during the Carnival, the coffee-houses in Paris shut up shortly after the close of the theatres, which is seldom later than twelve o'clock.

the plan of the early breakfast houses in London; they give you a supper or a breakfast, whichever you please."

On entering the coffee-room, we found ourselves enveloped in a dense cloud of smoke, which at first prevented us from discerning the corps of German musicians that were regaling a motley group of Europeans and Americans with some of the best compositions of their countrymen. In justice to the Americans, I am bound to say that nine-tenths of the whole company present were foreigners,—principally Frenchmen and Spaniards, who seemed to be very little afflicted with home-sickness,—enjoying, perhaps for the first time in their lives, their *petit verre* and cigar without the surveillance of the *haute police,* or the disagreeable intrusion of some municipal guards.

"These Frenchmen," said my friend, "cannot be happy without *cafés* and *estaminets.* Deprive them of their *demi-tasse,* their *petit verre,* and their *partie de domino,* and you set them at once in a state of rebellion; and yet I never saw a place in which they appear to be more at home than in New York."

"I have heard it said this morning that a Frenchman would rather live in New York than in any town of France, except Paris."

"And well he may," rejoined my friend. "There is nothing more tiresome than a residence in a provincial town of France."

"What surprises me most," resumed I, "is that the French in this country take so little interest in politics."

"That is easily accounted for," observed my friend. "Politics, in France, are the exclusive occupation of editors, from whom the people receive their daily allowance, with such seasoning as suits the peculiarity of their taste: in America, on the contrary, every man is called upon to take an active part in them, which is more than a man is willing to do who is as fond of amusement as a Frenchman."

While he was delivering his opinion in this manner, an elderly gentleman rose from behind a marble slab table, and, seizing the hand of my friend, exclaimed, in an accent which very strongly resembled the Gascon,

"*Que diable! faites-vous ici à cette heure-ci? Je croyais toujours qu'il n'y avait que les Français qui se tenaient débout après minuit! Et n'avez-vous pas peur qu'on vous dénonce demain dans les journaux,— vous qui êtes un homme public?*"

"*Taisez-vous donc, monsieur,*" whispered my friend; "*vous me trahissez.*"

"Is de gentleman vid you an American?" demanded the Frenchman in a low voice, and in broken English.

"To all intents and purposes he is," answered my friend.

"Je vous comprends," said the Frenchman with a significant nod. " 'T is is a very fine evening, sar!"

"Very fine, indeed," responded I.

"Do you tink it vil rain to-morrow?"

"I hope it may; it is most excessively warm."

"Dat is de reason I am 'ere," said the Frenchman; "I cannot slip ven it is so very 'ot!"

"And how is your lady?" demanded my friend.

"Very vel, I tank you, sar! Madame D***, you know, is most happy ven she is alone. *C'est son caractère Bréton."*

"Have you been at the theatre this evening?" continued my friend in his interrogatory.

"No, sar! I never go to de teatre," replied the Frenchman. "I have given lessons until very late, and just came 'ere to read *le Courier des Etats-Unis* before going to bed. *Puis-je vous offrir quelque chose?"*

"I am much obliged to you; but it is too late," replied my friend.

"Too late!" exclaimed the Frenchman with affected astonishment; then suddenly recollecting himself, and taking out his watch, *"Upon my honneur,"* cried he, "it is past two a clock. I 'ad no idee dat it vos so late;" and, without saying another word, the poor fellow took up his hat and cane, and vanished through the back entry.

"That Frenchman," observed my friend, "is one of the most arrant cowards I ever saw in this country. He has married an American lady; and is afraid lest his being seen at a public-house should exclude him from the society of his wife's acquaintance. We have a good many foreigners among us, on whom the dread of public opinion, and the peculiar fashions of our people, act as a similar restraint. You can hardly say of any man in this country that he is master *in his own house;* much less is he at liberty to act as he pleases *in public;* but there are very few Frenchmen among us, I assure you, at least among the wealthier classes, who do not think with Molière's *Tartuffe, 'que ce n'est pas pêcher que de pêcher en silence.'* But it's now high time to leave this place if we wish to take aught before going to bed." So saying, he threw some change on the plate which one of the musicians presented to him, and, snatching up his hat, opened the door for our exit.

When we re-entered Broadway, the moon had spread her mantle over the house-tops; a delicious breeze, which during the heat of day had been sleeping on the breast of the ocean, whispered comfort to the weary citizens; the dim noise of the multitude had wholly subsided; and the rattle of carriages, growing fainter and fainter, gradually died away at a distance. On approaching the neighbourhood of the Park, however, new traces of life appeared, until at last the brilliant façade of the theatre, surrounded by a host of liquor-shops, eating-houses, and oyster-cellars, presented itself through the dark-green foliage with the magic light of an enchanted castle.

"This part of the town," observed my friend, "is never quiet; it is the *perpetuum mobile* of America."

Accordingly, as we came near the corner, everything appeared to be animated: hackney-coaches stood in readiness to convey those who either did not feel disposed or were no longer able to walk, to any part of the city; and the doors of the eating-houses, tap-rooms, and oyster-cellars were thrown open for the reception of company.

My friend, who happened to be somewhat acquainted in New York, selected the establishment in the corner; which we entered, by descending six or seven steps into a capacious bar-room, furnished in very good style, and lit with gas as brilliantly as any saloon in London. This was a sort of reception hall, intended for those who *drank without stopping;* the real supper-rooms, with something like eighteen or twenty boxes to preserve the incognito of the visiters, being lodged in another part of the building.

The first thing which struck our attention was a large black board, on which there were printed, in the shape of a bill of fare, the nice little items of "wild duck," "wild turkey with oyster sauce," "roast chicken," "chicken salad," "roast oysters," "fried oysters," "stewed oysters," "scolloped oysters," &c. &c. &c.

We naturally took this as a favourable omen, and were about to betake ourselves to the only empty box that was yet left, when my friend recognized, in a gentleman that was entering the room, one of his former classmates, who had just returned from Paris, where he had devoted himself for several years to the study of medicine.

After the usual manifestations of joy, shaking of hands, and asking of questions, which neither of them pretended to answer but by asking fresh ones,—for my friend and his schoolfellow were both Southerners, and not in the habit of finishing a thing of that sort by a laconic "How d'ye do? I am very glad to see you,"—my friend at last succeeded in getting the companion of his youth seated by his side, and eliciting from him, as far as I am able to remember, the following honest confession of his experience in foreign parts, and the state of things he found on his return to his native country.

"I must freely confess to you," said he, "that what I saw of my countrymen abroad did not materially contribute to increase my respect for them; neither did I think it calculated to enhance the respect with which Europeans are wont to look upon the untried institutions of our country. They hunt men of hereditary titles and privileges just as much, and even more, than the English; the highest ambition which I ever knew them guilty of being the desire of associating with a count or a prince. And so different are their notions of rank and titles, of superiority and inferiority, from those of Europeans in general, that they make themselves not only hated by the admirers of republican principles, but also ridiculous in the eyes of every sensible Tory.

"If one of our business men were to-day invited to a prince's, and to-morrow to a count's or a baron's, you might be sure of his playing the aristocrat at the baron's house, merely because he was before asked to a prince's; and if, by accident, he had the day following met with one of his countrymen 'not yet as high up in society as himself,' he would have deemed it a duty due to his new standing 'to cut him dead,' though he might have known him from his infancy.

"The petty jealousies among the Americans have equally disgusted me in every part of Europe; and appeared to me the more ludicrous, as the being admitted into society depended frequently on circumstances altogether beyond their control. In one instance it was owing to a letter of introduction, for which they were indebted to the politeness of a friend, or the kind interference of a third person, to whom they were entirely unknown; in the other, to a high regard for the country of which they were, nominally at least, the representatives; and, in not a few cases, I can assure you, to mere curiosity. And yet you ought to have heard those people, who were thus by mere chance brought in contact with persons enjoying hereditary distinctions, talk 'of the different orders of society,' with the same degree of earnestness as if, by associating with the higher classes, they had actually partaken of their qualities!"

"And, then, what American, if he sets out to do it, cannot *force himself* into the best society by having recourse to a stratagem? which,

I believe, is altogether of our own invention, and consists in the practice of asking people to whom we are recommended, to introduce us to others with whom *they* are acquainted; and so on. Not only does our acquaintance, in this manner, wonderfully increase; but, as every one of our friends must necessarily know some two or three persons above him, we cannot but *'get up by degrees,'* until we reach a point infinitely above the level of our first introduction.* Some conceited Englishmen have called this practice 'the method of begging one's-self into society;' but, with our *élite,* nothing is deemed unfair which is not absolutely opposed to the established laws of the country."

"But some of our people keep elegant establishments in Paris, and, I am told, actually ruin themselves by entertaining the nobility," observed my friend.

"Some *may* injure themselves in that way," replied the young physician; "but I am sure others make money by it. Trust a Yankee to himself!"

"I do not quite understand you," observed my friend.

"The thing is plain enough," rejoined the physician; "the society of the nobility procures them the custom of their own countrymen, who consider a man of that sort as 'a stepping-stone to something better;' and he, poor innocent soul! makes them pay for the use they make of him."

"*A propos,*" demanded my friend, "have you dined with Mr. L***?"

"I was *invited* to dine there; but merely listened to the gentleman's own eulogy of his wines, and the eloquent description of every dish that was put upon the table, in order, afterwards, quietly to sneak off, and appease the cravings of my stomach at some snug little *restaurant* on the other side of the water. The gentleman you allude to has, moreover, lately turned jockey, and is now entertaining clergymen and physicians with nothing but horse-flesh. He probably thinks that this will ingratiate him with the English, and, in some respects, place him on the same footing with Lord S—r."

"All I have heard of that extraordinary little man, who, as I under-

---

* In some instances a mere name will answer the purpose of an introduction. Mr. ***, of Boston, meets in Paris Mr. W***, with whom he became acquainted in Philadelphia. "Do you know Chateaubriand?" asks the Bostonian.—"I meet him very often."—"Is he worth knowing?"—"Most assuredly."—"Adieu!"—The day following Mr. W*** meets Chateaubriand. *"Un drôle de corps* that!" says Chateaubriand, "you sent me yesterday." —"Who, I?"—"Yes, you, sir!"—"Whom?"—"The American." The conclusion of the dialogue may be imagined.

stand, has already risen to the dignity of *'un homme de passage,'** convinces me that he is acting the *bourgeois gentilhomme,* for the peculiar gratification of the less rich, but more refined, gentlemen of the old *régime;* only that he is not quite so generous as his original in the inimitable comedy of Molière."

"Neither does he trouble himself with so many *masters.* He is, in this respect at least, a true independent American, whose conversation would convince you in a moment that he has never had a master in his life. So far from it, he has himself turned schoolmaster, teaching a certain portion of his *raw* countrymen, not indeed the art of *eating,* but of *preparing* savoury dishes. Let one of those persons have the most trifling advantage over any of his fellow beings, and he is sure to use it as a means of establishing his superiority; for the scrambling for rank is born with them, and is only increased by a residence in Europe."

"Neither does it merely apply to such ordinary characters as you have just mentioned," added my friend. "I have known American *editors* assume in Paris—seldom, I believe, in London—an air of supercilious dignity, which would have been amusing if it had not been too absurd to be tolerated. They would *allow* Chevalier, and other writers of the French periodical press, to *cultivate* their acquaintance, and occasionally 'condescend to *receiving* them at their houses;' as if the hospitality they had received in Paris, and the willingness of certain people of fashion to come to their *soirées,* had actually given to their talents— which, if they had remained in America, would, in all probability, have never been known to the world—an additional lustre, that outshone the merits of their European contemporaries."

"There might have been another reason for the aristocratic presumption of the American editor," observed the physician. "The American may have kept a *valet,* while his French colleague was probably satisfied with the service of the *garçon* of his hotel. A thing of this sort separates an American man of letters from an European as effectually as if the ocean rolled its waves between them."

"That *must* be the case," resumed my friend; "for, if literary reputation were the sole basis of their respective ranks, I think our American editors would be obliged to give in."

"And yet they pretend to pity the political ignorance of the French,

---

* This, as is well known, is the term applied by the witty Parisians to those distinguished personages whose caricatured busts are exhibited in the principal arcades of the city.

and even the English; forgetting that those nations have two thousand years' history on their backs, which must necessarily form the precedent to the great majority of their conclusions."

"But have you not seen the famous Mr. Thistle?" demanded my friend. "I understand he keeps the crack house in Paris."

"He certainly does," replied the physician; "and there is at least something in his manner of entertaining people which appears to be frank and generous, though a great many of our first society think him excessively vulgar for not inviting them. The fact is, he can command better company in Paris than that of his own countrymen; and, under these circumstances, he is not to be censured for excluding those who otherwise would have excluded *him*. On the whole, I am rather glad that a character like his should be somewhere established in Europe; it is a living parody of the leading features of our aristocracy, illustrative of the true principle on which our 'first people' claim equality with the *noblesse* of Europe, and the conditions on which the latter are willing to admit it. Mr. Thistle, moreover, has quite a patrician bearing, which is truly burlesque when compared to the less than ordinary carriage of those who will have nothing to do with him, because they never associated with him in his own country."

"And what does Mr. Thistle care for the slander-hurling tongues of his countrymen?—he whose mansion has been repeatedly graced by the presence of princes of the blood? And where is the fashionable American who, in spite of his fox-like protestations to the contrary, would not be glad to have the *entrée* of a house, the *réunion* of the best and most ancient society of Paris?"

"Mr. Thistle is not merely admitted into the best society, he is actually one of them; though the preliminary steps of his promotion are kept as secret as those of the candidates for admission into the oldest fraternity on earth, and perhaps somewhat humiliating, as are said to be the first introductions to that honourable body. One little fact, however, could not entirely be concealed from the world; which is this, that when the *élite* of the *faubourg St. Germain,* who first took him by the hand, put it to the vote what persons should be admitted to his parties, the master of the house himself was excluded.

"The most sensible American I met in Paris," continued the physician, "was Mr. ***, a tailor from Boston; and the most insipid of my countrymen were those for whom he made the uniforms for presentation at court. These, in the absence of any fixed rule, (I have no doubt that, in case of Mr. Van Buren's being ousted, a bill will be introduced into Congress prescribing the uniforms to be worn by American citizens abroad,) were altogether left to the fancy of the artist, who never failed to recommend to every inexperienced Yankee courtier to put *a star* on his coat, in opposition to the *eagle* worn by the servants of the American minister. In this manner, he assured his patrons, they would neither risk being taken for servants, nor would they have to be ashamed of wearing plain coats by the side of persons all decorated with ribbons. Those who held a high rank in the militia he always advised to be presented in the uniform of colonel, that being the lowest title a respectable American ought ever to assume in Europe; and a military dress being the best excuse for the natural *brusquerie* of men fresh taken from business. In this manner the shrewd Yankee tailor not only acquires a fortune, but also sees his reputation travel, with his coats, from shore to shore; their being Americans that will never cross the British Channel without a suit of military clothes, in case they should be invited to dine or breakfast with a nobleman.

"But I do not wish to dwell any longer on the absurdities of our people abroad, for we are in this respect just like the English; our true character being only to be found at home, where it developes itself under the immediate influence of our institutions. Nothing, therefore, could be more preposterous than to judge us by the specimens we send abroad; and it was a wise remark of Thomas Jefferson, though, I believe, sufficiently misunderstood by his countrymen, that an American who has lived above seven years in Europe is a stranger to his own country, and no longer fit for any office of responsibility, even if he should have been employed during all that time as a diplomatic agent of his government."

"Thomas Jefferson," observed my friend, "has said a number of clever things, and warned us against a great many mistakes into which we have since fallen. He particularly dreaded the influence of British example on our public and private character; and the result has proved that he was not mistaken."

"And yet how little did he suspect that our political partisans would find professional statesmen willing to become the fee'd advocates of their doctrines, after the manner of O'Connell!" rejoined the physician.

"What do you mean?" interrupted I, astonished at the boldness of the remark.

"I mean what I say," replied he; "I know a senator for whom the manufacturers of his district are said to make an annual purse, on the ground that his Congressional duties interfere with the exercise of his profession as a lawyer."

"I cannot believe it," interrupted my friend with some vehemence; "and I will not believe it: but, even if it were true," added he, with a sardonic smile, "the honourable senator would, for the honour of his State, be the very reverse of the vulgar Irish agitator; one is paid by his rich and respectable constituents, the other by the very beggars of his country! None of our Whig senators, I am sure, would ever condescend to become the hired advocates of the mob."

"A fine piece of news this!" ejaculated the physician; "but I suspected as much as this when I saw the change wrought on the manners and customs of our people since my absence; how the simple, unsophisticated habits of our citizens have given way to cold formality and conceit,—and how the generous hospitality which was wont to grace our people is fast yielding to a vulgar and ostentatious display of wealth.

"I am actually afraid of meeting my old acquaintance, and it is for this reason you see me play the owl at this late hour; at which, at least, I am allowed to have my own way, without being intruded upon by my friends, or pushed aside by the busy multitude, to whom I must for ever remain an unprofitable stranger."

CHAPTER VIII

Return Home.—A Passage from the Edinburgh Review, apologetical of American Federalism.—Speculation on the Subject.—Little Reward of Democracy in the United States.—The Higher Classes contending for the Purse.—Consequence of this Policy.—Declaration of an American Reviewer with regard to American Poets—their Reward in Europe.— Falling asleep.—The Nightmare.

> "The earth has bubbles as the water has,
>   And these are of them."

Macbeth, Act i. Scene 3.

ON my return home, I found it impossible for me to go to sleep. The events of the day were yet fresh upon my mind, and I required some abstraction to set my thoughts to rest, and efface the disagreeable impressions produced by the conversation of the stranger. Undetermined as to the means of escaping from my own reflections, I searched the books and papers on my writing-table; where, unfortunately for my quiet, I happened to glance my eye on an American republication of the "Edinburgh Review," and a few scattered numbers of the "Southern Literary Messenger." I mechanically opened the first, and, as misfortune would have it, found my attention at once riveted by the following passage:

"Purge the British constitution of its corruptions," said Adams, "and give to the popular branch equality of representation, and it would be the most perfect institution ever devised by the wit of man."

"Purge it of its corruptions," replied Hamilton, "and it would become an *impracticable* government: as it stands at present, with all its supposed defects, it is the most perfect government that ever existed."

These remarks, I thought, proceeding from the two saints by which the American Whigs still swear on solemn occasions, prove at least Hamilton to have been the abler statesman, though they are both clearly indicative of the spirit which pervaded some of the leading patriots of the revolution.

Anxious to learn the opinion of a British writer on so interesting a subject, I read on, and was struck with the following good-natured apology for the doctrines and sentiments of the old Federalists.

"The leaning of the Federalists towards monarchy and aristocracy," says the reviewer, "has probably at all times been a good deal exaggerated by their antagonists. That there is, at the present time, hardly any such feeling, may be easily admitted; and it has probably been wearing out by degrees ever since the revolution, in proportion as men saw that realised without a struggle (!), which many in America, and still more in England, had deemed impossible,—the firm establishment of a republican government over many millions of people, with sufficient power to preserve order at home, and sufficient energy to maintain the relations of peace and war. *But, at the first, no reasonable doubt can be entertained of the fondness for monarchical institutions which prevailed among the leading Federalists.*"

The perusal of this passage, after a day spent, as I have described, in the city of New York, naturally gave rise to singular reflections. "What is it," said I to myself, "that the Americans have established without a struggle? And wherein consists the stability of their republican institutions, if it be not in the fact that the people from year to year conquer them anew from the wealthy opposition? And, as regards to the predilection for monarchical and aristocratic institutions, who that has observed the higher classes of Americans, at home or abroad, can doubt but that they are at this moment as strong as at the time of Thomas Jefferson?"

The old Federalists have not given up *one* of their former pretensions,—for there is no converting men in politics by argument; but they are probably satisfied that they must *wait for a favourable opportunity* of establishing them: they have become more cautious in their actions and expressions, because they now *fear* the people over whom they once expected to rule. All that I have been able to see in the United States convinces me that the wealthy classes are in no other country as much opposed to the existing government; and that, consequently, no other government can be considered as less permanently established, or more liable to changes, than that of the United States. And this state of danger the soft speeches of the Whigs try to conceal from the people by directing their attention almost exclusively to the financial concerns of the country. Wealth, in other countries,—as, for instance, in England,—acts as the *vis inertiæ* of the state; talent from above, and the wants of the labouring classes from below, acting as motors. In America the case is the reverse: the wealthy classes wishing for a change which the labouring ones resist; and talent, I am sorry to say, acting a subordinate part, ready to serve the cause of either party that promises to reward its exertions.

This, I am aware, is a sad picture of America, but nevertheless a true one; and I appeal to the history of the last half century, and to the biography of American statesmen, if an impartial one should ever be written, in confirmation of the general correctness of my statement. Exceptions to this rule exist, of course, in every State; but, without any particular predilection in favour of democracy, it is easy to perceive that these mostly occur on the popular side.

Whenever a man of talent or wealth embraces the cause of democracy, he becomes at once the butt of society, and the object of the most unrelenting persecution with all the "respectable" editors, lawyers, bankers, and business men in the large cities. To one democratic paper published in a city, there are generally from ten to twelve, sometimes twenty, Federal or Whig journals; which I take for the best possible proof that talent loves to be rewarded, and in republics, as well as in monarchies, naturally serves those who are best *able* to reward it.

The democrats have not the means of remunerating the services of their public men in the manner of the Whigs; for, with the exception of a few government offices, with mere pittances for salaries, and the election of senators and members of Congress,—persons "hired at the rate of eight dollars a day,"—all lucrative offices of trust and emolument are in the gift of the opposition, whose patronage, therefore, is a matter of infinitely higher consideration than that of the President and his cabinet.

The little pecuniary reward which the zealots and champions of democracy meet with in the United States, is, indeed, one of the reasons for which they are despised by their aristocratic opponents. "What talents," argue the latter, "can a man possess who will give up all manner of business, and devote himself exclusively to politics, in order, near the close of his life, to sit down contented with the editorship of a penny paper, a membership of Congress, or an office of from twelve hundred to two thousand dollars a year? Success in life is the best proof of ability; and who that will look upon the respective condition of our political partisans can for one moment be doubtful as to which of them have the *best side* of the question?"

It is for such and similar reasons that they take every opportunity of railing against the increased patronage of the government; as if the government of the United States were something apart from the people,—a power which the people have to contend with, and against which, therefore, they must direct their concentrated efforts! And a considerable portion of the people are actually duped in that way; they imagine that what is taken away from the government is gained by the community, forgetting that the government is of their own choice, and that the men placed at the head of it rise or fall at their beck. They do not seem to be aware that, as long as the government of the United States remains elective, all executive power vested in it increases but the sovereignty of the people, and that the patronage of the government is essentially their own.

On the subject of patronage the aristocratic press of America is truly eloquent; that being the point for which it most contends, the lever of its patriotism. What, indeed, would become of the flower of statesmen of the present Whig party, if the government of the country, or the people who elect that government, could reward the advocacy of their cause as princely as the "wealthy and enlightened" opposition?—if *money* were at the command of the public servants, as it is at the disposal of those who manage the great financial concerns of the country? Hence the people are warned against putting the sword and the purse into the same hands. "Let the government have the sword," say the Whigs, "provided we keep the purse."

The purse is the point round which the whole system of politics turned ever since the origin of the country. The war for and against a bank did, indeed, agitate the United States before they were quite ushered into existence; and has continued to throw the elements of state into confusion, and to act in a truly corrosive manner on every true source of national grandeur. What effect it had on the progress of literature and the arts is exultingly shown in an article of "The Southern Literary Messenger;" a copy of which, as I observed before, I found by accident on my writing-table.

"The intellectual character of our republic," says a writer in that clever periodical, in a paper bearing the title "Scriptural Anthology," "makes rapid advances in improvement. A very few years ago it was seriously argued whether or not the air of America was favourable to the inspirations of genius; now our artists, actors, and poets bid fair to take the lead of their European rivals. If the former fall short in anything,

'We ought to blame the culture, not the soil.'

It is now conceded on all sides that we have the stamina, or, (to speak
in a business-like tone,) the *raw material* of the first quality. No doubt
but we have had Homers in embryo, many a 'mute inglorious Milton,'
and many a Tasso, 'cabined, cribbed, and confined' by oppressive circumstances. But in spite of all those proverbial obstacles, to most of
which the *American* bard* is particularly liable, a poetical star sometimes gleams above our horizon. Such instances, it must be confessed,
are rare; and in what part of the world is the advent of a good poet *not*
a rare occurrence? With us but little encouragement is offered for any
man to devote his time and talents to this branch of literature; and,
without exclusive devotion, we are apt to suppose that excellence in
any art or science is but seldom attained. But, with respect to encouragement, matters are beginning to take a change for the better;—
in our literary world the golden age has been delayed to the last:
poetical speculations, albeit of an airy and immaterial nature, now
yield something substantial in the way of profit. Poets begin to have 'a
local habitiation,' not in the gaol or garret; and 'a name,' not synonymous with starvation. From being objects of cool regard or warm
persecution, they have become quite the lions of the day; *they visit*
foreign countries, associate with the nobility, and drink tea (or punch)
in the serene presence of the royal family. Even at home, the study (!)
of poetry has almost dared to compete with the absorbing calculations
of compound interest; and many a clerk is 'condemned to cross his
father's spirit,' as Chaucer saith, by penning a stanza 'when he should
make out a bill.' "

This sort of reasoning, in which I am half inclined to believe the
author was serious, together with the fact that the principal poets of
America are really obliged to seek "a local habitation and a name" in
Europe, may be considered as the best proof of the all-absorbing influence of the purse;—an influence which already acts restrictively on
genius and talent of the highest order, and will, if it be not counteracted by a more generous system of legislation, and a different spirit
diffused *among the people,* constantly absorb the main sources of
thought and action, which give to every nation its individual life and
character.

* The word "American" is in Italics in the original.

But I trust that the good sense of the people, the intelligence pervading the masses, and, above all, the high degree of morality and virtue which distinguishes the American above all other nations in the world, will be proof against the temptations of a handful of political sceptics; and that the country, blessed with Nature's richest gifts, and selected by Providence for the noblest experiment tried by man, will fulfil its mission,—which is not only the civilization of a new world, but the practical establishment of principles which heretofore have only had an ideal existence.

Thus cogitating, I pulled my night-cap over my head, put out the candle, and fell fast asleep. Agitated as I had been during the whole day, my sleep could not remain undisturbed by dreams. I imagined myself somewhere near the Hudson or the Delaware, in the midst of a large, flourishing city, besieged, stormed, and finally carried by a victorious Western army, whose gallant leader dictated laws written in blood to the affrighted populace. A deputation of "leading citizens," who had come to offer their riches as a ransom for their lives, he thus apostrophized in a stern and solemn voice:—"Fools that ye were to wish for artificial distinctions! Know that the origin of every aristocracy is the sword, not the purse, or the Jews would long ago have become the masters of the world! You have claimed the purse for yourself, and now the sword shall take it!"

PART II

CONTAINING A SHORT STAY
IN BOSTON AND PHILADELPHIA

CHAPTER IX

Arrival in Boston.—The Tremont House.—The Boston Common.—
Aristocratic Exclusiveness of the Higher Classes.—The Massachusetts
State-House.—Pathetic Elegy of a Boston Lawyer.—An Independent
Gentleman, not a Speculator.—American Aristocracy contrasted with
that of England.—The Aristocracy of America continually in contact
with the Lower Orders.—Anecdote illustrating the opposition of the
Lower Classes to Aristocracy.—An Aristocratic Patron.—Economy of the
American Aristocracy.—Northern and Southern Aristocracy contrasted.

> "If there's a hole in a' your coats,
> I rede you tent it;
> A chiel's amang ye takin' notes,
> And faith he'll prent it."

BURNS.

THE city of Boston, as may be known to many of my readers, is only
approachable by water and a long narrow isthmus, called "the neck."
For this reason it is said to be "the head of New England;" but the
people in the country, who are extremely jealous of the prerogatives
of "the townsfolks," merely call it "the great metropolis." When it was
first settled, which is more than two hundred years ago,—for which
reason it is termed "an ancient and honourable city,"and the families
descended from those settlers "ancient and honourable families,"—it
contained, somewhere in the neighbourhood of what is now called
"Beacon-street," three large promising bumps, which however, entirely
disappeared as the baby grew older, and are now smoothed down
almost to a flat.

The neck forms a large well-paved causeway, lined chiefly with
wooden houses, (in the principal streets the building are of stone or
brick,) and connects the city with the borough of Roxbury, which contains alone above ten thousand inhabitants. Coming from New York,
this is the regular entrance to the town; and through it therefore I
arrived, driving straight up to the Tremont House. This is a large,
massive building with a granite front and a brick back, situated in the

most eligible part of the city, and considered as the crack house of the place.

I found the interior very comfortable, and could have procured a parlour and chamber for the modicum of thirty-six dollars (about seven guineas) a week, if an acquaintance of mine, whom I accidentally met at the bar, had not advised me to content myself with a bedchamber, and dine at the ordinary; which, he said, would reduce my expenses to about one-third, without diminishing very materially my respectability. "Our *first* people," said he, "are satisfied with similar accommodations: they little care how and where they sleep, provided they live in a fashionable quarter; and prefer dining at an ordinary, because at a public table they get more to eat for less money. We are *republicans,*" added he, "especially in this city, which is called the *cradle* of liberty."

Not knowing whether he meant this as a satire, I proposed to take a walk with him before dinner, in order that I might have a *cicerone* to direct my first impressions of so classical a place; and accordingly we sallied forth, taking the direction down Tremont-street towards the Common.

"You see here at once the finest place in the whole city," said my cicerone; "one which might be enjoyed by all classes, if we had not already outgrown the *cradle*. The people who live in these houses, and who, with very few exceptions, have all been to England, do not like to be seen in public. They hate the arrogance of our grocers and mechanics, who would be apt to stare them out of countenance if they were to show themselves at a public walk. 'Humility,' they say, 'is not the besetting sin of the American people: on the contrary, the lower classes think themselves just as good as we are; and, what is worse, they *know* that they are our political masters.' This, they argue, is absolute madness, as a man may learn by a single trip to Europe. 'There *must* be a heaven's aristocracy of talent and knowledge, 'as one of our great men* used to say,' and consequently also a h—ll's democracy of ignorance and prejudice. The latter must not be encouraged in any way, and, least of all, by suffering ourselves to be confounded with it in private or public.'

"It was with the greatest difficulty," continued he, "that our aristocratic inhabitants of Beacon and Park streets† could be prevailed upon to suffer benches to be placed in the Mall. They had two reasons for

---

* Edward Everett, the present governor of Massachusetts.
† The two streets which face the Common.

opposing this popular measure: first, because it encouraged idleness, inducing people who ought to be at work or at home to come here and bask themselves in the sun; and, secondly, because it was possible from those benches either to see the people at the windows of the houses, which would be inconvenient,—or from the windows of those houses to see the people on the benches, which, as the sight of poverty and idleness does not particularly enhance the beauty of a landscape, would be 'shocking.' Malicious persons say that there are yet other reasons for opposing the benches; but I could never bring myself to believe them."

As we were ascending the little eminence on which stands the State-house, we were met by a lawyer, who, learning that I was a stranger come on purpose to see the capital of New England,—the *ideal* capital, namely, because New England is divided into six States, each of which has its own metropolis,—accompanied us, in order probably to become acquainted with my opinions, and in the evening report them to his friends.

For the information of my readers I must observe, that the Boston State-house is a heavy, clumsy piece of architecture, the style and arrangement of which are neither striking nor convenient. I was told that the building was originally intended to be erected on a much larger scale; but that, from motives of republican economy, its wings were afterwards clipped to their present dimensions,—the main body, for which there were sufficient funds on hand, remaining full as large as in the first design. The whole is crowned by a wooden cupola, of such enormous height as not even to leave the possibility of an illusion of its being made of stone, as in this case the walls would not be strong enough to support it. These are confessions which, in Boston, would not only render me unpopular, but actually expose me to being mobbed; but, at a distance of two hundred miles, (I write this in the city of New York,) one does feel less afraid of expressing one's opinions and sentiments. The interior of the house contains a statue of Washington, by Chantrey; a broad staircase; a large hall of representatives; and a number of smaller rooms for committees, and the several offices of the departments of state.

"This house," said the lawyer, after heaving a deep sigh, "once the receptacle of a *noble* body of men, is now open to every gingerbread man from the country; or you would see it built in a different style, worthy of the legislative assembly hall of a powerful republic, like that of Massachusetts! But the fact is, instead of great men, our house of representatives is now composed of members who advocate 'mackerel inspection,' cider-presses, fences, raising potatoes, and brewing small beer. Having no general ticket, each town or village must send its quota of advocates of its own particular industry; who, moreover, come here for no other purpose than to oppose the more elevated measures proposed by the more enlightened members for Boston."

"That is a fact," observed my cicerone; "our *city* representatives wish them all to *'where they don't rake up fire o' nights.'* They have so far degraded their station, that it is now a disgrace, and not an honour, to be delegated by the people."

"And what have they done to disgrace themselves?" demanded I.

"That is soon told," replied the lawyer; "every country member comes here with the determined purpose of opposing *us,* and, above all things, to let the Bostonians contribute largely to the expenses of the State. We pay nearly one-third of all the taxes; and yet we call this *a republican government!"*

"One of equal justice, you ought to have said," interrupted the cicerone.

"As if justice could co-exist with universal suffrage!" ejaculated the lawyer.

"I would pardon all," resumed the cicerone, with a sarcastic smile, "if our country members were to spend the money, which we pay them for lounging about town, in a liberal and gentlemanly manner: but, instead of that, they select the worst boarding-houses, from which they expel our journeymen mechanics, in order to live cheap; and, instead of wine and other liquors, which our merchants and grocers could make a profit of, consume immense quantities of that dreadful stuff which, under the name of 'New England cider,' is sometimes placed on our tables, and for which even our *sharpest* landlords dare not make a charge."

"The positive fact is," exclaimed the lawyer, "that few of our representatives are gentlemen."

"And that very few gentlemen will now-a-days consent to become representatives," added my cicerone, "except it be for Congress; and even that will not last long, if things go on much longer in the way they have for the last seven or eight years."

As the disposition of the higher classes of Bostonians to ridicule the institutions of their country were known to me, I paid no particular attention to their remarks, which were made as we were gazing on the statue *"of the hero of the revolution."* I only remember that the lawyer went on in a strain of uninterrupted eloquence, abusing the trial by jury, the vote by ballot, and, *à fortiori,* universal suffrage. "We just wanted that," he said, "to complete our misery! As if our mob had not enough power without it! Our democracy is of the worst kind; it does not strive for equality, but for supremacy. It becomes at once our jury, judge, legislator, and governor. You dare not act as you please in your own house; you dare not educate your children in your own way; you dare not express a wish of your own but what you have to dread to be exposed in public, and have your name paraded in the newspapers. Every man in this city is a spy on his neighbour, a voluntary, unpaid police-agent of the rabble, that pries into all your actions and motives, and is always ready to attribute them to the worst source. And yet we talk of personal liberty, as if such a thing could exist in a republic!"

"But is the description you give of your townsmen not applicable to all classes?" demanded I; "is it only the labouring classes, or 'the mob,' as you call them, which act as spies to the community?"

"We are all naturally a curious, inquisitive people," replied he; "and a cunning one too, because we hardly ever answer one question except by asking another; but all these faults are increased by the tendencies of our institutions."

"Have you been less curious or inquisitive before the revolution?"

"Not exactly that; but the inquisitiveness of the lower classes was less troublesome. Our gentlemen were not obliged to notice it; they were not directly responsible to the people; in short, *we* were in every respect more independent than we now are."

I thought it best not to continue this sort of conversation; so, quitting the house, and walking down Beacon-street, I pointed to a new build-ing which struck me as remarkably tasteful. "Here," said I, "is quite a stylish mansion! I did not expect to find so much neatness and com-fort in this city!"

"It is the mansion of Mr. ***," replied my cicerone. "Don't you think it a fine building? And in the Italian style, too! The owner is one of our richest men, the son of Mr. ***, who came to Boston in the year ——. He made all his money in the —— business, and must now be worth upwards of a million of dollars. He has a very nice family too. His wife was a Miss ***, daughter to Mr. ***, one of our most re-spectable merchants; quite an *intellectual* girl, with plenty of money.

I believe she brought him three hundred thousand dollars. Her sister married a Mr. ***, one of the most *influential men* in this city. They have been a good deal abroad, and furnished their house in the best style ——"

Fearing that I should be condemned to listen to a long description of the various articles of furniture brought home from London or Paris, and at last to the statistics of the gentleman's property,—a thing which is by no means unfrequent in Boston,—I abruptly changed the conversation by directing my cicerone's attention to an unfinished building, whose enormous height was entirely disproportionate to the small surface it covered on the ground.

"This house," I said, "seems to be perfectly new; how did it happen that so eligible a site for building remained so long a time unimproved?"

"It was a fine garden," replied my cicerone, "belonging to Mr. ***, living in the house adjoining it; but he sold it as a house-lot for the neat little sum of twelve thousand dollars. It's only a small piece of ground, just large enough for two parlours on a floor; but our houses are all three or four stories high, none of us wishing to be overlooked by his neighbour."

"Did he keep the ground on speculation?" demanded I.

"Bless your soul, sir!" exclaimed he; "do you think Mr. *** is a speculator? He is a rich man, sir! he does not care for the money; 'it's only for the conven'ance of it,' as the New Hampshire farmer said, when he dunned the gentleman for a bushel of potatoes. Who the deuce would not take twelve thousand dollars for a little garden, scarcely large enough to raise cabbage for the family?"

"Especially in a town where no man possesses anything he would not sell, provided a proper price be offered him," added the lawyer.

While we were thus talking, we had reached the mill-dam which leads over to Brooklyne, and from which we enjoyed a truly magnificent view of the panorama of Boston. I observed to my companions that their city was one of the finest in the Union; and that, as far as I might be allowed to judge, it could be made a most delightful residence.

"It *was* a delightful place," replied the lawyer; "but our old families are gradually losing their influence. Most of the fine houses you see here are inhabited by *roturiers;* our society is getting worse and worse every day; and, while we expend thousands for our public schools, we lose our manners."

"That is a fact," exclaimed my cicerone; "our young men are not half so polite as the old ones; and, what is worse, the influence of family is entirely lost. Our young ladies, for instance, do not value birth and good breeding half so much as money. They would rather marry a woodcutter, if he had shown himself 'clever' in making money, than the son of our oldest gentleman."

"But pray, gentlemen," interrupted I, half impatiently, "why cannot you enjoy the many blessings Heaven has bestowed on you, without being continually afraid of losing your dignity? I have heard more talk about aristocracy and family in the United States than during my whole previous life in Europe. You embitter your enjoyments and pleasures by endeavouring to exclude from them all that come after you; and, in doing so, wound the feelings of many an honest man, who, but for a little more urbanity on your part, would be your friend instead of your enemy. A question of interest which is now agitating the country* may for a moment unite you; but the union is an unnatural one, and on that account cannot last. Your state of society is such, that, in the ordinary intercourse with your fellow-citizens, you must necessarily offend more than you can gratify; and the mortifications which two-thirds of the whole population are constantly suffering from the small portion distinguished from the rest by nothing but success in business, must add to the natural jealousies felt by the labouring classes of all countries with regard to the rich. The distinction between the different orders of society may be more *apparent* in England,—as they are, from historical reasons, with all people of Saxon origin; but they are, nevertheless, far less offensive than yours.

"In all countries in which there exists an hereditary, wealthy nobility, there exists a sort of good-will towards the inferior classes which leads to the relation of patron and client, and through which many an apparent injustice is smoothed over by liberality and kindness; but the mere moneyed aristocracy which is establishing itself in this country, however you may disguise the fact by cunning and soft speeches, or an hyperbolical affectation of republicanism, *hates* the industrious masses over whom it strives to elevate itself.

"The exclusiveness of your wealthy brokers, that hoard money without *spending* it, offends the people without benefiting the artisan or the tradesman; and the meanness with which your first people bargain for every trifle to save a penny, renders their custom scarcely desirable to

* The United States Bank and the Sub-treasury system.

respectable tradespeople. You are extravagantly fond of splendour, and yet are afraid of displaying it. You must understand me right: I speak of the rich, calculating Bostonians, who really live on their property; not of your wealthy men in New York, who live on nine months' credit. Besides, you yourself will allow that your aristocracy is far from being generally well educated, and I do not see how this fault is to be remedied as long as wealth constitutes the chief title to good society.

"Your aristocracy, therefore, has not the power of dazzling the lower classes with that air of self-possession and dignity by which gentlemen of rank are at once recognised in Europe. On the contrary, the manners of your rich people in their intercourse with less successful aspirants to fortune are markedly coarse and vulgar, in order, I believe, to give the latter to understand that they are sufficiently *independent*—that, I think, is the word,—not to *care* for their opinion."

Here the lawyer pleaded a pressing engagement; and left us, without shaking of hands, or expressing a desire of seeing me again.

"You have made an enemy of that man," observed my cicerone, "who will make you a hundred more enemies if you should ever think of settling in this city."

"He did not seem to be offended," replied I; "or I should have checked my tongue before he left us."

"You can never tell when these people are offended," he rejoined; "but you may rely upon one thing,—they will never forgive you. They lock their wrath up, until a favourable opportunity presents itself for taking summary vengeance. If I were in your place, *I would make myself scarce.*"

"What do you mean by that?"

"I mean, I would not show myself too much in public, or in society; or perhaps engage my passage to New York."

"And you call this a free country!" exclaimed I, "and the manners of your people those of high-minded gentlemen! Good manners in other countries consist in putting every one at ease, which may be done without being in the least degree familiar; but here the higher classes seem to be determined upon making every one that is poorer than themselves feel his inferiority, in order to make him as uncomfortable as possible. And all this is done with an affectation of republican simplicity, which makes every species of arrogance only the more offensive as coming from an equal. The Southern people, whom you pronounce much more aristocratic, and who perhaps are so in the English sense of the word, are infinitely more amiable in their manners, merely because *their* exclusiveness relates to family and education, and because they are not continually in contact with the labouring classes.

"In order to make any kind of aristocracy tolerable, it is necessary that it should, in some shape or other, either protect the lower classes, or never come in contact with them. The aristocracy of the Atlantic cities is unfortunately neither a protector of the lower orders, with whom it is continually wrestling for power; nor is it, from its political position and mode of life, capable of avoiding incessant contact with them. Hence arises a continual jarring: the rich claiming a rank which the poor are unwilling to grant; and the poor provoked by the *unprofitable* arrogance of the rich, opposing to them a species of insolence which a labouring man in Europe would hardly dare to offer his equals.

"I recollect some time ago having travelled on board of a canal-boat from Harrisburg to Pittsburg. The accommodations on board of these boats, the most bigoted American—and I know I address myself to none such—could not but call miserable; and yet, the majority being satisfied, none dared to murmur. Our meals were shocking; cooked in the worst manner, and served as no man in England would place a piece of bread before a day labourer. During the night we were put on shelves, of which three were placed one above the other at a distance of not more than from sixteen to twenty inches, and so close together that the feet of one person touched the head of his neighbour, and *vice versâ*. To complete our misery, the cabin was not ventilated, the door being kept closed in order to prevent those who lay next to it from taking cold; and we slept without sheets, the same unwashed and uncleaned blankets having perhaps served in turn to a hundred different pedlars and emigrants. But the *ne plus ultra* was one of the captains,* a New-Englander by birth; a puny, pale, consumptive fellow with sharp grey eyes, thin pointed nose, long deeply-indented chin, and a dash across his face marking the opening of the mouth in the absence of lips. His voice, something between a growl and a grunt, seemed to proceed from a subterraneous cavern; while his hands, carefully concealed in his pockets, indicated, by their position, the usual current of his thoughts.

"This fellow, whom no man of correct judgment would have made

* These change at the different stopping-places of the boat.

keeper of a pack of hounds, used to look upon the whole company with an air of conscious superiority; strutting the deck as if he were commander of a frigate, and scarcely deigning to address a word to any of the passengers. You will excuse me for this digression, which you will readily forgive when you reflect that I but agree with you in the opinion that, much as the New-Englanders are to be esteemed at home,—and there is none more ready to pay homage to their public and private virtue than myself,—they are nevertheless among the dullest, driest, and most disagreeable adventurers one meets abroad. This man had the impudence to serve the same meat three times to his passengers: first, with tea and coffee in the morning; then, with pure water at noon; and lastly, though there was scarcely enough left to feed a dog, the remainder of the dinner was once more brought upon the table in the shape of a supper. Previous to that, we had been *kept,* as they call it, by a fat round-faced German, who gave us at least *plenty* to eat, and a friendly face in the bargain; but our Yankee captain seemed to be determined to make the most of our cash, without contracting the irregular polygon of his face into anything approaching a smile.

"Under these circumstances, a German gentleman, who, to judge from his merry voice, and two large bumps of alimentiveness gracing his circular forehead, was fond of humour and good cheer, was amusing the company in tolerable good English with a few unequivocal innuendoes in reference to their *English comforts;* which were no sooner uttered than the captain, probably thinking that the *foreigner* was an *aristocrat* not admiring the institutions of the country, told him that his conversation was 'most perfectly disgusting,' and that, if he did not 'hold his tongue,' he should be obliged to put him ashore. These, as far as I can recollect, were the very words of the ill-humoured blackguard; and such an effect did they produce on the company that none dared to remonstrate against his insulting conduct, though they *whispered* to one another that it was not altogether *gentlemanly* or *just.*

"Now, this man would not have been half so insolent if the gentleman whom he reprobated had not been decently dressed, so as to lead him to suppose that he wanted to play the aristocrat. It was a species of revenge against what he imagined to be the taunts and sneers of 'a vulgar upstart,' who, in spite of his money, resorted to this mode of travelling for the sake of saving expenses.

"If the higher classes claim superior respect, it is but just they should pay for it, as the higher classes do in Europe, where a man is charged according to his rank; but how few of your fashionable people are willing to lay out an additional groat for the distinction they so ardently covet. They want to be esteemed merely because they are rich, though their wealth does not benefit any of their fellow-citizens."

"I remember a young Bostonian," observed my cicerone, "who employed a second-rate barber to cut his hair. The task not being performed to his satisfaction, he indignantly rose from the chair, placed a piece of twelve and a half cents (the usual price being twenty-five) on the table, and, opening the door with great fury, told the affrighted little Frenchman that he should never *patronise* him again.

"Such instances of the liberality of our first people," he continued, "occur every day; as you may yourself witness by frequenting our market. Every one of our gentlemen purchases his own provisions, so as to render the collusion of the servants with the tradespeople, which you know exists to a lamentable extent in England, wholly impossible. Our aristocracy, I can assure you, are a shrewd people; but unfortunately for the comforts of domestic life, their servants are equally shrewd, and stay with their calculating masters no longer than they can *help* it.

"This state of things," added he, after a pause, "does not exist at the South. There the veriest fault of the people is generosity. The slaves, who enable them to be aristocratic without being mean, stand to them in the relation of vassals to their lords; and the planters, not fearing the power and political influence of their slaves, but, on the contrary, having an interest in their physical well-being, treat them generally with humanity and kindness. There never was a great moral evil, without producing also some good; and thus it is that the very relation between master and slave engenders ties and affections which no one can understand without having witnessed their effect. I have seen the wives of planters watch at the sick-bed of their slaves, and perform acts of charity which the misconstrued self-esteem of our Northern people would have deemed menial, merely because the feelings of *kindness* and *gratitude,* which are strongest in the Southern States, are, with us, construed into *obligation* and *payment;* two things which effectually destroy all poetry of life, even in the relation of parents to their children. I am not here disposed to underrate the miseries of slavery, as they will always appear to the mind of an European; but I cannot entirely overlook some of the advantages which result from it to the moral and social relations of the country."

And I could not but agree with my cicerone. If the tendency of wealth in the Northern States is towards an aristocracy of money, the aristocracy of the Southern States, founded on birth and education, is a sort of offset to it,—a means of preventing the degeneration of the high-minded democracy which once swayed the country, into a vulgar oligarchy of calculating machines without poetry, without arts, and without generosity.

"After all, the greatest benefactors of the American people were Southerners, from the great father of the country, down to its last chivalrous defender. Southern orators are yet the most eloquent; Southern statesmen the most disinterested in their views of national politics. Genius requires a heart as well as a head, or the seed lacks the warmth necessary for its germination. Give me the man whose blood flows quickly through his veins, with his ready perception and his high sense of honour! If aristocracy, the original sin of society, must be entailed upon man in every climate, then let me at once have that of the South. Give me an aristocracy above the cares and toils of ordinary life, which has the means and the leisure to devote itself to higher pursuits than mere pecuniary gain and profit,—an aristocracy to whom national honour and glory are not words without meaning, and whose estimation of a people's happiness is not deduced merely from its statistics of commerce and manufactures!

"I have always hoped, and still hope, that the democratic principle will, in America, prevail over all the others: but if this hope should prove delusive; if, in the phraseology of one of the ablest senators in the United States, 'the multiplied wants of the country' should beget an universal worship of Mammon as the means of satisfying them; then I would rather live surrounded by negroes, and, in the society of their aristocratic but high-minded and generous masters, seek some feeble consolation in the reflection that Rome and Greece were likewise cursed with slavery. I would prefer the aristocracy of the Southern States to that of the North, for precisely the same reason that I prefer, generally, a nobleman to a *roturier*.'"

"You are not very singular in your notions," observed my cicerone. "I do not remember a single European that came here but what expressed the same opinion; but this singular coincidence has not in the least changed the opinion of our people, who are perfectly satisfied that their city stands unrivalled in the world for virtue, wisdom, and patriotism."

CHAPTER X

Cross-examination of Foreigners in the United States.—Definition of Common Sense.—Its high value in America.—Aversion to Genius.— Sensible reply of a Boston Aristocrat with regard to a Parvenu from the country.—Ladies buying themselves a Professor.—Boys at school learning for Money.—A Boston fashionable Concert.—Description of the Musicians and the Audience.—High value of Morality in a Cantatrice.— Dangers of differing in matters of taste from the leading Coteries.— Secret Police in Boston.—Reflections.

"Unhappy he, who from the first of joys—
    Society—cut off, is left alone
Amid this world of death. Day after day
    Sad on the jetting eminence he sits,
And views the main that ever toils below."

THOMSON'S *Seasons.*

THE day after my arrival in Boston I delivered my letters of introduction. Some I merely sent with my card; others I carried in person, according to the custom of the country. My reception could not, of course, be equal to that of a well-recommended Englishman; the word "de" having, by my request, been suppressed in all my letters, and it not being known at that time that I was about to commit my impressions to paper. Yet was I received with politeness; subject, however, to a sort of cross-examination, of which, for the benefit of travellers, I will here furnish a short extract.

Question.—"How do you like this country?"

Answer (of course).—"Extremely well." (It will do no harm to show a little enthusiasm; the Bostonians, having little of that article themselves, like to see it in others.)

Question.—"How does this country appear to you compared with England?"

(This is a question never asked by the labouring class, who seem to care little or nothing about it; and proves at once your being in good society. You must answer it with great circumspection; as, if you give America the preference, they either think you a hypocrite, or a person

151

not used to society and the world; and, if you show yourself too great a partisan for England, their vanity will never forgive you.)

Question.—"Do you intend to settle here?"

(This question is best answered in the negative.)

Question.—"Are you married or single?"

(If the stranger be a man of moderate fortune, it will be best for him to call himself a married man; the fashionable society of Boston having a great dread of poor bachelors.)

Question.—"Do you not think we *enjoy* a very bad climate?"

(This they really believe; but it is prudent in Europeans stoutly to deny it. The fact is, it is really not half so bad as generally represented; there being more sunny days in America than, perhaps with the exception of Italy or Spain, in any part of Europe.

Question.—"Don't you think the transition from heat to cold very sudden?"

(Deny it by all means, even if there should have been a change of twenty degrees that very day.)

Then comes the praise of the American "falls," in which any one may join conscientiously; an American landscape in the month of October being, on account of the infinite variety in the colour of the woods, and the extreme serenity of the sky, the most beautiful thing in the world.

National vanity—a feeling which is totally distinct from patriotism—exists in no part of the United States to such an extent as in New England, and especially in Boston, whose inhabitants think themselves not only vastly superior to any people in Europe, but also infinitely more enlightened, especially as regards politics, than the rest of their countrymen. Thus the question has been seriously proposed to me, whether I had not been struck with the superior intelligence of the Bostonians, compared with the inhabitants of other cities in the United States and in Europe? and whether, on the whole, I had found any people in the world superior to those of New England?

These faults apart, I found the Bostonians quite an *entertaining,* I could not conscientiously say an *hospitable* people, because one does not feel at home amongst them, even after a residence of many years. The fact is, that though they boast of an unusual degree of "common sense" in their common transactions of life, very little of it is seen in their society. Society is the only sea with the navigation of which the New-Englanders are as yet unacquainted, in spite of the English,

French, and Italian charts they study for that purpose. The moment their ladies and gentlemen sit in state, they are affected and awkward; *et quand le bon ton parait, le bon sens se retire.*

What the wealthy Bostonians generally understand by common sense, and the influence which the latter exercises on society, I soon had an opportunity of learning, at the house of a fashionable gentleman, a president of a bank, with whom I had the pleasure of dining a few days after my arrival in the city.

The individual in question was between forty-five and fifty years of age; apparently of a high bilious temper, with a livid complexion, grey piercing eyes, straight hair, compressed lips, thin nose and chin,—in short, a figure which in any part of the world I should have at once recognised as belonging to a matter-of-fact man from New England. There were but two more gentlemen to dine with us, and no ladies besides the wife and daughters of our entertainer; so that conversation soon began to flag, until, the dessert being put on the table, the restraint was taken off from the gentlemen by the good-natured retiring of the ladies.

Mine host was the first person who broke in upon the monotony of the entertainment, by introducing a topic which at once commanded the attention of his friends.

"Common sense," he said, after having drunk the first glass of madeira and passed the bottle, "is the *genius,* or, as I do not like that word, the *essence* of society and good government; and I think," added he with a self-complacent smile, "no people in the world have inherited a larger share of this most invaluable commodity than our *cool, calm, calculating, money-making* Yankees. Did you" (addressing himself to me) "ever see a more intelligent people than our Bostonians? Did you ever see a city more quiet, more prosperous, more orderly than Boston?"

"The appearance of Boston," responded I, "certainly warrants all you say of it."

"Yes, sir," he rejoined; "and I can point out to you at least one hundred persons in that city worth upwards of a hundred thousand dollars."

"That certainly argues in favour of the industry and perseverance of its inhabitants."

"Say rather it argues in favour of their *common* sense," said he, "in which industry and perseverance are necessarily included. We are a common sense, matter-of-fact people," added he exultingly; "we leave genius and enthusiasm to Europeans."

"Thank Heaven!" exclaimed his neighbour on the left, "I have no genius in *my* family; my children are all brought up to be industrious."

"You may thank the Lord for that," replied our entertainer; "I never saw a genius yet who was either himself happy or capable of making others so. I have brought up my sons to become merchants and manufacturers; only Sam, the poor boy who is a little hard of hearing, and rather slow of comprehension, shall go to college. Our merchants, sir, are the most respectable part of the community."

"What college do you mean to send him to?" demanded I, in order to ascertain whether he had been serious.

"I shall send him to Harvard University," he replied; "the oldest literary institution in the country. Have you not yet been to see it?"

I told him that I had been but a few days in Boston, but that I should certainly take an early opportunity of visiting the institution.

"Do so," he said; "you will find it well worth your while; it will convince you that, while we have been making money, we have not altogether neglected arts and sciences."

"Which are your cleverest men in the various departments of science?" demanded I.

"Why, they are none of them very clever in *our* sense of the word. We consider professors as secondary men. Our practice is to give the different professorships away to young men, in order to induce them to devote themselves to the branch they are to teach. Our country is as yet too young for old professors; and, besides, they are too poorly paid to induce first-rate men to devote themselves to the business of lecturing."

"In this manner," rejoined I, "you will never have eminent men in the higher departments of philosophy."

"We have as yet no time to devote to abstract learning," he observed; "we are too young for that. Our principal acquirement consists in common sense; all the rest we consider as moonshine. You must know," he said, with a countenance in which superiority of knowledge was mingled with condenscension of manners, "that a young man learns as much in six months in a counting-room as in four years at college. My friends do not entirely agree with me; but I often told them that our colleges only made poor gentlemen, and spoiled clever tradesmen."

He then counted over the names of most of the rich men in Boston, who, he said, were all self-taught country boys, possessed of no other learning than the art of making dollars in a neat, handsome, clean manner. "This," he added, "has given them a higher standing in society than they could have acquired by all the philosophy in the world, and enabled them to marry into the oldest and most aristocratic families of the place.

"Take, for instance, the case of our friend ***. What does he know except making money? What has he ever learned except negociating, or rather *shaving* notes? What college did he ever go to, except that of our brokers in State-street? And has he not married the daughter of one of our richest men? Has he not got one of the largest fortunes with her? And is he not now connected with some of our first people—with the real back-bone of our Boston aristocracy? And do you know the answer his father-in-law gave to one of his old friends, who remonstrated with him for giving his daughter away to a *parvenu* from the country? 'I give my daughter to any man,' said he, 'who will come to Boston and have wit enough to make a hundred thousand dollars in six years.' There's common sense for you, I trust: that's what we call practical philosophy."

"It is certainly a melancholy fact," sighed the gentleman next to me, who now for the first time opened his lips, "that a great number of our young men, who have gone to college, have afterwards been unsuccessful in business. I think our education is not sufficiently practical;—we are still attached to the European system."

"Not only that," replied our entertainer, "but most of our students contract habits of idleness, which will never answer in this country. They want to imitate your English gentleman, when their patrimony— I mean their *share* in their father's fortune—is scarcely sufficient to keep them alive. Do you remember Mr. ***'s reply to a young gentleman who had asked him his advice as to what he ought to do in order to succeed in business? 'Take off your kid gloves,' said he, 'and go to work.' There's philosophy for you, equal to your Kants and Leibnitz! Mr. ***, you know, is a plain-spoken man, who came to Boston without out a cent in his pocket, and is now one of our most respectable citizens."

"But if this be the prevailing taste of your townsmen," said I, "why do you call Boston the Athens of the United States?"

"That appellation," replied he, "refers to our women, not to our gentlemen. Our ladies read a great deal. And why should they not? What else have they to do? And we have, besides, a lot of literary twaddles, manufactured by the wholesale at Cambridge, who attempt to turn the heads of our young girls with the nonsense they call 'poetry,' which fills nearly all our papers, instead of clever editorials. If we have one poet among us, we have at least fifty, the joint earnings of whom would not be sufficient to keep a dog. But then poets don't turn *our* heads, you see; we are too much occupied with business."

"But how do your literary men manage to get on?" demanded I: "I know several of them quite in easy circumstances."

"They marry rich women, who can afford paying for being entertained. They show their common sense in that. It's quite the fashion for our rich girls to *buy themselves a professor,* previous to taking a trip to Europe."

"And then," added my neighbour on the right, "literary reputations are in this city not acquired, as in other places, through the medium of public opinion; but by the aid of a small coterie, composed of a few 'leading citizens,' who have the power of setting a man up, or putting him down, just as they please;* the process being this: Mr. A. or Mr. B., wealthy gentlemen in Beacon-street, declare Mr. Smith a fine scholar; and immediately half a dozen of their clique will repeat the same assertion. The individual in question is thus made fashionable, so that any one speaking against him is considered unacquainted with the usages of society. Those, therefore, whose opinion—if they dare to have one—is different from Mr. A.'s and Mr. B.'s, are most likely to keep it to themselves; while every person aspiring to rank and fashion publicity swears to his scholarship: for our people, you must know, are accustomed to do everything from fear; nothing from love. If you want to succeed in anything,—if you want to carry any particular measure,—enlist half a dozen influential citizens in your behalf, and the rest will not dare *to back out.* That's the way things are done in this city.

"And the worst of it is," he continued, "that our coteries are small, and, for the most part, led by one or two *prominent members of society,* who, on all similar occasions, act as dictators. Add to this, that our fashionable men have not the advantages of education and leisure enjoyed by the higher classes in Europe, and that their manners are generally stiff, uncouth, and overbearing; and you will easily understand why our society, so far from resembling that of Athens, must

* Public opinion sways the country in all respects except in matters of taste, which are entirely settled by the higher orders.

necessarily counteract the independent development of mind and character.

"This habit of conforming to each other's opinion, and the penalty set upon every transgression of that kind, are sufficient to prevent a man from wearing a coat cut in a different fashion, or a shirt-collar no longer *à la mode,* or, in fact, to do, say, or appear anything which could render him unpopular among a certain set. In no other place, I believe, is there such a stress laid upon 'saving appearances.' I once asked a relation of mine for what sum of money he might be prevailed upon to suffer his mustachoes to grow? He demanded twenty-four hours 'to figure it out,' and then told me the next day that he could not do it for one cent less than ten thousand dollars. He reasoned thus: 'I am a man of moderate property, the interest of my patrimony being barely sufficient to pay for my board, I am therefore obliged to work, in part, for my living; but, my wants being few, an additional six hundred dollars would cover all my expenses. These I hope to earn by practising law, to which profession I was bred, and, for which I feel a natural predilection. Now, if I wear mustachoes, I must resign my practice as a lawyer; for with mustachoes I can neither go to court, nor obtain a respectable chamber practice. Six hundred dollars are the interest, at six per cent. per annum, of ten thousand dollars, which, therefore, would be sufficient to make up for my loss; for I can manage to live without society.' "

"A few singularities of that sort may be charged to every people," observed the gentleman of the house; "and, besides, I really do not see what business a young man has to wear mustachoes: I would certainly not employ him in a counting-room. We are a young people; and, as such, must endeavour to get on by hard work, not by dandyism. Some of our instructors have the good sense to inculcate this doctrine even into our children; and I do not see why grown persons should be permitted to set up a different rule for themselves."

"And pray, sir," demanded I, "in what manner do your instructors teach children the necessity of working?"

"In the best manner," replied he, "common sense could dictate. *They make them study for money.* They distribute annually a certain sum,—say, from eighty to a hundred dollars,—in the shape of prize-money, among those who obtain the highest marks at the different recitations, for which the pupils are numbered as high as *plus* seven, and as low as *minus* seven; a certain number of positive marks entitling the child to one cent prize-money. At the end of the school-term accounts are made out, when each child receives a check on a bookseller or stationer for the amount due to him; for which he may now select a book, a pen-knife, or some other trifling article, according to his own pleasure; on which, moreover, the instructor himself enjoys a liberal discount."

"But does not this practice," I said, "introduce sordid habits at an age in which the mind is most susceptible of receiving impressions, and in which it is of the greatest importance to instil into children more elevated notions of honour and justice?"

"You are entirely mistaken," replied he; "and one can at once see from your remarks that you are a little dyed in the speculative philosophy of your country. No stimulus to learning can be half as great as when a boy can figure it out on his slate how many dollars and cents his geography, grammar, spelling, reading, and good conduct come to *per annum.*"

This *common sense* of the Bostonians, thought I, as I was walking home, is, after all, very narrowly circumscribed; referring in most cases merely to immediate wants, and the means of satisfying them. But it is in referring actions to ultimate principles that men rise above commonplace, in proportion, perhaps, as they render themselves liable to error. Common sense is a sort of instinct sufficient to guide men through the lower spheres of life; but of itself incapable of raising them to a high moral elevation. Common sense, in fact, is the genius of mediocrity. It does not expand or liberalize the mind, or communicate to it any great and generous impulse. It refers to a sort of *intérêt bien entendu;* and is, on that account, not in very high repute among a large portion of the Southern people. I remember what a Southern Jacksonian once told me with regard to the politics of Massachusetts. "We do not want that State," he said, "to come over to our side, because it would prejudice the rest of the Union. People would immediately ask what concession has Government made to the particular *interests* of that State?" This is the idea which the Americans themselves entertain of the common sense of the leading citizens of Boston.—*Point d'argent, point de Suisses!*

In the evening I saw again my cicerone, who proposed going to the concert, which he promised me would be one of the most fashionable ones of the season. We accordingly shaped our course towards Masonic Hall,—a building in style slightly approaching the Gothic, but in size not much larger than an ordinary dwelling-house,—which, ever since freemasonry became unpopular in Boston, has been changed into a temple of the Muses.

On looking over the bill, I found that the performers had a peculiar way of recommending themselves to the notice of the higher classes of Americans. In the first place, all of them were professors, members of different philharmonic societies in Europe, whose favourite airs, duettos, concerts, &c. had met with universal applause in London, Paris, and St. Petersburg. Then they were all composers; the bill expressly announcing a favourite air from "La Gazza Ladra," arranged by Professor ***; duetto from "Gli Italiani in Algieri," with variations by Mr. ***, Professor of the Royal Conservatory of ***; &c. A Spaniard even went so far as to give notice that a grand rondo, originally composed for the violin by Mayseder, would be performed with variations by Professor ***, late first flute-player to his Majesty the ex-Emperor of Brazil.

I communicated to my friend my astonishment at the fashionable people of America being so easily duped by high-sounding titles, which in Europe would at once stamp a man as a charlatan or a village performer; but was assured that this was the regular way of proceeding in all the Atlantic cities, the judgment of the higher classes in matters of taste confirming, without a single exception, the verdict pronounced by the connoisseurs of Europe.

"You will," he said, "to-night hear the voice of a woman who in England would at best be considered a tolerable good ballad-singer for a provincial theatre, but you will witness the storm of applause with which she will be received *here*. It is such a fine opportunity for all who have taste, to show their superiority over those who have not had an opportunity of improving themselves in Europe. This songstress, moreover, is introduced to some of our first people, who will collect here to-night, and by their significant nods and half-subdued 'bravos' induce the multitude to the clapping of hands. Our *leading citizens* think themselves bound by hospitality to applaud an English *cantatrice:* for which reason the second, third, and fourth rows of benches are occupied by *tout ce qu'il y a de mieux,*—that is, by *tout ce qui a de cent à cinq cents mille écus;* the first benches being declined by all, either from modesty, or from fear of making themselves too conspicuous before the public.

"An American aristocrat, you must know," continued my cicerone, "is a gentleman of very nice feelings, who, while he is most anxious to avoid notoriety among *the people,* in order to avoid public censure, is at the same time particularly solicitous to push himself forward in his coterie, in order by his social standing to make up for the injustice of politics."

"I presume," said I, "most of the gentlemen on the forward benches are merchants?"

"Let me see," he said, standing on tiptoe. "They are mostly merchants; but I also discover two lawyers, and a fashionable clergyman. There is, however, not a man amongst them worth less than one hundred thousand dollars."

"Pray, is a rich man here supposed to understand something about music?" demanded I.

"Most assuredly he is," replied he. "You will always find the richest men give the first sign of approbation, after which the minor fortunes venture to signalize theirs. Our society is so small that every man in it is known; so that no individual can be guilty of a breach of etiquette without having at once the whole clique against him. There is more social tyranny in this place than you could find anywhere in Europe. Every principle of morals, politics, or religion is set up as an article of faith; our infallible moneyed men proclaiming in their counting-rooms, and on 'change, the Polish doctrine *Nulla salus extra ecclesiam Catholicam.*"

While we were thus discussing *la haute société* of Boston, Mrs. ***, from London, made her appearance, and—her morality being endorsed by three responsible merchants—was received with thundering applause; the *Honourable* Mr. *** giving, as drum-major, the signal with a beautiful cane, which was immediately answered by *"the middling interests"* in the centre, and at last echoed by the mechanics, perched up in the rear. Mrs. *** courtesied. Renewed applause; during which she, at last, opened her cherub lips, and, with a great deal of common sense,—that is, without any of the coquetry of a French actress, or the *agaceries* of an Italian *prima donna,*—sang off two or three verses of one of those English ballads which sound so prettily in a private parlour, and so badly in a large concert-room. The worst of it was, that instead of the simple melody, which in most English or German compositions is exceedingly touching, she endeavoured to show her school, and the scope of her voice, by introducing variations, which were duly acknowledged by the people to whom she had been recommended. The *ladies,* especially, seemed not so much to admire her voice, as her modesty in not looking once from the music on the fashionable young men whose eyes were fastened upon her.

English women, being fine and tall, charm sufficiently by their placid beauty, and a certain *laisser aller* which they carry off admirably. French and Italian women, on the contrary, are, as a race, far less handsome, but considerably more *piquantes. Ces sont des femmes caressantes.* An English woman is made to be wooed; a French one entices *you* by a thousand little trifles, which it is the study of her life to practise with success. One is, perhaps, truly amiable; the other *interests* you by her very peevishness. The fair songstress seemed to be amiable in the English fashion, for she was all good nature—the usual concomitant of a certain *embonpoint,* and smiled continually—on her music-book.

"But how is it possible," said I to my cicerone, "to applaud such singing as this? There is neither simplicity nor taste, neither feeling nor execution in her performance, and yet the storm of applause is not abating."

"For the Lord's sake!" exclaimed he, "do not say that loud enough for other people to hear you. It would deprive you of many an innocent pleasure you would perhaps otherwise enjoy during your stay in this city. Our *élite* never forgive such a difference of opinon to one of their own clique; how much more, then, must a foreigner be on his guard! And in this case, too, where Mr. and Mrs. *** have taken the songstress under their protection! It would be sufficient to exclude you at once from society. This is a *free* country, sir! every man may do or think what he pleases, only he must not let other people know it. You might just as well attack one of our fashionable preachers as Mrs. ***."

"If this is what you call freedom in Boston," said I, "I will not go to another concert, if Paganini himself were to perform here."

"And yet, if you heard an oratorio performed by our 'Handel and Haydn Society,' you would, perhaps, change your opinion. That society is almost wholly composed of mechanics, who cultivate music from taste, and pay their German leader, a good scientific musician, a very handsome salary."

"Singular city this!" exclaimed I, "in which the labouring classes cultivate music from taste, and in which the rich people listen to it from obligation. I shall be obliged to leave the room. Will you not accompany me?"

"I should like to do so," whispered he; "but it would be observed. I am obliged to live with these people; and you know the proverb,

'Among Romans do as Romans do.' *A propos;* if any one should ask you about the concert, and especially about Mrs. ***, say you were *'delighted;'* that's the word now. There is no use in making yourself enemies; *delighted,* sir! Don't forget your cue."

What an extraordinary phenomenon, thought I as I went home, this state of society must be to an European! And is it a wonder if, under such circumstances, the most paltry scribbler thinks himself justified in caricaturing it? Here is a free people voluntarily reducing itself to a state of the most odious social bondage, for no other object but to maintain an imaginary superiority over those classes in whom, according to the constitution of their country, all real power is vested; and here are the labouring classes, probably for the first time permitted to legislate for themselves, worshipping wealth in its most hideous colours! Here, then, is a society formed as nearly as possible on the abstract theory of equality; and this is the state to which it has become reduced by the aspirings of a few wealthy families in less than a century! If such is the tendency towards decay in all human institutions, how jealous ought the people to be of the most trifling privileges, arrogated exclusively by certain classes.

And what species of tyranny is worse than that which attempts to control a man's private actions, his worship, his domestic arrangements, and his pleasures? What can be more absurd than for a certain class, for the most part not a whit better educated than the rest, to assume the dictatorship in all matters relating to politics, religion, or the arts? And how can it be reconciled with the spirit of independence, manifested more or less by every American, to see so large a portion of their countrymen governed by the tinsel logic of such a coterie? Nothing can excite the contempt of an educated European more than the continual fears and apprehensions in which even the "most enlightened citizens" of the United States seem to live with regard to their next neighbours, lest their actions, principles, opinions, and beliefs should be condemned by their fellow creatures!

I have heard it seriously asserted in America, that there are no better policemen than the ordinary run of Bostonians; and that, as long as their natural inquisitiveness remained, there was no need of a secret tribunal; every citizen taking upon himself the several offices of spy, juryman, justice, and—*vide* Lynch law—executioner. This is by some called the wholesome restraint of public opinion: but, in order that public opinion may be just, it must not be biased by the particular faith of a coterie; and there are transactions in private life of which the public ought never to be made the judge.

There is scarcely a degree of political freedom which can compensate a man for the loss of independence in his private transactions, and the want of a generous liberality in the community at large. There are individuals whose tastes and dispositions are not likely to involve them in any political or religious controversy, and who therefore can be comparatively free, even under a despotic government; but, in a community like Boston, no abstract rule of conduct can be laid down, capable of protecting a man against censure and retaliation. This peculiarity in the composition of its society I do not, however, like so many others, ascribe to the political institutions of the country, which, on the contrary, are constantly counteracting its effects; but to the aristocracy of money, unmitigated as it is by superior education, and unlimited in its influence either by the existence of a real nobility or a powerful sovereign.

The *moveable,* moneyed aristocracy of our times I consider as the greatest enemy of mankind, in comparison to which all the terrors of the feudal system are as nothing. The nobility of the middle ages offered to the people protection for vassalage, and set them the example of chivalry and valour. A mere moneyed aristocracy, on the contrary, enslaves the people without giving them an equivalent, introducing everywhere the most sordid principles of selfishness, to the exclusion of every noble and disinterested sentiment. A mere moneyed preponderance of one class of citizens over the other, does not form an historical link between the present and the past; neither does it, like the masses, represent the interests of mankind in general. All its tendencies are downwards, reducing a people gradually to a degree of moral degradation, from which perhaps they might have been saved by the presence of a powerful nobility of family.

CHAPTER XI

Maternal Affections of American Ladies—their Cause.—Want of Romance in the Lives of American Gentlemen.—Moral and Religious Cant. —Daniel Webster's Principle of resisting arrogant Innovation.—Reflections on the Democratic, Aristocratic, and Monarchical Forms of Government.—The Bunker Hill Monument.—Want of Patriotism in the Higher Classes of Americans.—The English Feeling in Boston.—Americans passing for Englishmen in Europe.—Anecdotes.—The American Aristocracy take the House of Lords under their Protection.—Their Contempt for the Western Settlers.—The American Character not understood in Europe.

"And as for Heaven 'being love,' why not say 'honey
Is wax?' Heaven is not love, 'tis matrimony."

BYRON.

WHEN I again saw my cicerone, I communicated to him my surprise at seeing so few women frequenting theatres, concerts, and other places of amusement. To one lady seen at the theatre there are at least three or four gentlemen; whereas at church the relation is the reverse, proving the ladies to be much more piously inclined than the men.

"Our women," he said, "are too much confined at home, attending on their children; and yet this, and going to church, constitute their only pleasures in this world. Ours is yet a country in which preachers are better paid than actors and musicians; and a seat in a pew of one of our fashionable 'meeting-houses' is offered you with the same ceremonious politeness, as, in Italy, a box at the opera."

"I have always heard that American women made the best mothers," said I.

"As regards the maternal affections of our women," replied he, "I can easily conceive why they should be strong. It is nearly all the romance (!) they enjoy; the duties they assume in marrying overbalancing infinitely the caresses and attentions bestowed upon them by their husbands. Our young men are an industrious, steady, persevering, but not an amiable race of beings. They have a high respect for ladies in general; but they are not devoted to them beyond the forms and usages of society. Money-making is the principal pursuit to which they are devoted; and which so completely absorbs their time, that, between business and politics, they hardly find time for the cultivation of affections.

"And our rich people," he continued, "are, in this respect, more to be pitied than the poor. The latter spend their few leisure hours, or rather *minutes,* at home, in the circle of their families; while the former are compelled to waste them in society. And what society is that? It does not consist of a few friends whom accident assembles round the fireside, to pass away an evening in agreeable chit-chat. Our fashionable people are not fond of this cheap, unostentatious sort of amusement; and, besides, it does not suit the taste of our boys and girls, who are only satisfied with a dance. For this reason our parties are expensive, and afford little or no relaxation to men of sense. I once heard a diplomatist say, that a young man, in order to form his manners and judgment, ought to choose his female society from among ladies not under thirty, and his male companions from gentlemen not under forty years of age; but certainly, if manners and judgment are to be acquired only on such terms, our state of society is such that our young men must for ever remain deficient in them.

"If our married women were to be compensated for the loss they sustain in society by increased attention from their husbands, they might perhaps profit by the exchange. But our business men have no time for cooing. Their first object is trade; everything else is subordinate. There is a great deal of domestic comfort in the United States, resulting from sound principles of morality and religion, especially on the part of the women; but I have hardly ever seen that tender affection—that union of souls, in which two persons require nothing but each other's consent for the completion of their happiness. That state, I am aware, requires either absolute poverty, or a degree of wealth and refinement which, from the vain attempt to satisfy the heart with the gratification of artificial wants, returns once more to the legitimate source of all human happiness. Both cases are as yet unknown in America; labour securing a competency to every industrious man, and the laws and institutions of the country preventing the accumulation of property.

"These circumstances make us a practical and active, but not an enthusiastic or imaginative people. We choose our fair companions according to the dictates of good sense, not after 'some fanciful creation of the mind.' Our country is not yet a land of *beaux idéals."*

"On this account," proceeded my travelled cicerone, "we are not subject to disappointment when the dreams of our youth are not realized; and the organization of society prevents us even from perceiving our error. Suppose one of our young men to marry a woman whose tastes, disposition, and character are essentially different from his own; it would not necessarily follow that the union must, on this account, prove an unhappy one. The points of contact are so few, the sphere of action of each party so well defined by custom and law, and the occupation of the man out of the house so constant, that he may become the father of a large family, and even die without finding out his mistake. This assertion seems to be absurd, and yet it is true to the very letter. And it is this sort of a passiveness in all matters not relating to business or politics, which, though it may not constitute the most amiable or interesting feature of our character, is nevertheless the principal cause of the universal content which pervades our community.

"A similar match in Europe would be the source of endless misery. The comparative leisure enjoyed even by the labouring classes would prove a source of pain to two minds not perfectly tuned in unison. Nothing creates so many artificial wants,—nothing is, in itself, such exquisite luxury as leisure.* Our rich, industrious population may pity the poor *lazzarone,* who is badly fed, scarcely covered, and who has no other couch to lay his limbs upon but the marble steps of a palace or a church; and yet how many such vagabonds would be willing to exchange their position with that of our most opulent citizens? Such is the difference in men's ideas of happiness.

"An European computes his *time,* or rather his *leisure moments,* better than his money; in America the case is reversed. In Europe, wealth is comparatively within the reach of few; but every one has his little share of leisure, from the day-labourer who has his hour at noon and his vesper, to the *rentier* who lives in idleness. Under these circumstances, the choice of a companion determines a man's happiness for life. Great and many are the calls on each other's sympathy in pleasure and in affliction, and a single discord destroys the harmony for ever. A

---

* Those of my readers who are disposed to doubt the possibility of such sentiments proceeding from an American, must be informed that my cicerone, being the son of a government envoy of high rank, was born and educated in Europe.

man may live with a woman of different tastes,—he may eat and drink with her,—he may see her at specified hours of the day,—he may share his fortune or anything else with her without being unhappy; but who can describe the feelings of an enthusiast whose wife remains motionless at one of Shakspeare's plays?—at the sight of the ocean or the Alps?

"These inequalities of taste and disposition become a true source of misery in proportion as we have leisure to give scope to our imagination. In active life, in the pursuits of agriculture, commerce, or manufactures, they are hardly noticed. What time, I would ask you, has one of our young men to be unhappy?—when in the morning he rises, to read the papers; then takes his breakfast, at which his fair partner presents him with her own white hands two cups of hyson or pekoe, with the trifling addition of a steak or a chop; then goes to his counting-room, where he remains until one; then passes the hour from one till two on 'change; then returns home to eat his beef and pudding, which he accomplishes in about ten minutes; then returns once more to his counting-room, where he remains till sunset; then comes home to swallow his two or three cups of tea; after which, if there be no political *caucas,* no evening lecture, or late arrival of the mail, he is heartily glad to go to rest, in order to gather strength for the work of the next day? What can it matter to him whether his wife be sentimental? whether she have imagination or taste? whether she be an admirer of the drama?

" 'What's Hecuba to him, or he to Hecuba?'

"Our *fashionable* men," continued he, with a sarcastic contraction of his lips, which was his usual substitute for a smile, "are less fortunate. They are not permitted to go to bed when they are tired. *Society* has claims upon them; they must contribute their share to the entertainment of the evening. Accordingly, they are obliged to wash and dress, put on kid gloves, and prepare, in every other respect, for the sacrifice, to which they are led by their wives like so many sheep to the slaughterhouse. Being, as married people, excluded from dancing, and cards being abolished among us, they are obliged to amuse themselves with taking refreshments, which I believe they always do, until, towards ten, a regular supper rewards their patience; after which the majority of the company get into their hacks, swearing that it was a capital entertainment, at which there was plenty to eat, and a great profusion of choice and exquisite wines.

"As regards our women, they are, with the exception of the time consumed at meals, the whole day left to themselves; a circumstance which is not calculated to render their existence a happy one, unless they are blessed with children to break in upon its monotony, and afford fresh scope for their affections. Hence our women love their offspring passionately; while for their husbands they feel a sort of half-distant respect, wholly opposed to that tender familiarity without which it is impossible to penetrate into a woman's heart.

"In this manner our men are cheated—or rather cheat themselves—out of the poetical part of matrimony; but are also saved from a vast deal of mortification. At any rate, our hard-featured, industrious Yankees, who are accustomed to act from principle, not from impulse,—from conviction, not from inclination,—have shown themselves worthy of living under free institutions, which seem to compensate them for the absence of those pleasures which a higher degree of refinement and an abundance of leisure secure to the higher classes of Europe; and the remark of a celebrated European statesman was, perhaps, a wise one, when he said 'that a people is fit for liberal institutions in exactly the same proportion as its whole time is employed in satisfying its physical wants.' "

"But how is it possible," demanded I, "that with all this political liberty, and the constant occupation of all classes of society, you should have become reduced to a degree of social bondage, of which no city in Europe, and scarcely one in Asia, furnishes an example? Remember, I have not yet forgotten the advice you gave me at the concert."

"All this," replied he, "is owing to the excessive prudence which pervades our higher society, and which, in reality, makes them believe that no European can fathom them. Our gentlemen are, indeed, not endowed with the faculty of second sight; but they have what they call 'second thoughts,' a sort of *arrière pensée,* which it is not always easy to decipher, and is frequently the whole substitute for profundity or research. Thus they have always two motives for one and the same act,—a public and a *private* one; and, as many Europeans who come here to study our character are ingenuous enough to consider one motive quite sufficient for each act, it is an even chance they are mistaken, whether they have a view to our private or public motives. If you stay long enough among us, you will hear morality, politics, and even religion advocated from more than one *prudent* motive. High, exalted views, or enthusiasm for one or the other of these all-important subjects, you will, indeed, meet with occasionally; but, in general, we look upon all such sentiments as unhealthy, feverish, unbecoming a 'calm,' 'sober,' 'calculating' people. We delight in prose, though we frequently *talk* poetry. Poetry with us is a *public* consideration, for which reason its place is usually the newspapers. It is food for the multitude; our *private* motives seldom rise beyond a clear view of our own immediate interests. In the inimitable language of one of our most fashionable young ladies, we *admire* roast beef, and *dote* on oyster pies.

"This is in some degree the origin of our cant in morality and religion, which our politicians, when there is no other absorbing topic, such as manufactures, commerce, fisheries, &c. employ for the purpose of 'making a hit.' In the absence of enthusiasm, which would inspire them with natural eloquence, they seek to maintain themselves at a certain elevation by pressing hard on lofty topics; having no wings, they endeavour to support themselves in the air by a *parachute*. Thus the words 'virtue,' 'patriotism,' 'morality,' 'religion,' 'piety,' are in every one's mouth. All these terms had originally a distinct meaning attached to them, and to the mass of the people they are still full of import; but, being thus used on the most trifling occasion, they must sooner or later become degraded to mere figures of speech.

"The same holds of our republican manners. You will see many of our public characters wear the garb of humility in the presence of their meanest fellow-citizens; they carry their own *portemanteaux* when landing from a steam-boat, shake hands with everybody on election day, and, like *Hildebrand,* assume, when walking or standing, an inclined posture; but let them once be elected, and you will see them draw themselves up to their full height, exclaiming *'Ego sum papa!'* With all our democratic machinery, our Atlantic cities contain more lingering, pining, 'aspirants to honourable distinction,' than perhaps could be found in any equal number of men in Europe.

"Besides," continued he, "our rich people, who, in the absence of a law of primogeniture, preserve their wealth by marrying cousins,* and our young merchants, who become rich by successful speculations, are somewhat tired of their monotonous state of existence. Many of them

---

* Against this practice, Dr. Spurzheim, the lecturer on phrenology, strongly remonstrated while in Boston, pointing to the pernicious consequences on the health and vigour of the rising generation.

have been in Europe, where their property has enabled them, occasionally, to associate with the higher orders. They have witnessed the importance attached in *civilized* countries to rank and fortune, and are therefore, out of pure philanthropy, anxious to introduce the same high degree of civilization in America. *'Do we not see the world prosper around us?'* asks Mr. Daniel Webster, the great Massachusetts statesman and orator;* 'do we not see OTHER GOVERNMENTS, and OTHER NATIONS, enlightened by experience, and rejecting ARROGANT INNOVATIONS and THEORETIC DREAMS, accomplishing the great ends of society?'

"Now is not this Conservatism with a vengeance! Would an English Tory have dared to make such an avowal before a British parliament? Where would England be, if her born or chosen legislators had looked round for precedents among other nations? What would have become of the United States, if the representatives of the people, in 1776, had held the same language? What better argument can be made in favour of absolute despotism in any country, than that 'other nations, and other governments, reject *arrogant innovations* and *theoretic dreams'*? The decree of the Emperor of China against the introduction of Christianity is not more profound in its argument; and yet Mr. Webster is, in this respect, nothing but a plagiary! Arrogant innovations were resisted in China long before the birth of the honourable senator for Massachusetts.

"Such doctrines as these will explain to you, at the same time, the views of our Whigs. Compare them to the principles of Toryism in England, and the conviction will irresistibly be forced upon you that the latter are a thousand times more liberal, and compatible with the freedom of the people. How many measures for the welfare of the English people have emanated from the nobility! But these *Whigs,* who are just one or two steps removed from the masses, think themselves beset by dogs, and are continually kicking for fear of being bitten.

"These sentiments will not surprise any one who has heard 'the most influential citizens' assert that the republic has secured no great and signal benefit to the United States; that they were just as free, and certain classes even freer, under the British Government; that there can be nothing worse than the present mob-government, &c. These sentiments, I say, had ceased to astonish me; they only served to convince

* Daniel Webster's second speech on the Sub-treasury System proposed by the present administration.

me of the necessity of trusting to institutions, not to men, the welfare of the state."

In the present struggle for power, ambitious men may yet hope to arrive at honourable distinction through legitimate means—through the suffrages of the people; and hence the decision of every great question is still referred to the latter, although in a manner so distorted by cunning and sophistry that the people can scarcely see the true point at issue. For this reason the United States are, as yet, free from secret societies, private meetings and assemblies for political purposes, and leagues of powerful families for the furtherance of treasonable objects. Neither of the two parties, the would-be-aristocratic or the democratic, is as yet firmly established in power, or can hope to acquire and retain it for any length of time; but it is even this unsettled state which, by some, is taken for a surety of the continuance of the republican government.

Every institution, democratic, aristocratic, or monarchical, was originally good, and remained so as long as it answered the purpose for which it was first established. For this reason it is absurd to praise or censure, in the abstract, either of these forms of society. The elements of each of them probably co-existed at all times, even under governments the most republican or despotic: all calamities which ever befell mankind arose from their misapplication, or from the disproportion between the progress of society (no matter in what direction) and the relative preponderance of one or the other of these three principles.

If any of the two great parties which divide the United States, as they do the rest of the world, should ever succeed in breaking up and destroying the other; if any one of them were to establish itself so firmly in power, as to make its political antagonists wholly despair of overthrowing it by constitutional means; then one of two great evils would necessarily ensue,—political indifference on the part of a great number of industrious and wealthy citizens; or a lawless opposition, not to the party in power, but to the *institutions* under which they hold it. Something of the kind—at least the former of the two cases—actually occurred during the latter part of the administration of General Jackson; at which time a large portion of wealthy, and formerly influential citizens, believing it in vain to make any farther resistance to the sway of democracy, entirely withdrew from politics, and frankly expressed, at home and abroad, in conversation and in public prints, their contempt for the government and institutions of America. Now that, by a series of changes which it is not here the place to explain, political influence and power seem to be once more within their reach, they begin again to take an active part in public affairs, recommencing their opposition to democracy with renewed vigour.

The government of the United States requires, more than any other, a strong opposition, in order to prevent a powerful faction from assuming a monarchical sway through one or more of its leaders. Democracies and aristocracies may eventually terminate in monarchies; their most critical moment being always that in which one of two great parties has gained some signal victory over the other. The power obtained by the conquerors is necessarily concentrated in the hands of a few political champions; who, being on such occasions, for a time at least, independent of public opinion, or having that opinion in their favour, may dictate law. Such a moment is fraught with dangers, even if the democratic party be the conqueror; the transition from democracy to monarchy being far more easy than that from aristocracy to the government of a single individual. The latter is, indeed, impossible until the aristocracy is completely absorbed by the democratic element, and by degrees spoliated of its prerogatives.

For this reason a powerful aristocracy of family has always been the strongest bulwark against arbitrary power, and the preserver of liberty in the middle ages. But, in order that the aristocratic element shall fulfil its high destination, it must have an *historical* basis;—it must date from the origin of the country, and, like the aristocracy of England, have contributed to the foundation of the state. A mere mushroom aristocracy of money, taken yesterday from behind the counter, possesses none of these essential qualities; and is on that account neither capable of protecting the lower classes, nor of forming by itself a powerful political party. What a commercial aristocracy may do for the happiness of a people, even when reflecting on its historical grandeur, we have seen in the example of Venice, from the time the signory elected the chief magistrate, in 1173, to that in which she stooped

> "——————— to be
> A province for an empire, petty town
> In lieu of capitol, with slaves for senates,
> Beggars for nobles, panders for a people."

The establishment of a purely democratic government—that is, of one in which the democratic prevails over the aristocratic and monarchical principles,—is an historical problem which, under the most favourable circumstances ever combined, was intrusted to the American people. These circumstances will continue to act for centuries in their favour; and suppose the government finally to become modified, could such an event disprove the fact that, as long as the republic *did* last, the people were prosperous and happy, the nation respected abroad, and its domestic affairs managed with skill and integrity? Is it an argument against democratic institutions that they cannot last for ever? Might you not just as well despise youth and vigour, because they are doomed to old age and decrepitude? If it be true that all republics finally changed into aristocracies or monarchies, it ought to make the Americans only the more jealous of preserving the purity of their institutions, in order that, if an aristocracy *must* come, it may not be one of mere wealthy stock-jobbers.

————

"Come," said my cicerone, "let us take a walk over to Charlestown, 'the mob quarter,' as our enlightened citizens call that independent suburb of Boston. We shall have a fine view of the city and the harbour from Bunker's Hill monument, the most classical object in this neighbourhood."

"How far is it now completed?" demanded I. "I was told they did not go on with it from want of funds."

"That monument," replied he, "of which no one can tell when it will be finished, is a sad proof of the preference given by the Bostonians to *realities,* rather than to fictions of honour and glory. Our people are not fond of the poetry of history. They seem to have fought for liberty because it was a thing worth fighting for, without being fired with that enthusiasm for a great and noble cause with which we have seen millions of Europeans rush into battle as into a banquet-room.

"We Yankees are not like the heroes of antiquity; we are not ambitious, and do not even think it worth our while to leave traces of our virtues and achievements to posterity. We are not easily moved by historical recollections, and therefore think it a useless vanity to erect monuments for our children, in order to stimulate them to great and generous actions. This is a new illustration of our common sense. Being less exposed to invasions from a foreign enemy, and less dreading the aspirings of a powerful faction within, we do not see our institutions surrounded by those dangers, in the struggle against which love of liberty and of country become the absorbing passions of a people. Liberty, with us, constitutes a quiet possession, which we hope to retain rather by prudence and economy than by enthusiasm and courage."

"I have heard a number of Bostonians," observed I, "animadvert seriously against the celebration of the 4th of July, the anniversary of the Declaration of Independence; and especially against the reading of that instrument from the pulpit, because it contains expressions offensive to a power with which the Americans are now living in peace and amity."

"We do not wish our children to imbibe that tender affection for liberty," replied he, "which a lover cherishes for his mistress; we want them to be wedded to it in the good old Puritan fashion, without going through the tedium of a sentimental courtship. Our liberal institutions are, with us, a sort of household furniture intended for common use, well kept and guarded from injury, but no object of ardent attachment or devotion."

The total absence of enthusiasm among the higher classes of Americans, I found, indeed, one of the most remarkable features of their character. They consider the democratic institutions of their country *opposed* to national grandeur; and feel, therefore, little inclined to commemorate events which could either flatter the vanity, or excite the emulation, of the lower classes. They seem to be of opinion that the people of the United States have full as much liberty as they can bear, and that a little more would unavoidably upset the whole. This will be considered as a gross slander on the patriotism of the aristocracy; but it is nevertheless a conclusion I have deliberately come to, after a long series of observation. Love of liberty and of country I found infinitely stronger among the labouring classes, who do not enjoy the advantage of finishing their education in Europe; absolute contempt, and sometimes hatred of the institutions of their country, among those who have had the means of spending several years abroad. What is the world to argue from it?

The monument at Bunker's, or rather Breed's Hill,—for the Americans mistook their position in the night, and fortified Breed's Hill instead of Bunker's Hill,—was intended, I believe, for a plain obelisk, which, if it were completed, would command a most superb view of the city and the harbour: as it now stands, it is nothing but a modern ruin,—a lasting reproach to the want of *nationality* of the Bostonians. Want of *public spirit* it cannot be; because the Bostonians have given a thousand proofs of their readiness to make large pecuniary sacrifices in order to further the establishment of institutions calculated to benefit the community. The establishment of the Athenæum, principally through the munificence of a merchant; the Asylum for the Blind, towards which Mr. Perkins contributed alone ten thousand pounds sterling; the great liberality of all classes whenever an appeal is made to their charity; and lastly, the large sums paid annually for the support of common schools and public lectures, do not allow me to entertain the least doubt on the subject.

But, in the case of the monument at Bunker's Hill, "the English feeling," for which the higher classes of Boston were always distingushed, seems to have acted as a counterpoise; and to have, if not absolutely prevented its completion, at least withheld those sums which would have been readily contributed for another object. The *Boston ladies,* who, it is said, have a good deal of public spirit, made an attempt to revive the national pride of the gentlemen, but without effect; the outward respect paid by the Americans "to the sex" being essentially different from that species of gallantry which makes men delight in anticipating the wishes of women without being regularly pressed into the service. The "appeal of the ladies," therefore, remained without effect, and a few of the forward ones barely escaped being ridiculed in the public prints. "This is a sad state of society," say the disciples of Miss Martineau; "but all this will be changed when the ladies will vote, and hold public meetings for the propagation of patriotism."

"If the *English feeling* of our aristocracy," observed my cicerone, "were to manifest itself only by the omission of expensive monuments, it would, perhaps, less expose us to the censure of our patriots, or the just ridicule of Europeans. But I have known gentlemen whose highest glory consisted in not being recognised as Americans while in England, and whose delight it was to pass on the Continent *pour des Mylords Anglais.* One of them, a youngster of not more than twenty-one years of age, was, on his stay in Paris, particularly afraid of being taken for an American savage. He spoke on all occasions of England as his native country—(our fashionable young men, you know, talk of going *home* to England,)—and commenced and finished his sentences with '*Nous autres en Angleterre,*' '*nous autres à Londres;*' &c. In the travellers' books he signed himself Mr. ***, '*Rentier de Londres;*' his clothes were made by a London tailor, his hat was English; and he even imitated the bad English accent when speaking French, though he could speak the language tolerably well when he wanted to shine before Americans.

"A year or two ago," he continued, "I met, on the Rhine, with a still more extraordinary phenomenon. It was nearly in the middle of the month of August, when I went in a steamer from Mayence to Coblentz. There were a number of Englishmen on board, who, according to their custom, avoided as much as possible every kind of contact with the rest of the company. They were seated on one side of the boat, gazing on the moving panorama of the river; occasionally ejaculating 'fine!' 'pretty!' 'very fine!' 'too much at once!' At a little distance from them, towards the stern of the vessel, sat, 'solitary and alone,' as a celebrated senator has it, a gentleman in a macintosh, buttoned up to the chin, supporting his body, which was bent forward, by a huge cane, and keeping his eyes fixed on the ground in the deepest meditation.

"This Pythagorean attitude and silence, which were admirably becoming a thinking Englishman, excited the mirth of all the passengers, and especially of the Germans, who ironically remarked 'that the English had a very philosophical way of travelling, always reasoning and reflecting when other people are satisfied with the mere looks of things.'

"After the lapse of I should think an hour, the supposed Englishman, whose back must have ached considerably, drew himself up to his full height, enabling me to recognize in him a young gentleman of my acquaintance, who had gone to Europe for his health, and was at the same time carefully improving his manners. 'How long is it since you left ***?' demanded I, rushing up to him in order to shake him by the hand. 'Hush!' whispered he; 'I have been coming down all the way from Strasbourg with these Englishmen here, and none of them has recognised me as an American.'

"The fact is," continued my cicerone, "our higher classes, in spite of their continual croaking, have no other standard to go by but the English. They pique themselves on dressing like the English, talking like the English, thinking like the English, and behaving like the English, and on having English sentiments with regard to politics and religion. Some of 'the aristocracy' are even more orthodox than the English themselves; especially with regard to the Irish, who, since their emancipation, are much more unpopular with certain classes of Americans than O'Connell can possibly be in a British assembly of Tories.

"For the same reason have our aristocracy taken the House of Lords under their protection; 'because the English nobility is such a glorious institution!' 'it contributes so much to the national splendour!' and there are so many high families in America *connected* with the first people in England! They probably think that, as long as aristocracy finds a stronghold in the old institutions of Britain, there remains at least a hope of introducing something similar to them in the United States; but they forget that, from the historical aristocracy of England, to the nameless money-dealers of America, there is a greater transition than from the substance to the shadow of a thing. Incorporated companies and banks are as yet the only armories that furnish weapons to the chivalrous knights composing the nobility of the New World; and there is scarcely an American squire that would not be willing to sell horse and lance provided a proper price be offered him.

"Another generic feature which marks our wealthy *parvenus,* while, at the same time, it furnishes a curious index to the human heart, is the little sympathy felt or expressed with regard to the enterprising Western settlers, and the contemptuous language held by our 'respectable editors' when speaking of those unfortunate exiles from the refinement of 'the Old States.' Mrs. Trollope's caricatures of the 'half-horse and half-alligator race make the reader laugh; those drawn in our own papers are calculated to make one *despise* them. They use precisely the same language formerly employed by British writers with regard to the early settlers of the American colonies:—'lawless adventurers,' 'fugitives from justice,' 'outcasts from society,' 'dregs of humanity,' 'candidates for the state's prison or the gallows.'

"By these gentle appellations do the mushroom aristocracy of a few trading places stigmatise the steady, laborious, enterprising race of men that fertilize the Western wilderness, and create new markets for manufactures and commerce. Scarcely a couple of generations removed from the original settlers, they already play the old families, without having in their ephemeral existence done *one* thing deserving to be recorded in history; for we cannot disguise the fact, that all we have thus far accomplished, all that distinguishes our people from the idle and vicious population of Europe, all that has contributed to our boundless national prosperity, is owing to the virtue, enterprise, and perseverance of the *labouring* classes, and in no small proportion to those very 'adventurers' whom our Atlantic satraps affect to despise.

"Our higher classes," added my cicerone, "seldom get angry at foreigners for abusing their government in the abstract; but let any one attempt to prove that there are no elements of a different administration to be found amongst them, and they will raise a hue and cry against the audacious slanderer. Tell them that they are 'no republicans,' and they will feel themselves flattered, though they may pout like some affected prude with whom a man takes some pleasing liberty. But attack their *aristocracy;* say that it is a noisy, shapeless, monster, with many tails and no head,—or, what is worse, say that you discover *no* aristocracy in the country,—and you will set them raving.

"I remember a poor, little, innocent woman who nearly fainted at a duke's telling her that he had understood there was no *noblesse* in America; but merely an educated (?) wealthy *bourgeoisie.* Poor thing! she little expected such a mortification; and from such a quarter too! And yet she was a great stickler for human rights; just like some fashionable reformer, who can see no reason for the extraordinary prerogatives of the nobility, but is wide awake to the chasm which separates *him* from the multitude.

"We may safely call ourselves the vainest people on earth," concluded my cicerone, "and yet we dare not have an opinion which is not sanctioned abroad. We constantly refer each other's manners, doctrines, and principles to those which are current in Europe; but, when an European ventures to imitate our example, we cannot contain our wrath at his impertinence. We do not object to the standard of comparison, but to the comparison itself; because we claim for ourselves the exclusive faculty of arriving at just conclusions. Our best society is but a sorry caricature of that of Europe, and yet we get angry when an European attempts to depict it. Our fate is indeed the most singular. No one can understand us; and yet we are constantly talking about ourselves, and throwing out hints as to where observers may look for an explanation of our manners. The good people of England especially seem, in reference to us, to be in precisely the same predicament as Dr. Johnson was with regard to the Scotch,—the more we talk, the less they know about us."

CHAPTER XII

A party of English Gentlemen at Dinner—their Patriotism.—Character
of John Bull in America.—The Englishman's Speech.—The American
Answer.—Modesty of British Commercial Agents in the United States.—
Anecdote characteristic of the Second Society.

"Peace, I say! hear mine host of the Garter! Am I politic? Am I subtile? Am I
a Machiavel? Shall I lose my doctor? No; he gives me the potions, and the
motions. Shall I lose my parson? My priest? My Sir Hugh? No; he gives me the
proverbs and the no-verbs."

Merry Wives of Windsor, Act iii. Scene 1.

To-DAY I dined with an English gentleman, who had been settled a
great number of years in the country, and was married to an American
lady of very good family.

The company was composed principally of merchants and manufacturers, with an admixture of a few travelling agents of British commercial houses, whom it was not difficult to recognise as the lions of
the party. They were not, properly speaking, members of the first
society, because foreigners who are once married and settled in the
country seldom belong to it, unless they are immensely rich; but they
thought themselves nevertheless considerably above the second, not one
of them having accepted an invitation to the latter for the last six
months,—preferring infinitely no society at all to the degradation of
mixing with inferior persons. Besides, one of them, having of late
moved into "a more respectable neighbourhood," was preparing to
entertain his new fashionable acquaintance with a large, sumptuous
party, which he hoped would at once open to his sons and daughters—"the old man and woman" are not so easily promoted—the road
to the highest circles.

Dinner, which was one of the plainest I ever made in the United
States, was served in the usual manner; only that the gentleman of the
house piqued himself on having everything cooked in the true English
fashion. I believe he had a beef-steak brought upon the table for the
sole purpose of showing the difference between the English and Ameri-

can ways of dressing it. "This is an English steak," said he; "at least you do not see it besmeared with rancid butter, and N.B. cooked with Liverpool coal." The *roast beef* was recommended in the same manner, as being "roasted in the true English style;" and the same was said of the parboiled vegetables, and at last of the fire-proof pudding.

"I hope," said one of the gentlemen, who was an American at the head of a large manufacturing establishment, "none of our friends is troubled with dyspepsia."

"I like the English kitchen better than any other," replied our entertainer, "whatever preference my friends may give to the French or Italian."

"At any rate it is preferable to the American," observed another Englishman.

"And if not that, we at least know how to eat," remarked another.

"That," said our host, "no one will deny. The custom of eating against time exists only in America."

"Why," observed the manufacturer peevishly, "I have seen many an Englishman, sitting down at our public tables, play as good a knife and fork, and as quickly too, as one of our 'natives.'"

"That was done in self-defence," cried the Englishman, "if it was done at all."

"If the custom of dining at *table d'hôte* existed in England," rejoined the manufacturer, "your people would soon learn *speed* and *ingenuity* in eating."

"I hope, sir, such a custom will never be introduced."

"And then you forget that at a public table in America you frequently meet with people who, in England, would be content to make their dinner at a beef-shop."

"I often suspected something of the kind."

"Why, sir, this is a republican country; we have no *public* distinction of classes."

"So much the worse for you."

"But is it not very strange," observed the manufacturer, somewhat angrily, "that you Englishmen, who come here for no other purpose in the world but to make money, who 'underwork and undersell' us wherever you can, should be constantly railing against this country? I have seen Scotchmen, Irishmen, Frenchmen, and Germans who were all satisfied to live amongst us and acquire property; but I do not remember a single Englishman that was not constantly talking of the

superiority of England over America. The English are the only foreigners that never become *bonâ fide* citizens. They always have a leaning towards their own country, however they may have forsworn their
sovereign, and pledged fidelity and allegiance to the United States."

"I consider all you have said as highly in our favour," said our host.

"But I do not," remarked the manufacturer. "I consider it downright perjury to come and settle amongst us,—to apply for the privileges
of citizenship,—to go through the requisite formalities,—to pledge an
oath of allegiance to the country,—to renounce publicly one's former
sovereign,—to exercise all the rights of native Americans conferred by
these acts,—and then, after all, to remain a foreigner at heart, and to
abuse this country whenever an opportunity presents itself of doing so
with impunity. If you dislike this country so much, why do you stay
in it?"

"Because I cannot do better," replied the Englishman.

"That's an old, but nevertheless a good one," remarked one of the
company.

"Oh!" exclaimed the manufacturer, "we know *your* principles well
enough. Your John-Bullism is past redemption."

"I trust it is," said the gentleman, colouring to his ears. "Nothing,
God willing, shall transform me into a Yankee!"

"But you are married in this country; you have children born in
America;—what countrymen shall *they* be? They cannot be called
Englishmen, I am sure."

"I am sorry for it; but that is not my fault. I will, at least, give them
an *English education*."

"Pray, are you a naturalized citizen?"

"I have never perjured myself," replied the sturdy representative of
John Bull.

"But did I not see you the other day at the polls?"

"I did not vote, I merely distributed tickets."

"What a nice distinction this is; you did not vote, you merely elec-
tioneered!"

"That was done from principle."

"What principle can that be? What interest can you take in our
politics without being a citizen?"

"I have no interest at all in it. I merely do my duty by exerting myself to the utmost of my power to insure the election of the worst candi-

dates, in order that you may the sooner be cured of your republican notions."

"If this is really your object, you ought to have been lynched long ago."

"I tell this merely to my friends."

"Pray, do not quarrel with him," interrupted one of the guests, addressing himself to the manufacturer; "our friend has always exerted himself on *your side* of the question."

"That is a fact," observed another. "Though you start from apparently very different premises, and appear to have very different motives, there is really no great difference between you in the end; so I think you had better shake hands, and drink to *England and the United States!*"

"England and the United States!" echoed the company.

"England and the United States!" repeated our host; "and may the latter never forget *what they owe* to the former!"

"John Bull to the back-bone!" cried the manufacturer. "All in his own house too!"

"But is it true," demanded another Englishman, who, I was told, was an ironmonger, "that Mr. *** is not yet naturalized?"

"I am," said he, "to all intents and purposes a *British subject.*"

"That's no answer to my question," replied the ironmonger; "a man may be a British subject, and still for all purposes in *this* country a naturalized American. I am a citizen of *both* countries. I hold real estate in Nova Scotia and in the United States."

"Then you do not hold it according to law."

"Pshaw!" ejaculated the ironmonger, "who cares for that? Millions of acres of land in this country belong to foreigners."

"But you cannot be a *bonâ fide* holder of real estate in the United States without being a citizen, and you cannot become a citizen without renouncing all allegiance to foreign countries. You must have perjured yourself with regard to England or America."

"Poh! poh! Talk of perjury in such matters! It's a sort of custom-house oath which binds a person no farther than his word. I would not be such a fool as to give up my rights as a British subject. Times may change;—would you have me put all my eggs into one basket?"

"A nice creed this!" cried the manufacturer; "and such are the men that govern our elections! And you vote just like the rest of us?"

"And why should I not?"

"Pray, don't quarrel," said the same mediator that had before reconciled the manufacturer with our host; "*he,* too, votes on *your* side. Why do you scrutinize his motives if his *acts* coincide with your own? *England and the United States!* I say,—*their interests are one and the same; may they never be divided by party spirit!*"

This toast was drunk with all the honours; after which the gentleman of the house rose, and made, as far as I can recollect, the following *speech:*—

"Gentlemen,

"I am glad to see that you are by degrees coming to your senses. You cannot but agree with me, that it is the best policy of the United States to cultivate the friendship of Great Britain. It is, I am sure, the wisest thing you can do, after having been so foolish as to separate from us. As for *us,* we do not care three straws for that separation; we can get *along* without you."

"That's an Americanism," remarked one of the company: "he is a stickler for Old England, and talks of going *along!*"

"I plead guilty to the charge," replied the host. "The fact is, I have been so long in the United States that I have almost forgotten the English language."

"Go on, sir! Go on!" cried the company; "never mind the language."

"Well, gentlemen, I said we did not care three straws for that separation; neither do we, for our annual commercial balances against you are now greater than they ever were before the revolution. I only wish we could get rid of Canada in the same way. As for your *independence,* it's all my eye and Betty Martin, as the saying goes, as long as you borrow money, and we are the ones that lend it you. A man in debt has lost his freedom, and the same holds of a nation.

"As regards the good understanding which exists between England and the United States, it is based, I am sure, on the most rational basis: the creditor likes to see his debtor prosper, in order that he may have a chance of being paid; and the debtor does not wish to break with his creditor, in order that the latter may not be too hard upon him, and, perhaps, trust him again. This, I believe, is all the sympathy which exists between the two countries at present; the antagonistical principles of their respective governments admitting of none other. With regard to myself, gentlemen, I can only say that, as the partner of an English house, I have always found the Americans an honest, clever, enterprising people; a little too enterprising by the by, especially with regard to manufactures" (here he cast a side glance at the representative of 'the American system'); "but, as this has done *them* more harm than *us,* I am not disposed to quarrel with them. The Americans are, no doubt, our best customers; for which reason we like to see them in Liverpool, Manchester, Leeds, &c. in precisely the same manner as we Englishmen meet with more civility in Boston, New York, Philadelphia, and Baltimore, than in any other part of the Union. This is all natural enough; and, in proportion as *trade* increases, our *friendship* must increase with it: and as I, for one, am really disposed to promote the latter as far as lies in *my* power, I will give you 'The trade between England and America!' "

The trade between England and America was then drunk in a bumper; when, after sundry coughs and expectorations, the manufacturer rose and delivered himself in these terms:—

"Gentlemen,

"I am a manufacturer,—I presume you all know what that means; and I am *proud* to be one." (To the host.) "I think, sir, that without manufactures this country would be entirely dependent on Great Britain. Our manufactures, sir, make us independent; without manufactures we should still be the slaves of the old country." ("Oh, oh!" and cries of "Go on, go on!") "But, sir, I will go further; I will come to the point; I will go beyond it! What, sir, would become of this country without manufactures in case of a war with England?"— (Several gentlemen, "We don't want war; we want peace.")—"Gentlemen, if you interrupt me, I will sit down."

("No, no! go on! Let us have it in true style.")

"Well, gentlemen, I have asked the gentleman what would become of us without manufactures in case of a war? Here is a question! will you answer me that? Can you deny that our manufactures are destined at some future day not only to compete with those of England, but to *beat* them? And as to the insinuation, sir, that the establishment of manufactures has hurt this country, I look upon it with scorn; and what is worse than scorn, with *pity,*—nay, with perfect contempt."

(Cries of, "That is personal;" "that won't do, Mr. ***; you are out of order.")

"If I was out of order, I am sorry for it; I did not mean to be personal; I only wished to state the truth, the whole truth, and nothing but the truth. The gentleman hinted that we have not enough capital or perseverance to carry on that branch of industry; at least, I understood him to say so; but *I guess* he will find himself mistaken. If we have not enough perseverance, we have at least 'an awful sight of hang-on.'" (Shouts of "That's right; give it to him!" and laughter.) "But, sir, I gladly reciprocate; nay, I feel absolutely obliged to you for the kind sentiments you expressed in reference to this country. I hope the friendship between England and this country will be eternal; I mean to say, *I trust* it will last for ever. England cannot but *profit* by it, and so must *we*. Why then should we be eternally quarrelling with one another. I can see no good arising from it in any shape; so far from it, on the contrary, *a pretty considerable deal* of evil.

"It has been the custom of a few ignorant Englishmen to underrate the American character; but *I calculate* the English *nation* had nothing to do with it, and must, since Lord Brougham's establishment of common schools, have learnt the true character of our people. But, as I always say, gentlemen, there is not the least cause of enmity between us. We both speak the same language, and were originally one and the same people; we intermarry and trade with one another; and, in short, do all things which mark us as civilized nations. On this account, gentlemen, and because it does not behove a Christian people (as one of our orators said), even in time of war, to harbour any ill will towards one another,* I give you, gentlemen, and I trust it may be a sentiment to which you will all cordially respond,—'Success to the enterprise of both countries; and may they never forget *their common stock!*'"

"A fine *stump speaker*† this!" observed one of the Americans.

"Rather too *Kentuckical,* though," remarked another; "but the fact is, there are so many *nice* shades of our meaning, that we cannot express them in any other language."

———

I again saw my cicerone in the evening, and related to him the conversation I had listened to, expressing my surprise at the continual feuds between the English and Americans.

* Mr. Quincy was, during the last war, one of the leading members of the opposition; and, as such, introduced a resolution "that it was unbecoming a Christian people to exult in the triumphs over their enemies." This resolution was afterwards voted to be erased from the journal of the house.

† One who speaks *extempore;* because in the Western country they use the stump of a tree for a rostrum.

"This ought not to astonish you," observed he: "most of the commercial agents, who come here either to settle or to reside, find themselves, for the first time in their lives, in what is called 'the first society,' apparently on a par with our most influential, *i. e.* moneyed citizens. This, of course, strikes them as extraordinary, and leads them to the conclusion that the first society in America must be essentially different from the society called 'the first' in England or Europe in general; to which they could not, possibly, procure themselves an introduction. This, as you may perceive, must be the natural effect of their modesty, for which you ought not to blame them, and for which I, for one, am rather disposed to give them credit; especially as I have seen the same persons, who in America flourished in the most fashionable circles, on their return to England not even admitted to the society of a London club, but content with a place in the counting-room of their employers, and a table in a city coffee-room. Though occasionally thrown into the company of *our* statesmen, they never approached, by chance, a member of parliament in their own country; and, although here considered as men of ability, they were satisfied with living in obscurity at home.

"As regards their political opinions," he continued, "few of them, I believe, have received a liberal education, so as to be able to view our institutions with an enlarged, impartial mind, or to separate an accidental evil from the general good of which they may be productive to the great mass of the people. Instead of seeing in our government a practical illustration of the political doctrines abstracted from the experience of all countries and of every age, they view in it only a modification of the government of England, and apply to it the scale of their own country.

"For this we can the less blame them, as many of our most distinguished statesmen and politicians take precisely the same view of our institutions; referring them constantly to the British model, and considering nothing as legitimate which cannot be directly traced to, or deduced from, a similar institution in Great Britain. If you believe them, no other people but the English are born with a political understanding or forecast: why then should the English, who come here, not apply the same doctrines also to the Americans? and why should they not, occasionally, join our own fashionable people in depreciating the advantages of our government, and speak disrespectfully of those whom ourselves are accustomed to treat with so little ceremony?

"When the English, who come here to live among us, declare our government a mere experiment, and our institutions destructive to the ends of society, they re-echo but the sentiments of our first people, whom they are obliged to imitate if they wish to be considered fashionable; for, believe me, an Englishman who would praise our government, and who in consequence would be suspected of Radicalism, would be infinitely less popular in Boston than one who, by abusing us, proves himself to have belonged to the fashionable school of politics in his own country.

"The great evil of our society consists in its being constantly acted upon by two entirely heterogeneous principles,—the democratic institutions of the country impelling our people one way, while the aristocratic aspirings of the upper classes communicate to them an impulse in the opposite direction. The resulting motion, therefore, is neither *straight forward,* nor directly ascending; but a sort of compromising diagonal, which in the inimitable language of our people is characteristically called 'slantendicular.'

"This is the great historical origin of the doctrine of double motives which sways our best society; and which is, perhaps, the principal cause of all the incongruities, contradictions, and downright absurdities for which we have been ridiculed by Europeans. I, for my own part, tell you frankly that I dislike in the extreme the 'slantendicular' conduct of certain classes. I prefer a downright aristocracy with *avowed* motives and principles, to a jesuitical nobility of 'influential citizens.' You must respect the perseverance and iron consequence of a Duke of Wellington; but you cannot but despise the cringing pride of *our* Tory politicians. If we are doomed to have artificial distinctions,—if we must have an aristocracy after the model of that of Europe,—let us, for mercy's sake! *import it ready made;* the gradual process of growing it ourselves is too tedious, and the minute details too disgusting, not to put the best of us out of humour.

"I never want to see an aristocrat until he is ready to put on white gloves; our 'ungloved,' 'unwashed' aristocrats are to me an object of horror. No tyranny is more odious than that of an overgrown *bourgeoisie.* Being less removed from the lower classes, their tyranny is more felt; and not being placed sufficiently above competition, they are incapable of taking any lofty, disinterested views with regard to the government of the people, whom they half fear and half dispise. These faults, at least, are among those which are seldom to be found in an

hereditary aristocracy, until it becomes reduced to a position in which it
is obliged to enter with the people on a contest for power.

*   *   *   *

"Having told you so much about our 'first people,'" said my cicerone,
taking a bottle from his closet, and filling two glasses with I do not
now remember what, "I will, as a *pendant* to them, relate to you an
anecdote which will throw some light also on our *second* society. Only
let us drink fast, and let me soon remove the glasses; I should not like
my servants to know that I am in a habit of taking a thing of this kind.
There is no use in making one's self unpopular, you know.

"The town of Boston," he commenced, "if it were not already remarkable as the 'cradle of liberty,' and the place where the first American *tea-party* was given, would long ago have become so by the hospitality and convivial talents of its inhabitants.

"At the South-end of the town, at the very spot where General
Washington raised a fort from which he forced the departure of the
British army, stands now, not a monument to commemorate the deed,
but an excellent hotel, where a man may get the best things in the
shape of viands and wines, if he be willing to pay for them. To this
place, called 'Mount Washington Hotel,' many an excellent family,
probably out of patriotism, retires in the summer, not only to enjoy the
sea-breeze, and to escape from the noise of the town, but also in order
to be able to say that they have spent the summer at a watering-place;
New Port, Longbranch, and Saratoga Springs being much more expensive, and society too exclusive to enable people of moderate fortune
to participate in the entertainments of the season. The Washington
Hotel, therefore, is frequented by such gentlemen and ladies as have
acquired competency without wealth, respectability without family
dating of more than one generation, and a common-place routine of
fashion without having had the advantage of a trip to Europe,—in
short, by such as in Boston form the second society, and with whom the
first society never, even by chance, exchange any kind of civility.

"Notwithstanding these apparent disadvantages," continued my
cicerone, filling himself another glass, "nothing could be prettier than
this second society if its members could be made to agree amongst themselves. This, however, is altogether out of the question, owing to the
numerous coteries and subdivisions to which it is again subjected. Our
second society, namely, has again its first, second, and third rank, each

of which is again subdivided into still smaller circles, which are again numbered; so that it requires the nicety of a mathematician to ascertain what sort of company a man is likely to be with when invited to a party. Owing to this trifling circumstance, the members of the second society live with each other somewhat after the manner of cats and dogs; making but too frequently foreigners witnesses of their broils, and affording them, as will appear from my story, occasionally an opportunity of acting the peace-makers.

"An instance of this kind happened last year, when a Polish gentleman arriving in Boston, and finding the town too hot in the summer, was induced to take up his residence at the 'Washington Hotel,' which he was told, and with great justice too, furnished excellent accommodations at moderate prices, and commanded a fine view of the harbour.

"Scarcely had he removed thither, before his being announced 'as a count,' 'a real count,' 'a count that was *known* to be a count,' and who had brought letters proving him to be 'every inch a count,' caused such a sensation in the house, that the ladies refused to eat, drink, and even *talk,* except in company of 'the count.' The count could not but be flattered by these attentions, and in turn omitted nothing by which to testify his gratitude. He listened with the utmost patience to the accounts of their chivalrous ancestors,—for in Boston even the second society have *ancestors,*—sat without opening his lips when they mutually abused one another, and with incredible skill managed to remain on good terms with the various sets, divisions, and subdivisions, whose every-day regret it was to be obliged, 'owing to the ridiculous American custom,' *to dine together at the same table.*

"At last the melancholy hour drew near when the count was about to depart. When this sad intelligence was received, the ladies, with that tenderness which belongs to their sex, and the peculiar generosity which marks 'the second society,' determined to pay to the count a tribute of their respect, and accordingly met in conclave to consult as to the best manner of manifesting their sentiments. At first, the first section of the second society met, and agreed to give the count *a ball*. Then came the second, then the third, then again the *élite* of each section; and, wonderful! on this subject they all agreed.

"It was therefore intimated to the count that he must defer his departure until after the ball, to which the cavalier readily consented; assuring the ladies that their kindness should be engraven on his heart, and that he should never forget the amicable reception he had met with in Boston. The rest of my story is easily told. The evening was fixed for the party, the 'ladies patronesses' chosen from each set, (because, the count having been polite to all, none could very well be omitted,) and invitations sent out to three or four hundred people to pay to the count the tribute due to his rank and quality.

"At last the appointed evening arrived. The ball was superb,—the hall magnificently decorated,—the music exquisite,—the refreshments in excellent taste and in the greatest profusion. There was also a supper;—not indeed equal to one of Crockford's, but, notwithstanding, nice, delicate, blending the French with the English art of cookery, and arranged in a style worthy of a *prince*. The selection of madeira and sherry corresponded with the supper; and there was a profusion of iced champaign for the ladies. The whole went off prosperously, with the exception of a single mistake; which, however, the count did not discover till the next morning, when the landlord, stepping into his room, presented him with a small piece of paper containing the disagreeable item of—

" 'To Ball, 1000 dollars.'

"The count was stupified,—changed colour,—declared that the ball had been given to him, and that he had nothing to do with settling the bill.

"The landlord withdrew; handed the bill to the 'ladies patronesses,' and respectfully demanded an explanation. Hereupon a grand meeting of all the sets was immediately convened, at which the best understanding prevailed throughout, the whole assembly coming to the unanimous resolution 'that the count was a shabby fellow.'

"The day following, the count paid the bill and quitted the hotel, without leaving a single p. p c. for any of its inmates."

Here my cicerone finished his glass, locked the bottle and the empty tumblers carefully up in the closet, and, having put the key in his pocket, told me in the most solemn voice that it was not the custom in Boston to keep late hours, and that, in order not to lose his reputation as a moral man, he was now obliged to wish me a good night.

CHAPTER XIII

A Literary Party.—The American Press.—Character of Editors—their Rise and Progress.—Influence of Advertisements.—Old and New Federalists.—Mode of operating on the People.

"A field of glory is a field for all."

Pope's *Dunciad*.

I PASSED an evening at the house of a genuine specimen of a Yankee,—at a sort of literary party, to which nearly the whole Boston tribe of the quill were invited; the master of the house being well able to act as president. My Boston friends, on reading this, will imagine I refer to a gentleman in B***-street; but I can assure them that they are mistaken. I do not mean a man who has at once been promoted to the rank of king of literature, master of the pamphlet and magazine writers of New England, by his wealth and the agreeable manners he acquired in Europe; but a hard-working man, who served his apprenticeship in a printer's shop, and by dint of perseverance and talent became one of the most powerful organs of public opinion, and a correct English writer. His politics were, from the beginning, those of the Federal school, but honest; his style clear and flowing, his arguments logical and to the point; and he possessed a fund of wit and humour to season the productions of his pen. In his younger days he submitted himself to the arduous and unprofitable task of exposing some of the most glaring follies of his countrymen; for which, though he became in an eminent degree a public benefactor, he was frequently sued for libel, and condemned to heavy fines. Notwithstanding these reverses he had prospered, and become the father of a large family, most of the members of which were distinguished for great ability.

On this occasion he had convened his friends and acquaintances in order to communicate to them his resolution to add a new monthly periodical to the list of those already in existence, and to ask their contribution to so laudable an undertaking. He also told them that for one year at least he was ready to continue it at a loss, remunerating liberally the best papers on politics and *belles lettres,* to which he proposed to direct his principal attention.

The proposition was received with enthusiasm by the whole company. They agreed unanimously that such an undertaking was highly patriotic, and that the time being was particularly propitious to an undertaking of that sort; that the condition of the country, and the progress of literature and science in the United States, "loudly call for such a periodical," &c.; and, as a mark of their sincerity, pledged their entertainer in a bumper of hock, which seemed to augur favourably for their taste and judgment.

While they were thus engaged in expressing their sympathy with literature and the arts, I had an opportunity of observing their countenances, which partook of the usual shrewdness of New-Englanders, but were otherwise far from being remarkable or striking. Fortunately for my democratic sentiments, they were all representatives of the Whig or American Tory press; though some of the *English* editors of that denomination would not, perhaps, feel flattered by this extension of the fraternity.

What was most interesting to me was, the little ease which prevailed amongst them; none seeming to know his true position. They approached each other with great caution, as if they dreaded each other's malice. I am sure they did not venture a single expression which they would not have liked to see in print. In addition to this, they watched each other's motions, and the greater or less degree of intimacy which existed between their entertainer and his invited colleagues; in short, they wanted nothing but tact and manners to pass for a tolerable body of diplomatists at a provincial court in Germany.

I could not help making some reflections on those poor mortals, who, like other players, "fretted their hour upon the stage;" though their *parts* were not many, and the play but too often not worth the candle. I believe I am not altogether wrong in asserting that the American daily press, though its influence on national politics is prodigious, is nevertheless in its composition, character, and moral force, scarcely to be compared to the mass of talent employed in this branch of literature in Europe.

There is scarcely a paper in any of the large cities of the United States which has a decided political character—advocating some great historical principle, and employing in its warfare other weapons than common-place dialectics, and constant appeals to the passions of its subscribers. The effect produced by the American papers is due to their number; there being not one of them which can boast of a subscription sufficiently large to make it a true representative of public opinion. Their power is owing to combination. No great central institution has as yet taken the lead; but they have a wonderful faculty in communicating each other's ideas, either by direct quotations or by dressing up the same thought in a variety of manners. An American paper, in fact, is said to be edited *with great talent* when it contains in each number from half a column to a column of original matter: the rest consists of extracts and advertisements. The latter constitute the pecuniary resources of an editor; the subscriptions being so low that, unless a "fair advertising patronage" can be obtained, little profit or absolute loss must necessarily attend the publication.

From this single circumstance the leading character of American newspapers may at once be inferred. The commercial part of the community advertise the most,—their interests, therefore, are sure to be advocated; while those principles which refer to the higher branches of statesmanship or political economy are rarely made the subject of newspaper controversy, except perhaps in the Southern States. The Southerners are the only people in the Union who study politics as a science, having both the education and leisure for that purpose. The Southern papers, therefore, are, on an average, much better edited than those of the North; though from their higher standard, and the peculiar composition of Southern society, they have comparatively a small number of readers.

The practical men at the North call the Southerners, and especially the Virginians, "Metaphysical politicians," in contradistinction to those whose immediate object is the increase of trade and traffic. The Northern papers advocate each only *a particular part* of a political system: one, a bank of fifty millions; another, one of forty millions; one, a bank in New York; another, one in Philadelphia, &c. just as it suits the convenience of their subscribers. It is not the press which leads the public,—it is the public which leads the press. What is likely to succeed—that principle which promises to become popular, which gratifies the peculiar *penchant* of the leading portion of the public, is sure to be maintained, if not with spirit, at least with great obstinacy; but a great truth, which is not yet universally received, which meets with a strong opposition from wealth and prejudice, which is calculated to benefit future generations and not the present one, often pleads in vain for a single enunciation in a daily print. The proverb, *"Point d'argent, point de Suisses,"* applies as much to the gentlemen of the press as to the hired soldiers of Helvetia; with this difference only, that, once engaged in fight, they do not always defend their masters with the same unalterable faith and courage.

The fact is, a truth which clashes with the interests of a certain portion of society is seldom introduced by men not entirely independent in their circumstances; and for this reason a powerful aristocracy, or an absolute monarchy, has often done more for the emancipation of a people than could have been effected by the variously-directed efforts of the wealthy middle classes. The history of all countries up to the present day furnishes ample proofs of this assertion, and the state of America itself forms no exception to the rule.

The Southern planters, who, not without cause, are reproached with aristocratic principles and sentiments, are nevertheless the stronghold of American liberty, without which the variety of commercial, manufacturing, and agricultural interests would soon produce a conflict of principles, which would ultimately endanger the Union. The very opposition to the Southern interests obliges the higher classes of the North to live in peace with the inferior orders.

The industrious labourer at the North has no better ally than the Southern planter, who, from his position, is more independent, more generous, and better able to protect him against the rich monopolist than the *roturier,* who is his competitor. From the South emanated all the democratic measures, together with the doctrine of the sovereignty of the people as it is now understood in the United States. Southern statesmen advocated the rights of the poor; and broke down the monopoly of trade and manufactures, which threatened to enrich one class of citizens at the expense of all the rest.

There is a species of republicanism which may assume all the odious features of aristocracy; and there is an aristocracy, in the true sense of the word, which may act as a stimulus to liberty and national honour. If there be one truth which the history of modern times has proved beyond the possibility of a doubt, it is this,—that the wealthy *bourgeoisie,* where it succeeded in obtaining power, has been a ruder tyrant of the lower classes than the hereditary nobility whom it deprived of their political influence. As my friend truly observed,—the more nearly an aristocracy is allied to the people, the more intolerable are its presumptions; the less are these qualities redeemed by refinement, education, and that peculiar sense of honour which, even at the worst stage of corruption, seldom entirely quits those descended from a long line of ancestors. If Michel Chevalier is right in believing that the nature of man is too corrupt to be governed by a pure democracy, then I would, with my Boston cicerone, prefer at once an aristocracy of family and *hereditary* property, with chivalrous notions of honour and justice, to a cold, calculating preponderance of moneyed men, which, though it may to a certain extent stimulate enterprise and industry, establishes nevertheless a mean *numerical* scale of worth, the most distressing of all to the lofty aspirations of high-minded men.

The aristocratic *super-position* of society, as it exists in Europe and in the Southern States of America, has far less tendency to circumscribe the liberty of the people* than the democratic *juxta-position* of different ranks and fortunes, with an incessant *struggle* for individual distinction. In short, I prefer the white-gloved democrat of the South, with his *aristocratic* bearing, to the ungloved aristocrat of the North, with his republican humility, and his cravings after popularity and power.

> "Ourself and Bushy, Bagot here and Green,
> Observed his courtship to the common people,—
> How he did seem to dive into their hearts
> With humble and familiar courtesy;—
> What reverence he did throw away on slaves,
> Wooing poor craftsmen with the craft of smiles,
> And patient underbearing of his fortune,
> As 'twere to banish their effects with him.
> Off goes his bonnet to an oyster wench;
> A brace of draymen bid—God speed him well!
> And has the tribute of his supple knee
> With '*Thanks, my countrymen, my loving friends!*' "

As I was thus pondering on the relative merits of the North and South, I observed a gentleman whom I had once met in a stage-coach talking to the master of the house in a manner from which it was easy to infer that *I* formed the subject of their conversation. Shortly after he rushed up to me, and, seizing both my hands,

"Don't you remember me?" exclaimed he; "we travelled together in the same coach from Baltimore to Washington."

I was glad to find some one to converse with freely, without being

* These remarks can, of course, only be understood as applying to the *white* population of those States.

every third word stopped by such prases as these: "Why, sir! I don't exactly know;" "I sometimes think;" "I am half inclined to suppose;" "I rather guess;" "I should *swan,*" (for, "I should swear,") &c.; or cross-examined as to my intentions, views, inclinations, tastes, and habits, which I knew would be considered as absurd if they did not entirely correspond with the stereotype patterns of the leading moralists of the city. During my stay in Boston I have often felt gratified with the attention shown me by many of its inhabitants; and there are, perhaps, few cities which, in proportion to their population, can boast of so large a number of educated men and women: but I cannot refrain from alluding to the want of moral independence, not only in their private and public acts, but also in their *conversation.* I communicated these thoughts to the Carolinian, who, seizing both my hands, exclaimed,

"You have spoken my very heart. I could live twenty years in this city without feeling myself at home in it. There is a degree of cere- moniousness, watchfulness, and prudence, even in the hospitality of these people, which destroys that familiar conviviality to which we are accustomed at the South. The same holds of the women. There is a cer- tain severity—*une rigueur poussée trop loin*—about the loveliest faces in New England, which acts as a disenchanter on enthusiasm. You gaze, you admire, you respect; but you are almost *afraid* to love; such a distance does there seem between yourself and the object of your fancy."

From these topics our conversation turned on literature and the representatives of the press.

"Our editors," said he, "think themselves competent for the solution of every question, whether it refer to politics or poetry, to the settlement of the Western country or to Greek and Roman archæology. Once armed with a quill, they care not whom they meet in the arena. Fortu- nately it is their practice to praise indiscriminately every book, pam- phlet, or poem, of which a copy is sent them 'for notice;' except when the author attacks their favourite doctrines, or pretends to be wiser than themselves. In such cases they exhibit an *esprit du corps,* and woe to the unfortunate offender that provokes a power so formidable! Not only will judgment be pronounced on him *editorially;* but also in an infinite number of *anonymous* articles, furnished by the legion of literary twaddles which surround our 'independent press,' and claim the oc- casional insertion of a squib as a *bonus* for the amount of their annual subscription. This species of assassination is considered perfectly lawful, and is practised by lawyers, physicians, clergymen, merchants, manufacturers, and tradespeople of all sorts. Whoever subscribes to a paper considers himself *the editor's patron,* and obliges the latter to give publicly to his duly lucubrations.

"An editor, in order to reject these voluntary contributions, must be very independent in his circumstances, or possess a fund of wit and sarcasm to make people afraid of him, as is, for instance, the case with our entertainer; but by far the majority are glad to avail themselves of these opportunities of filling their columns without personal exertion or trouble. You know how the democratic tendency of Cooper's novels was treated in our prints; how the youths of our colleges, and the clerks of our dry-goods-men, exerted themselves to the utmost to counteract their pernicious tendency."*

"I do not remember many of those newspaper squibs," said I; "but I think Cooper showed very little taste or good sense in answering them at large in *'A Letter to my Countrymen.'* "

"And in republishing that letter in England," added the Carolinian; "making the English public judge between himself and the American people."

"And yet, what remedy has an American author in such a case, except to appeal from a small and prejudiced public to a large and liberal one?"

"I do not think," rejoined the Carolinian, "the English public is much more liberal than our own. But, then, in England every man sticks to his trade, so that the criticism of the periodical press, and even of the daily papers, proceeds at least from persons competent to judge, and who have made literature their principal occupation in life. If it were not for English critics, we should not know or esteem our own poets; for it is only after they have acquired a standing *there,* that they are admitted into society in this country. I remember what an American lady from this very city told a gentleman in Paris, when she heard a certain bard was visiting the highest society in England: 'I cannot conceive of it,' said she; 'he never visited in the first society *with us.'* 'Then,' observed a sarcastic Scotchman, 'the first society in England must be very differently constituted from the first society in America.' "

"You are too severe on your own countrymen," said I.

---

* Since Mr. Cooper's last publications on France, Italy, Switzerland, &c. he is less abused by his countrymen. The nice things he tells them about the *palaces* of Europe, and the society of princes to which he *himself* was invited, have put the critics in good-humour with the author.

"I am accustomed to speak my opinion frankly," replied the Southerner. "How many of the gentlemen present do you think fit to edit a respectable paper in England?"

"That is a difficult question."

"Oh, not at all, sir! I will answer it for you. Hardly one besides our entertainer, who, though perhaps no longer equal to what he was, possesses, nevertheless, more business tact, and writes better English, than any one of his colleagues. And yet all these men have pretensions to literature, and imagine themselves capable of judging the literary productions of others. What man of talent would under such circumstances not rather appeal to England, and be judged by his peers, than trust to the decisions of his countrymen? The greatest praise of the American press is, after all, but a dubious testimony of an author's merits, even with a great portion of the American public; while its censure becomes doubly severe from the circumstance of its rare occurrence, and the great ease with which it may be avoided. I remember an instance in which one of this gallant body of editors 'cut up' a book, and that too one which has since been republished in England, merely because the author had forgotten to send him a copy;—a tribute which no poor devil of a writer ought to forget to pay to those sovereign princes of literature, if he do not wish to see himself damned. But, if the work has once gone through an edition in *England*, all is hushed in silence; for, although we declaim continually against British influence, we have scarcely an editor who dares to hold an opinion different from that of the English public. The love of independence is, indeed, inherent in them; but in such matters a mere *declaration* does not answer the purpose."

"And what is the usual career of one of your editors?" demanded I.

"That is easily told," replied he. "A man fails in business, or is otherwise unfortunate; he does not succeed in his profession, or has had some other falling-out with the world. Then he turns politician, and commences generally by being a democrat. Democracy is the easiest and best commencement of a politician. He is serving his apprenticeship with the people, as a young physician first practices on the poor before he ventures his skill on those who are able to pay him. The majority of our 'most respectable editors' commenced in this manner, by advocating 'the greatest good to the greatest number;' but, once brought into notice, the transition from Radicalism to Whiggism, and from that to Toryism, is effected with little difficulty.

"You may always doubt a democratic editor's sincerity when his *advertisements* begin to increase. He is then sure of making himself agreeable to a certain portion of the *commercial* community, and to meet soon with the proper reward of his new political faith. You may then expect to see him promoted in society and on 'change; and ten chances to one he will be able to settle with his creditors. After that, he begins to differ in one or the other point from the leading principles of the democratic party, (for it is seldom that a man changes *at once* from a democrat to a Whig,) until by degrees he renounces the whole doctrine as unworthy 'of a gentleman and a scholar.' Then he begins his abuse against the *mob,* declaiming loudly against anarchy and usurpation; because new converts to a doctrine must show more zeal than those who have been brought up in it, and in order to exhibit their contempt for the class of society from which they themselves have sprung. These abuses are afterwards returned with interest by those who have remained faithful to their cause, or who have not yet had a chance of promotion. Hence arises a newspaper controversy, which is neither calculated to elevate the style of our writers, nor to throw much light on the great principles for which they are contending. After subtracting the personal abuse and common party slang of our papers, there remains scarcely enough matter to elicit one generous thought, or a single truth capable of adding to our political knowledge.

"Our editors are so much bent on discussing men and characters, that they scarcely ever find time for examining a principle; and hence it is that foreigners not acquainted with our public men cannot form a correct notion of our politics. It is our boast that Europeans do not understand our institutions; but I believe the same reproach applies to ourselves, and particularly to our editors. How many of these, I would ask, understand the true meaning of aristocracy and democracy? and what historical idea do they associate with these terms?

"Immediately after the revolutionary war, we had Whigs and Tories; that is, men that were honest enough openly to avow their sentiments. These *had* a political system, and defended it logically with philosophical arguments. And I will be sincere with you: a large portion of our public men *was* then inclined towards Whiggism, or rather to a moderate Toryism, as might have been expected from a people principally descended from England, and versed only in the British school of politics. These men, however, soon discovered the impossibility of establishing, in America, a government after the English model. Their principles and doctrines became unpopular; until, at last, their motives were suspected, and they themselves held up as traitors to the country.

"The French revolution had given a fresh impulse to the democracy of the country; and the champions of the old school—the Federalists as they were called—were obliged to leave the field to their victorious antagonists. Since that period their party has tried to *smuggle* itself into power. They assumed a variety of insignificant names by which to deceive the multitude, and within the last few years sailed under false colours. They are no longer the plain honest men who come out with their principles in broad daylight; they do not advocate openly and manly the system they once gloried in, but only certain detached parts of it. They administer their politics to the people, like some disagreeable medicine, in exceedingly small doses, in order not to disgust the public stomach.

"The great majority of editors are, in every respect, the mere tools of party. They do not set up or maintain a principle, they merely spread it over a wider surface. Their *modus operandi* consists in appealing to the passions of the multitude, upon whose decision their success mainly depends; and the same is the case with our statesmen. The democrats may do so without apparent inconsequence; they *acknowledge* the people as their sovereign, and may do them homage: but when a party, which agrees in nothing except in the conviction that the people are unfit to govern, bends its knees before that very people in order humbly to crave some of the offices and distinctions in its gift, then I can no longer remain an indifferent spectator; I feel indignant at the base conduct of these crafty flatterers, and become ashamed of the principles of the party to which my whole family and myself have always belonged."

"You are a Federalist then?" demanded I.

"Yes, sir, one of the *old* school; for I believe that an aristocracy not linked with, but, on the contrary, separated and opposed to the people, must for ever remain powerless; and that the people of no country are to be won by empty praise and sycophancy, but by the conferring of some substantial benefit."

"Our rich people do not even understand how to strike the lower classes with the exhibition of wealth and splendour; a practice which is rarely entirely without effect when that exhibition benefits a large number of tradespeople. So far from seeking the appearance of liberality, they hoard money in the most miserly manner; as if the mere possession of wealth, and not the skilful application of it, were capable of procuring them political influence. There is not a branch of industry in which they are not striving to grind the face of the poor, and yet they expect the latter to promote their interests! Nothing but an entire stupefaction of the people can ever make them attain their object. The people give nothing without an equivalent, and are only rendered more obstinate by the fine speeches and flattery of those who pretend to be their superiors. In one word, our aristocrats are fond of power and distinction; but they are unwilling to pay for them. Money is, and remains, their highest consideration; and the acquisition of it the principal object of their lives. Hence the privilege of making money, and of borrowing and lending it, has become the rallying point of their party. How far this will assist them it is at present difficult to tell; but one thing they may rely upon with certainty,—that the people, though for a time espousing their cause, will again desert them at the first clashing of interests.

"Among the Western hunters and warriors there are better materials for a future aristocracy than can be found in the Atlantic cities. They are, at least, owners of real estate, and possess the soil on which they play the lords. In short, the persons who are now called 'the aristocracy of the Northern States' must change their manners, habits, principles, and education, before they can expect to gain a hold on the sympathy of the people."

"But why do you remain with a party with which you have so little sympathy?" demanded I.

"Because I do not wish to be called an 'apostate.' I am so far disgusted with politics, that I will not have anything to do with them hereafter. The great interests of democracy claim in every country, even in absolute monarchies, the utmost attention of the legislator. All wise statesmen, whether kings or senators, have been attached to its leading principles; but men have ever been too corrupt to give it a systematic development. This circumstance makes me sometimes doubt its success among us; though I, for one, am no longer opposed to the experiment."

"The press!" shouted the company,—"the press!" and the editors pledged it in a bumper.

CHAPTER XIV

Unitarian Preaching.—Doctor Channing.—Character of his Audience.—
Religious Party on the Sabbath.—Discussion of Dr. Channing's Merits.—
Moral Cant.—General Characteristics of New England Society.—Women
the only Aristocracy.

> "Love, and meekness, lord,
> Become a churchman better than ambition."
>
> *King Henry VIII.* Act v. Scene 2.

"La Religione e la Filosofia commandare l'una e l'altra energico volere, e
giudizio pacato, e senza queste unite condizioni non esservi nè giustizia, nè
dignità, nè principii securi."

> SILVIO PELLICO.—*"Le mie prigioni."*

THIS being Sabbath, and the last day of my stay in Boston, I went to
the "first Unitarian church" to hear Dr. Channing, a gentleman of
wide-spread reputation in America, and of late considerably known also
in England. He is considered the prophet of Unitarianism in the
United States, and I am not disposed to derogate from his reputation.
He has undoubtedly contributed much to the popularity of the sect in
Boston, and to its spreading in several parts of the Union, where a
large portion of the population consists of New-Englanders.

I once heard a clever man assert, that the world stood in expectation
of a great man who should unite the three principal creeds, Christian-
ism, Judaism, and Islamism, into one, and thus bring unity and concord among the different believers in one God. Whether such a man
would have to clothe his doctrines in pious mysticism, in order to affect
the heart as well as the mind, and to embrace all the peculiarities of
these creeds, he did not say; but, since I have heard Dr. Channing, I
am inclined to think that he is the man, and that he intends to solve
the grand problem by philosophical *analysis*. It is possible, namely,
instead of inventing a form which shall contain each of these creeds as
a co-ordinate part, to make use of the dissecting-knife in order to cut
off all that is not perfectly homogeneous: the remaining trunks, with
their "sublime moral," would then so little differ from one another,

that the one might be safely substituted for the other, and *vice versâ*. How much the world would gain by such a simplification, I leave political economists and female philosophers to judge, who perhaps are best able to appreciate the advantages and beauty of such a system.

The sermon I heard was one of the doctor's best. It was "on the character of Christ," and I must do him the justice to say that he handled his subject with great skill. It was a perfect epopee—almost equal to the *Henriade,* only that it was in prose. The effect on the audience was electric. Instead of the ladies fanning themselves, and the gentlemen sleeping as they are wont to do at this season of the year, they all looked "at the doctor," and at each other, as if doubting the reality of so extraordinary an effort. I expected at every moment a public manifestation of their feelings, but was disappointed; for hardly had he finished, and a psalm been sung by the choir, before his hearers —who, I was told, were composed of the "genteelest" and "most *fashionable* part of the community"—left church with that peculiar English propriety and undisturbed countenance, which would have led an European from the Continent to suppose they had never been affected.

It is usual in Boston to make sermons a peculiar branch of literature, and to discuss them in lieu of other literary matter at dinner or tea, especially on Sundays. This practice, by which many an European has undoubtedly been edified, I was to-day doomed to become a victim of, in a very nice family. I took tea at a gentleman's house, who, though he had seen a good deal of the world, thought it nevertheless *prudent* to conform to the customs of society; especially as he had grown-up daughters, whose prospects in life might have suffered from an open confession of the liberality of his principles. Having arrived at the conviction that religion is absolutely necessary to the *moral and political* well-being of the community, and that it is a powerful means of repressing the vices and passions of the *multitude,* he espoused, on his return to America, that creed which most nearly approached his mode of thinking, and put the least restraint on his habits. His family were inclined towards orthodoxy; but, the father worshipping at an Unitarian church, the daughters followed his example, and listened to the eloquent discourses of Dr. Channing.

Scarcely had I entered the room, and, in the good New England fashion, bowed separately to all the ladies, and shaken each of the gentlemen present by the hand, before the eldest daughter—a beautiful dark-eyed girl, with black hair and ruby lips—addressed me in the most solemn manner in these terms:—

"Well, Mr. ***, whom did you hear to-day?"*

"I heard Dr. Channing," replied I.

"Were you not delighted?"

I somewhat hesitated for an answer.

"It was certainly a great effort," said the gentleman, observing my embarrassment.

"But is he not a charming preacher?—I mean, is not his *style* beautiful?" demanded the girl.

"It is *glorious, glorious, glorious!*" echoed the women.

"And the doctor is not only one of our greatest preachers, but also one of our first literary characters," resumed the young lady. "He has written an excellent sermon against General Jackson, and a most glorious article against Napoleon in the North American Review."

"Is he also a politician?" demanded I.

"Yes, sir, and a most *glorious* one; he wrote against the tariff, and of late also against slavery."

"Why did he not write sooner against it?"

"Because he waited for the proper time, just after the subject had been taken up in England."

"Are you an abolitionist, Miss ***?"

"I was taught never to speak of it," said the girl, blushing. "It is a question in which we dare not act, as we are told by our minister."

"For G—d's sake!" cried the old gentleman; "let us not have *abolition*. Those blackguards are already stirring up the country in every direction, and will not be satisfied until they will have produced a separation of the Union. I think Dr. Channing had better turn his wits to something else."

"But what induced him to preach against General Jackson?" demanded I.

"Because General Jackson was very nigh involving the country in a war with France, and Dr. Channing is opposed to war, on account of its wickedness. It completely obscures 'moral grandeur,' and sets a high premium on the lower qualities of the mind, such as courage, patriotism, and the like. He is in general opposed to 'military greatness,' and is just as severe on Napoleon, Nelson, Wellington, and Jackson, as Pope was upon women; only he is not quite so satirical," observed the

* This is the Sunday "How do you do?" of the Bostonians.

old gentleman. "He thinks those men will have 'a very low standing' in the other world. Isn't it so, my child?"

"Precisely so, father; Dr. Channing always speaks of Napoleon as of 'the miscalled great man.'"

"Then the French were right in calling him *le* PETIT *caporal.*"

"Why, the doctor calls Napoleon only a *third-rate man!*"

"Then, I assure you, he has been sinking the bathos in a professional manner. Such a speech might have been *piquant* some twenty-five or thirty years ago at a nobleman's table; but no one can venture on it now without betraying the most profound ignorance of history, and the most ridiculous conceit at the same time. None but great men do great things; the saying and writing them is left to inferior minds, and often to mere scribblers. Napoleon tamed the revolution, he changed its corrosive nature; which alone ought to have entitled him to the respect of the Tories."

"It is the misfortune of our people," continued the old gentleman, "that they cram everything under the head of morality. Morality is the cant and crack word of the place. If you go to our fashionable churches, you will hear the fashionable clergyman preach 'morality;' if you visit a private gentleman's house, he is sure to entertain you with 'morality;' if you attend a public meeting, the 'moral' speaker will address his 'moral' fellow-citizens on the subject of 'public morals;' if you listen to the partisan harangues of our professional politicians, they will conjure the people 'in the name of morality' to outvote the profligate antagonist faction, &c. Morality seems to be the great lever of society; the difficulty only consists in finding its fulcrum."

"I believe Dr. Channing is very popular in England," observed one of the visiters.

"Among the Unitarians at least," replied the master of the house; "but the assertion of some of his friends here, that he is the best English writer now living, is, I can assure you, wholly gratuitous. We are apt to overdo things on this side of the Atlantic, and are either too lavishing in our praise or too severe in our censure. We always deal in superlatives, even in common conversation; which is the surest sign of our imagination being void of images. Everything with us is 'most beautiful,' 'most sublime,' 'most glorious,' from a turnip up to our ministers, lawyers, and statesmen; so that, on occasions when we are really moved, we have no other terms to express our feelings than those whose signification is already worn out by common use.

"As regards Dr. Channing's merits as an author, no one can deny, I believe, that he is a correct and tasteful writer, though by no means a powerful one. There is throughout his productions a visible want of originality and strength, which a skilful rhetoric and a nice selection of terms are incapable of concealing even from ordinary readers. His ideas are less striking than the garb in which they are dressed, and remind one constantly of some pretty little miniature painting, in which the artist is more successful in the drapery than in the face. In addition to this, he is, like all New-Englanders, prone to argument, and in the course of it but too frequently betrays the want of logic and sound scholarship.

"This is most apparent in his little pamphlet on Slavery, and the annexation of Texas. He there ventured on a subject in which the popular feeling was already in his favour, and yet did not set forth a single new idea capable of adding strength to his cause. He merely reiterated, and dressed in new garbs, the general argument against slavery, used by European writers nearly a hundred years ago; and, in so doing, but followed the example of hundreds of his countrymen, who did the same thing at a time when it was dangerous to advance such doctrines in America. I naturally expected to see the subject treated, not in the English manner, but applied to the condition of the Southern States. I thought he would allude to the forlorn condition of the *free* negroes at the North, and propose some means of elevating their character, in order gradually to prepare them for a rational state of freedom. I thought he would reproach his own fellow-citizens for refusing negro children to be educated at our public schools, for excluding them from our churches, our theatres, our public houses, our stage-coaches, and even our burying-grounds! And yet it is evident that, as long as the feelings of our Northern population do not change with regard to the negroes, emancipation can do them no good; for, while it gives them liberty, it prevents them from becoming respectable,—it takes away the master's whip in order to transfer the slave to the pillory and the gallows.

"I expected Dr. Channing to propose a scheme for gradually emancipating the negroes, without absolutely ruining the planters; but, instead of all this, he contented himself with declaiming against slavery in the abstract, and in appealing to the *political* prejudices of the Northern people."

"But," objected one of the gentlemen, "Dr. Channing, in his pamphlet on Slavery, and in his 'Letter to Henry Clay, on the annexation of Texas,' says that he is aware that these publications will make him unpopular with a large portion of his readers; but that he is prepared to meet their disapprobation, rather than omit to do his duty."

"Oh! that's nothing," rejoined the master of the house, "but a display of courage in times of peace. Let him preach the same doctrines to the Southerners, or, as I said before, allude to the forlorn condition of the free negroes amongst ourselves, and I will believe in his moral fortitude. Many a clergyman in the United States has exposed himself to being mobbed, and some *were* mobbed, for daring to preach what Dr. Channing published with the greatest possible security in Boston; and yet those men earned no reputation for their martyrdom."

"Neither did these men employ the proper means for abolishing slavery; they preached revolt."

"And Dr. Channing," resumed the old gentleman, "the doctrine of political equality. He pressed the subject of slavery on his Northern brethren, not with the calm, impressive voice of an apostle of Christianity,* but with the malice of a political demagogue, jealous of the mental superiority of the South. Riches he neither condemns nor despises; but he is inexorable on the subject of leisure, which enables the Southern planters to be gentlemen and professional politicians. Here" (pointing to a little pamphlet lying on the table) "is the best proof of his sincerity and courage. See what he says of the South and North in his Letter to Henry Clay. If the company will allow me, I will read the passage. It is worth perusing, as it contains an illustration of the character of our leading people.

" 'I now proceed,' says Dr. Channing, 'to another important argument against the annexation of Texas to our country,—the argument drawn from the bearings of the measure on our national Union. Next to liberty, union is our great political interest; and this cannot but be loosened—it may be dissolved—by the proposed extension of our territory. I will not say that *every* extension must be pernicious; that our government cannot hold together even our present confederacy; that the central heart (?) cannot send its influences to the remote states which are to spring up within our present borders. Old theories must be cautiously applied to this country. If the federal government will abstain from *minute* legislation, and rigidly confine itself within constitutional bounds, it may be a bond of

---

* In his Letter to Henry Clay he avers that he has prepared himself for his task by "self-purification;" but in what manner he does not mention.

union to more extensive communities than were ever comprehended under one sway.' "

"Capital logic, this!" exclaimed one of the visitors. "Do not pretend to rule, and you will sway over extensive communities. And what does he mean by *minute* legislation? What do the Southerners claim but non-interference with their internal regulations? and yet, while Dr. Channing preaches the same doctrine, he stirs up a question which, sooner or later, must interfere with the sovereignty of the States."

"This is not all," replied the old gentleman: "he contradicts himself every third or fourth line, preaching union on one hand, and the dissolution of it on the other. Let me read to you another passage.

" 'Undoubtedly there is peril in extending ourselves; and yet the chief benefit of the Union, which is the preservation of peaceful relations among neighbouring states, is so vast that some risk should be taken to secure it in the greatest possible degree. The objection to the annexation of Texas, drawn from the unwieldiness it would give to the country, though very serious, is not decisive. A far more serious objection is, that it should be annexed to us for the avowed purpose of multiplying slave-holding States, and thus giving POLITICAL POWER. *This* cannot, ought not to be borne. It will *justify*, it will at length DEMAND a separation of the States.' "

"Did I not always tell you," interrupted the same visitor, "that the doctrine of nullification originated in Massachusetts? This is but a repetition of sentiments expressed here more than twenty years ago. But we change opinions according to circumstances."

"Hear on!" cried the master of the house. "You interrupted me in the best part of Channing's letter.

" 'We maintain," he says, 'that this policy is altogether without reason on the part of the South. The South has exerted, and cannot help exerting, a disproportionate share of influence on the confederacy. The slave-holding States have already advantages of co-operation, and for swaying the country, which the others do not possess. *The free States have no common interest like slavery to hold them together*. They differ in character, feelings, and pursuits. They agree but on one point, and that a negative one,—the absence of slavery; and this distinction, as is well known, makes no lively impression on the consciousness, and in no degree counteracts the influences which divide them from one another. To this may be added the well-known fact, that in the free States the subject of politics is of secondary importance, whilst in the South it is paramount. In the North, every man must toil for subsistence; and, amidst the feverish competitions and anxieties of the eager and universal pursuit of gain, political power is sought with little comparative avidity. *In some districts it is hard to find fit representatives for Congress,* so backward are *superior men* to forego the emoluments of their vocation,—the prospect of independence,—for the uncertainties of public life.'"

"Under such circumstances," interrupted I, "and with such an exalted patriotism on the part of your *superior* men in the North, the American people ought to be glad to find Southern legislators in Congress; else their senate and house of representatives would contain nothing but men of straw."

"It is precisely that mental aristocracy of the South which our people dislike the most," responded the old gentleman. "They cannot pardon elegant manners and superior education. But hear what parallel Dr. Channing draws between the South and North.

" 'What contrast does the South form with the divided and slumbering North! There, one strong broad distinction exists, of which all the members of the community have a perfect consciousness; there a peculiar element is found, which spreads its influence through the mass, and impresses itself on the whole constitution of society. Nothing decides the character of a people more than the form and determination of labour. Hence we find a unity in the South unknown in the North. In the South, too, the proprietors, released from the necessity of labour, and having little of the machinery of association to engage their attention, devote themselves to politics with a concentration of zeal which a Northerner can only comprehend by being on the spot. *Hence the South has professional politicians,* a character hardly known in the free States.'

"You hear," cried the reader, *"our* politicians are mere *dilettanti.*

" 'The result is plain,' continues Dr. Channing. 'The South has generally ruled the country. It must always have an undue power. United, as the North cannot be, it can always link to itself some discontented portion in the North, which it can liberally reward by the patronage which the possession of the government confers.'

"This, gentlemen," exclaimed the master of the house, "is the manner in which the doctor preaches against slavery! He shows the whole value of it to the South, and then calls upon the South to renounce it, in order to put itself on a level with the North. An *advocate* of slavery could not have selected a better argument for pressing the continuance of the institution on the Southern planters, and yet he expects them to become convinced of its wickedness. He has, indeed, a most peculiar way of exhorting sinners; he shows them all the nice things they may get by offending against the law, and then says, "All these you shall *not* have by following me."

"And what does all his argument come to," observed one of the visitors, "but this?—Our moneyed men in the North revere nothing more than money; but, because each of us is determined to make money, we are divided into as many different castes as there are ways and means of making money. We, Northerners, have no rallying point; because every one makes money for himself, and not for his neighbour. This, however, is not enough to give us political strength; and for this reason the Southerners, who by their slaves are placed above the necessity of making money, rule over us by superior talent and education. This is a state of things not to be endured; and, since we cannot become clever ourselves, we must at least prevent others from becoming so. With us, politics come after money; in the South, they take the lead in all human pursuits. If, therefore, we want to get the upper hand with those Southerners, we must abolish slavery, or, in other words, force the planters to make money for themselves; then we shall see who can make money faster, the South or the North. In the North all work for money; and, as politics with us are no very lucrative pursuit, our *superior* (rich?) men will have nothing to do with them. They prefer the prospect of money to that of political distinction, and the actual possession of it to everything else in the world."

"Capital!" cried the old gentleman; "that's the point Dr. Channing is going to make. We would like to become like the Southerners, if we could do so without pecuniary sacrifice; but, as this is entirely out of the question, we must reduce those who are above us to our own level. In this manner we shall promote equality and justice, and, in addition, obtain credit with the world for philanthropy and true Christian charity."

"You may say what you please against the doctor," said the eldest girl, visibly displeased by the turn the conversation had taken. "I shall always believe him *a charming preacher*."

"I am myself very fond of his sermons," added the old lady; "only I prefer reading them at home to hearing them at church."

"And I," observed an elderly gentleman, "do not like his explanation of the Scriptures by their general scope, and the disbelief of their being written by Divine inspiration; though I heard his colleague assert, that, *rather than disbelieve* THE WHOLE, *he would take every part of them* FOR GOSPEL."

*   *   *   *

And now I must bid good-b'ye to Boston and its remarkable inhabitants, who, I am afraid, have already occupied my attention more than is agreeable to my readers, and, perhaps, to the Bostonians themselves. "Common sense" is certainly the staple commodity of *New England;* but I cannot say I have always found it in the *metropolis.* The Bostonians are too much flattered by their own public men and the press, not to be occasionally benefited by the remarks of "a foreigner." They all call themselves an enthusiastic people,—comparing themselves to the Athenians; but, during my whole stay in the United States, I have not known one of them moved by the tender passion, which, strange to say, never attacks an educated Bostonian *mal à propos.*

The gentlemen of that city never do anything out of season. Whenever one of them falls in love, you may be sure he is quite ready to get married, and that the object of his affection is a legitimate one. He does not throw away his sentiment on some unattainable object, for he husbands his feelings as he does his property. No man remembers better than he the words of Bacon: "When it (love) entereth men's minds, it troubleth men's *business;*" and, the latter constituting by far the most important object of his life, it is comparatively a rare case to see him *look out for a wife* "before he sees his way clear ahead." In this manner he avoids a great deal of romance and vice; but all this prudence and calculation, this impossibility of being betrayed into some rash inconsiderate act, lend to his character a degree of hardness and severity, which, though it may admirably qualify him for public life, renders him, nevertheless, the most unamiable creature in society.

I have heard it said that the New-Englanders in general have a quicker perception, and are shrewder, than Europeans or the rest of the Americans. The Bostonians pride themselves on being "sharper" than the Jews, and on preventing them from making a living in their city; but I cannot say that this agrees with my experience. As regards quickness of perception, they are certainly inferior to the Italians, and in part even to the French; but they make up for it by their greater calmness, which renders them less liable to error. They have not, as a certain English writer believes, two heads; their clearness of judgment arises only from the absence of emotions. Where men have but *one* aim, and that a definite and finite one, they are seldom deterred from it; so that the vulgar, who merely judge by the success, often ascribe to them great mental powers: but there is a kind of genius which, from its very elevation, and its necessary incommensurability with the common mind, is doomed to unceasing strife; and with this the New-Englanders have in general but little sympathy.

The great difficulty which Europeans, and even Jews, find in acquiring property in New England, is not so much owing to the superior business-talent or cunning of the New-Englanders, as to the practice of "every man's doing every man's business;" which reduces the price of all kinds of labour by excessive competition, and leaves no room for interlopers of any description. No species of industry is deemed vulgar or degrading; and, while a European or a Southerner is obliged to do an hundred things *honoris causâ,* the New-Englander undertakes nothing without a prospect of advantage or reward.

Another deficiency in the composition of the New-Englander is the absence of humour. I have, indeed, been shown a number of persons who were said to possess a great deal of what is called "dry wit;" but which, after all, was but an odd way of expressing common-place ideas. Their conversation, generally, wants seasoning,—the spice of imagination and taste. In sarcasm they succeed better; simply because they have more judgment than fancy, and understand dissection better than composition. I shall never forget the definition which a Southern gentleman, a member of Congress, gave of the satirical powers of a distinguished politician of the North. "He has no imagination," said he, "no humour, no keenness of wit; but his sarcasm resembles a very cold razor, which takes off the skin without requiring an edge."

These are some of the dark points in the character of the New-Englander. His bright ones are exhibited in his relation to the community as a citizen. Few people have so great a respect for the law, and are so well able to govern themselves. In no other country are the labouring classes so well instructed, so orderly, and, I may add, so respectable,—in the *European* sense of the word,—as in New England. Though their State politics have generally been inclined towards Whig, and even Toryism, they are nevertheless the most thorough Radicals in principle, and, perhaps, the only people capable of enjoying so large a portion of liberty without abusing it. In addition to this they are sober, industrious, and, with the exception of a few straggling pedlars, from whom it would be absurd to draw a general conclusion, just and honourable in their dealings. In short, nature has done everything to make them calm sober republicans; but reserved every agreeable and amiable quality exclusively for the *women*. Not only are "the ladies" better educated than "the gentlemen;" but also, owing to their entire separation from trade and traffic, more imaginative, high-minded, and patriotic. If the Bostonians, and the New-Englanders in general, have been remarkable for deeds of public and national charity, I am inclined to believe it was principally owing to

> . . . "th' balm that draps on wounds of woe
> Frae woman's pitying e'e."

The women, in fact, are the real *aristocracy* of New England; and I shall go to live in Boston when Miss Martineau's plan is realized, and the women emancipated from thraldom.

CHAPTER XV

The Nobleman's Journal becomes more and more Aristocratic.—Wistar Parties in Philadelphia.—Literary Gentlemen in Philadelphia.—The Girard College.—Character of the late Stephen Girard.—The Quakers.—Their Aristocratic Sentiments.—Quaker Dress.—Philadelphia Ladies.—Good Living in Philadelphia.—The Mansion-house in Third-street.—Apostrophe to the Fashionable Young Men and to the Men of Family.

> "Still stranger much, that when at last mankind
> Had reach'd the sinewy firmness of their youth,
> And could discriminate and argue well
> On subjects more mysterious, they were yet
> Babes in the cause of freedom, and should fear
> And quake before the gods themselves had made;
> But above measure strange that neither proof
> Of sad experience, nor example set
> By some, whose patriot virtue had prevail'd,
> Can even now, when they are grown mature
> In wisdom, and with philosophic deeds
> Familiar, serve t' emancipate the rest!"
>
> Cowper's *Task,* Canto v.

THE journal of my friend I found was too long for publication. Besides, I could discover his aristocratic propensities to grow stronger and stronger in exact proportion to his intercourse with the higher classes; so that I was obliged to omit his notes on the society of Philadelphia and Baltimore, in order to find room for his observations on Washington. Two circumstances, however, I must not suffer to pass unnoticed; his admiration of the Quakers, and his dislike of the Wistar parties,—a sort of half literary, half fashionable, weekly convention of gentlemen, at which a tolerable supper is added to a great deal of indifferent conversation on ordinary topics.

"There is," says my friend, in one of his notes, "a much greater number of literary and scientific gentlemen in Philadelphia than can be found in any other city of the United States; but they are, as yet, far from forming 'a republic of letters.' As long as literary and scientific men without fortune are merely tolerated by their wealthy but less clever colleagues; as long as science and literature in the United States are judged, not by their high intrinsic value, but by the advantages which may result from them in the common transactions of life; as long as arts and sciences remain without influential patrons or public consideration, it is in vain to attempt their promotion by pampering poets and painters with a weekly supper. These 'literary *réunions,*' as they are called in Philadelphia, are not calculated to put a man of letters at his ease, or to elicit new thoughts by familiar conversation. On the contrary, they are stiff, unsociable, full of that *gênante étiquette* which prevails in all the higher American coteries to the exclusion of mirth and familiarity. The Athenæum and Garrick clubs in London contain daily a thousand times better opportunities of improvement to young literary men, than the Wistar parties of Philadelphia in the course of a century. There are, in fact, no establishments similar to those in the United States; though there are *very respectable* gambling clubs in New York, Philadelphia, Baltimore, and even in the godly city of Boston."

"The newly established Girard College," observes my friend in another note, "will not prove so great a blessing to the Philadelphians as is generally imagined. With the munificent donation of its founder, and the truly royal splendour of its execution, it will, I am afraid, become after all little more than an ordinary school of arts and trades. The whole system of education in the United States, and the tone of society, must materially change, before an institution like the Polytechnic School of France can possibly succeed in forming scholars in the higher departments of science. The peculiar foundation and organization of Girard College does not seem to me to be much calculated to improve the system of hand-to-mouth learning produced by the material tendency, and the desire of pecuniary gain and profit, which form the index to the character of the greater part of professional men in America. The founder himself, though in many respects a public-spirited, and in his own way a clever man, had but a vulgar appreciation of genius, and a very high respect for money. This is undoubtedly the reason why he chose none but wealthy men for trustees of the college which was to bear his name, though it is more than probable some literary men might have been found in the United States, who, without being able to give *bonds,* would have proved of some advantage in establishing and organizing a college.

"All I have heard of that vain old Frenchman confirms me in the opinion that, even in his acts of generosity, he was but a vulgar plebeian; never consulting the feelings of those he wished to benefit, but first wounding with a rude hand their inmost soul, in order afterwards to apply the healing plaster in the shape of a bank-note. Thus, he would lecture one of his most faithful servants engaged to be married, on the vexations and follies of matrimony; drawing in a brutal manner the veil from nature's holiest mysteries, and refusing to give him aid and protection, until, perceiving that his victim, dreading the consequences of his temper, remained, like some obedient cur, silent at the abuses of his master, he signed a bank-check in his favour to the amount, I believe, of some thousand pounds. I have heard other anecdotes about him of a similar nature, from which I could not help drawing the conclusion that it was his peculiar delight to make his friends and clients forswear every other god and goddess before he introduced them to the temple of Mammon;—or did the cunning Gaul do so from a knowledge of the society in which he wished to gain an ascendency? What reason, after all, had the Philadelphians to be proud of such a man? And what difference is there between an American banker leaving several millions of dollars to a rich and populous city, in order that his name may be perpetuated by the building of a school; and an honest English boot-black, who leaves an hundred thousand pounds for the establishment of an hospital?*—I can see none; unless it be that the act of the former proceeded from vanity, while that of the latter took its origin in charity and true Christian piety.

"The most interesting part of Philadelphia society are the Quakers; as a body the most singular, as individuals the most respectable, Christians in the United States. I do not here speak of their religious tenets, which are sufficiently known to the world; but of the fact of their being throughout a moral people, by mutual support almost universally in easy circumstances, and from their habits of industry and frugality seldom led into temptation. No other Christian society is held together by such strong ties of affection and brotherhood; no other set of men bear in their manners, habits, dress, and character so strongly the imprints of their faith. They carry their religion—a thing unknown in these times of moral and political advancement—into every act of their private and public lives; and, though they sometimes obtrude it in a manner not the most pleasant or refined on the notice of strangers, show at least on all occasions that Christianity with them is a living

* Mr. Day, of the firm of Day and Martin.

principle, not an abstract doctrine to be remembered only on the Sabbath.

"I like aristocracy in every shape, whenever it has a solid foundation; but I despise aristocratic pretensions in a vulgar rich man. The aristocracy of the Quakers consists not so much in wealth as in family, and this circumstance has given to the society of Philadelphia a tone decidedly superior to that of New York. Though much more exclusive and less hospitable than the New-Yorkers, the Philadelphians are more agreeable and elegant in their manners. They have more of the *à-plomb* of gentlemen. There is less motion and more dignity in their carriage; and you can see, from an hundred little circumstances, that the higher classes have the advantage of a generation over the ordinary run of aristocrats in the United States.

"The Quakers, who are still among those who directly or indirectly influence the fashions of society, have introduced a patrician simplicity in dress, manners, and habits, which forms a singular contrast with the gaudy ostentatious display of wealth with which one is occasionally struck in New York. The Philadelphia ladies dress with more taste than any others in the Union; they walk, dance, sing, and talk better than those of the Northern cities; and their manners in general are more finished. They do not study Latin and Greek, like some of the New England belles; but they prattle French and Spanish, and sometimes Italian, with tolerable facility. They cultivate the *agrémens* of society; while a great portion of the Northern women puzzle their heads, and those of their admirers, with philosophy and the classics. Yet it is but justice to say, that the women of New England, even those of the highest classes, remain unsurpassed as wives and mothers, and set, in this respect, the example to all other females in the United States.

"In point of shape, the ladies of Philadelphia are believed to be unrivalled; their necks, shoulders, and waists being admirably wrought, and their hands and feet of the most aristocratic littleness. Their complexions are not so clear and fresh as those of the women of New England; but the expression of their countenances is more *distinguée,* inclining somewhat towards the Spanish. I was also told that they had a taste for the romantic; several 'droll' engagements taking place annually, and a small number of run-away matches furnishing from time to time sufficient matter for the *chronique scandaleuse* of the town. Things of this kind are of rare occurrence in the North; though, as I observed during my stay in Boston, there is no lack of imagination on the part of the *women*. But where should a young Bostonian find time to run away with a lady? What business or matter-of-fact man is sufficiently amiable for a woman to risk her reputation on his account?

"The Quaker ladies, in general, are renowned for their beauty. They dress plainly, but in the richest materials; showing that their aristocracy consists in substance, not in forms. The colour of their dresses, which is usually of a light grey, is not ill suited to a fair complexion; but the cut is too Old-English not to form a glaring contrast with the Paris fashions weekly imported into the United States. At the time of William Penn, the Quaker dress was not distinguished from the fashions of the day by all that was inelegant, odd, contrary to the prevailing taste; and on that account did not obtrude itself on every one's notice. But at present the case is reversed; the very simplicity of the apparel becomes an arrogant distinction, or may at least be considered as such by those who do not look upon it as a part of their religious creed. Every man or woman owes something to society, so that a total disregard of its established rules and customs is usually considered as proceeding either from extreme vulgarity, or a degree of elevation which need not descend to the level of others: a wise person avoids the dilemma.

"For this reason, and perhaps also because the French fashions of the day are far more becoming to a pretty face, and exhibit *taille, tournure,* &c. to much greater advantage, a portion of 'the Society of Friends' have of late relaxed from their original severity, and adopted certain unobjectionable parts of Parisian millinery. The selection they made shows their tact and sense of propriety; and it is now a common saying with travelled men, that, in order to see a well-dressed lady, one must either see a Parisian woman of the higher classes, or a '*gay Quakeress* of Philadelphia.' The gentlemen, too, begin to trim their hats, and allow the fashionable scissors to be applied to their coats, without dreading the immediate downfall of Christianity. They are also said to have grown more attentive to ladies; having at last arrived at the conviction that the hearts of women are more easily attached by the silken thread of trifling cares and attentions, than by the chain-cable of constant toil and sacrifice.

"A number of Quakers of Philadelphia occupy themselves exclusively with science and literature; few of them are not members of some charitable or other association for the benefit of mankind. Yet they have, from the commencement of the revolutionary war, been denounced as *Tories:* partly because they did not take an active part in the struggle for independence; and partly because, as politicians, they have always been in favour of a federal government. If it be true that family, education, and even property, are, from the principle of self-preservation, inclined towards a strong protective government, the Quakers as a body must naturally be advocates of Conservatism; but in a country like America, where political principles and parties are constantly changing, where the power of the government and the opposition are so nearly balanced, and where the clashing interests of society sometimes completely paralyze the course of politics adopted by the Congress of the nation, I can see no evil come from a small part of the community being attached to existing forms, or united, if this were possible, for the purpose of resisting the rapidity of public events.

"The American government, as I have often said, requires, more than any other, a strong opposition. The aristocratic and democratic principles mutually excite and increase one another, like positive and negative electricity in the metallic plates of a galvanic chain; only, that from time to time they require *cleaning.* Each principle without the presence of the other would soon degenerate; and it is, in this situation of public affairs, perhaps a fortunate circumstance that there should exist at least *one* class of society capable of representing with some sort of dignity the aristocratic element of State.

"The time, after all, must come when the United States will have their history; when the present will be linked to the past; when the names of American statesmen and patriots will go for something in the estimation of the public. Then the influence of family will and must be felt by the people as the historical representative of their political existence. This period is now delayed by the apparent opposition between the higher and lower classes; but it will arrive as soon as the real *élite* of society will *join* the lower orders against the tyranny of mediocrity—in the shape of the government of the rich *bourgeoisie.*

"The society of Philadelphia is, on the whole, better than that of Boston or New York. There is less vulgar aristocracy than in other Northern cities. Not that I mean to say that there are not people to be found in Boston and New York that could rival the Philadelphians in point of 'gentility;' but in the good 'city of brotherly love' there is, probably owing to a seasonable admixture of a large number of European, and especially French families, a higher tone, greater elegance, and, in every respect, more *agrémens.* The New-Englanders are an arguing people, and annoy you, even in society, with mathematical and political demonstrations. The Philadelphians have more taste, and *have the best cooks in the United States.*

"There is nothing more aristocratic than the keeping of an excellent cook; nothing so vulgar as not to care what one is eating or drinking. *'Dis-moi ce que tu manges, et je te dirai qui tu es,'* said the celebrated author of *'La Physiologie du Goût;'* and, certes, no Philadelphian will in this respect be found wanting in the scale. There is a nice little house in Third-street, kept by a man, or, as I should say, 'a gentleman,' who spent upwards of an hundred thousand dollars in Europe in learning how to eat and drink, and who is now teaching the same science to a select circle of his countrymen; charging them for his trouble a little less than some of the quack professors of the culinary art in New York and Boston, who think a dinner excellent when it consists of joints, and show their barbarism by putting ice in their claret.

"Mr. H—d, of the Mansion-house in Philadelphia, has been long enough in Europe to know the difference between gravy and melted butter; and if every American that goes to Europe to improve himself would *only learn as much,* there would be no harm, and much substantial benefit, arising from it to the country. I have, at his house, eaten fricassees that would have done credit to old Véry;—his son inherited the money, not the taste of his father;—and sauces with which, as Prince Puckler Muskau has it, 'a man could have eaten his own grandfather!' In short, one is more comfortable at the neat little house in Third-street, than anywhere else in the United States. An Englishman himself could live there without missing any of the luxuries of his own country, if the bar-keeper were not a stupid old negro, and Mr. H—d, jun. more of a gentleman than a landlord.

"A word in parting to you," says my German traveller, apostrophising the fashionable young men of Philadelphia; "you are much mistaken if you take the terms 'idler,' and 'gentleman,' as synonymous. There is a vast difference between a gentleman of leisure, and a vagrant that walks up and down Chestnut-street, and stares women out of countenance. You seem to think that a certain bold unabashed look marks the gentleman of *ton,*—the fashionable rake, whose position in society enables him to disregard the prejudices of the multitude. You pamper your fancy in the *salons,* in order afterwards to feed upon a common pasture. This is but a miserable way of imitating the refined *roué* of Europe. If you cannot affect sentiment, conceal at least your passion, or curb your inordinate fancy. There is nothing so vulgar as imagination without taste.—And you men of family, without fashion! study aristocracy in the classics, rather than in the newspaper polemics of the day; or, if this should prove too tedious, read the history of the Italian republics. There was a time in Florence when every nobleman was obliged to have a trade, and yet Florence produced the *Medici;* why should you be ashamed to imitate so high an example? or are you afraid lest all your tradespeople should wish to become noblemen?"*

* Trade and traffic are less popular in Philadelphia than in other parts of the Union; the young men delighting in being called "gentlemen of leisure."

PART III

CONTAINING A TRIP TO WASHINGTON, AND A SHORT
STAY IN THE METROPOLIS.

CHAPTER XVI

Journey to Baltimore.—Arrival in the City.—Barnum's Hotel.—The Washington Letter-writer.—His Views of Politics.—Arrival in Washington.—Street Manners of the People.—Hotels and Boarding-houses.—High Life in the Metropolis.—The Epicure House.

"Quando si parte il giuoco della zara
Colui che perde si riman dolente
Ripetendo le volte e tristo impara;
Con l' altro se ne va tutta la gente."

DANTE.

ONE morning, early in the month of March, I left Philadelphia in a steamer for Baltimore. It was a frosty cold day, and we were obliged to have a fire in the cabin; round which the gentlemen—the ladies occupying, as usual, a separate, more elegantly furnished room,—formed at first a small, but, in proportion as the company increased, a larger circle. The manners of the people had already a touch of the South in them: scarcely would a gentleman approach the stove before those who were already seated made room for him; an attention which, trifling as it was, marked a certain consideration for the feelings of others, which it is always gratifying to notice wherever we are. The captains of the boats from Philadelphia to Frenchtown, and from Newcastle to Baltimore,—the distance from Frenchtown to Newcastle is made on a railroad,—were noted for their civility to the passengers; and, on the whole, I do not remember having travelled more at my ease in any part of the United States.

We arrived in Baltimore early in the afternoon of the same day; and the greater part of the company putting up at Barnum's hotel, I concluded to go thither also. On entering the spacious bar-room I at once asked for a separate room, and ordered my luggage to be taken up to it; but was told "that I must not be in a hurry," and that no room could be given away to any gentleman without the bar-keeper having made his "calculation." I then perceived that the gentlemen, one after the other, stepped up to him, telling him their names; which he put down on a slate, together with the number of rooms they asked for, precisely in the same manner as the burgomaster of some small town in Germany would set down the names of the officers of a regiment which is to be quartered upon it. It finally became my turn to speak.

"What's your name, sir?" demanded the bar-keeper.

"Mr. ***," said I, taking care to omit the "De."

"Are you alone, sir?"

"Yes; but that is the reason I want a room by myself."

"All single rooms are engaged long ago. I shall have to put you in a room with one or two other gentlemen."

"Then I shall not stay here."

"You may do as you please; but I cannot accommodate you better. We have to turn away people every day, and we *must* serve our old customers."

"You had better stop here," whispered one of the gentlemen in my ear; "you will be satisfied with the house in every other respect, and I am quite sure you will not be able to do better in Baltimore."

"But, sir," said I to the bar-keeper, "cannot you manage to put me into a room with only one other person?"

"I will see what I can do for you, but I cannot promise; I must first make my *calculation.*"

"And you will of course put me together with a *gentleman?*"

"Nobody stops here but gentlemen; you need not have any scruples about *that,*" replied the bar-keeper rather indignantly.

I thought it best to be silent if I wanted to sleep that night at all, and thus quietly awaited my sentence. At last the bar-keeper had completed the distribution of the rooms; and began to call out the names of the gentlemen, telling each the number of the room he was to occupy. When he called out my name he smiled; and turning to me with a sarcastic expression, "We have to put you in a room with one gentle-man," said he; "but, should you stay longer, we can to-morrow give you a room by yourself." I bowed in token of acknowledgment, and betook myself at once to the quarters assigned to me.

"Also going to Washington?" demanded my chum as I entered the room.

"Yes, sir; are you going?"

"I am *obliged* to go," replied he (with an air of importance); "I am always there during the session of Congress."

"Perhaps I have the honour of addressing a senator?"

"No, not exactly."

"Or a representative?"

"Nor that either."

"Then you must have some business there?"

"Certainly, sir; I am a correspondent of the New York ***."

"Oh! you write the letters from Washington for that paper?"

"Precisely so; and it is a more difficult task to write a good letter than to make a bad speech."

"No doubt of that, sir; you may often be employed in making the best of a bad argument."

"What do you mean, sir?"

"I mean, by improving what has been said by a senator or representative."

"Not only that, but it is *we* that give the cue to every argument. Our representatives take up a question as they find it stated in the papers."

"And it is you that govern the country?"

"It's the press, sir, and nothing but the press, which governs a free people."

"But is not the press liable to error?"

"All human institutions are; but *we* have such abundant means of correcting and preventing it, that it is almost impossible for us to be in the wrong. In the first place, *our* press has the money by which (drawing himself up to his full height) it can secure the best talents; and, secondly, our people are too 'cool' to be easily wrought into a passion. We are a 'calculating' people."

"But your papers are full of personal abuse. Do you think *that* an advantage?"

"Not exactly; but it is unquestionably a great help—a seasoning of dull editorials. Our people have so much ordinary conversation in the course of the day, that, if it were not for the slander contained in our newspapers, they would not be amused at all. *Papers,* sir, are 'the eating, drink, and fuel' of the Americans; and on that account they can never be too hot for them."

"But very high seasoning marks a bad taste; I should think the best papers on what is called 'the aristocratic side' would scorn personal abuse."

"Quite the reverse, sir, I assure you. It's the only means of attracting notoriety, and of pleasing our first people. Besides, it would be useless to play the part of a gentleman in *that respect,* when all the rest are blackguards. We want strength, sir! strength! and nothing but strength!—none of your 'milk and molasses' productions, of which a man can make neither head nor tail. If we give a man a beating, we do not want him to get up again; 'we go the whole hog.' When we attack a man, we assail at once his moral, political, religious, and domestic relations. Every little helps, you know. 'Give a dog a bad name, and hang him!' says the proverb, and it is just so with our politicians."

By this time I began to be afraid of the man, lest, if he should not "steal my purse," he might publish me in the papers. He looked, indeed, like a desperate fellow; though his self-sufficiency was quite amusing, and the smacking of his lips and the stroking of his chin, with which he accompanied every one of his sayings, were sufficiently ludicrous to destroy the effect of the ferocious manner in which he paced the room. I therefore made no farther reply, but began to dress for supper. This untimely cessation of conversation seemed to annoy him, as it probably prevented him from showing off, and impressing me with a proper respect for his station. He therefore drew a parcel of papers from his pocket, and throwing them violently on the table—

"Here," exclaimed he, "is the last news. I dare say you know it already. We have triumphed in every part of the country. Our State is carried 'high and dry.' "

"I do not care much about politics," replied I.

"You don't?" said he. "Why, then, do you stay in the country?"

"Cannot you imagine a man to have any other business but politics?"

"Oh, certainly, sir! a man may be a merchant, a doctor, or a tradesman; but, I mean, how do you *amuse* yourself? I for my part should go mad if I had not politics to divert myself." (With pride,) "I *need* not be a politician, thank God! I have money enough without it; but I *love* politics on account of the pleasure they give me. I glory in them! There is such fun in being on the side that beats. One hundred and fifty guns, sir, are to be fired from Albany to New York, and from New York back again to Albany, in honour of our last victory. Where is the pleasure to be compared to that, sir? To carry a whole State 'smack, smooth, and no mistake!' "

"But it must be very annoying to be beaten."

"That never occurs to me, sir. I never stay long with the beaten party. If you study our politics, you will always find that our most 'talented men' desert a party just before it is going to break up. We always like to be on the conquering side. That's the way to 'get along' in this country, sir, if you want to be a politician. But is there no bell in this room? I'll see how long it will take *to raise a waiter.*"

"What do you want, sir?" grinned a negro almost instantaneously.

"Some brandy and water and half-a-dozen cigars: I am going to write an article."

"Then I do not wish to disturb you," said I, grateful for an opportunity of escaping from the room.

Scarcely was I half an hour down in the reading-room before a huge bell rang for supper. I expected, as usual, a rush into the dining-hall; but was much surprised in perceiving the quiet gentlemanly manner in which every one took his seat. The supper was excellent, and, what is more, it was well served. I began to perceive that I had fallen into good hands, and was only sorry that an establishment in every respect so unexceptionable should have adopted the vexatious custom of having the roll of travellers called by the bar-keeper, in the manner of some surly sergeant, before accommodating them with a room. A great deal of unpleasant feeling arises from mere mistakes in forms, which may easily be corrected by a little attention to the usages of the world, and which, therefore, cannot be sufficiently recommended to innkeepers.

Early the next morning I found myself safely seated in one of the huge railroad cars which leave Baltimore every morning for Washington. This railroad, I believe, is one of the worst in the United States; the travelling on it being excessively tedious, the stoppages frequent, and the rate very slow. I believe we did not go faster than seven or eight miles an hour, so that we required nearly half a day to complete a journey of about forty English miles. Nothing can be more barren than the country through which the railroad is laid; and the approach to the metropolis is anything but striking, although the entrance is by the way of the Capitol.

Washington is, indeed, a city *sui generis,* of which no European who has not actually seen it can form an adequate idea. Mr. Serullier, formerly minister of France, used to call it "a city of magnificent distances;" but, though this be true, I should rather call it "a city without streets." The Capitol, a magnificent palace, situated on an eminence called Capitol-hill, and the White-house, the dwelling of the President, are the only two specimens of architecture in the whole town; the rest being mere hovels, and even the public buildings, such as the Treasury, War and Navy Departments, and the General Post-office, little superior to the most ordinary dwelling-houses in Europe. The whole town is, in fact, but an appendix to those two public buildings, a sort of ante-chamber either to the Capitol or to the house of the chief magistrate. If such a town were situated in Europe, one would imagine those buildings to be the residences of princes, and the rest the humble dwellings of their dependants.

The only thing that approaches a street in Washington is Pennsylvania Avenue, a sometimes single, sometimes double row of houses, leading from the Capitol to the White-house. In this street are the two principal hotels of the city, and a considerable number of boarding-houses. The former are two large barracks, capable of holding each from one hundred and fifty to two hundred people; the latter are, for the most part, mean insignificant-looking dens, in which a man finds the worst accommodations at the most exorbitant prices, and must often be glad to be accommodated at all.

The most aristocratic inn in Washington is Gadsby's, though I consider this "to be a mere matter of taste;" the pretensions to aristocracy resting on four clean walls, and a triple row of galleries in the court, which render the distribution of the rooms convenient, and the rooms themselves agreeable and airy. In every other respect I found no difference between Gadsby's and Brown's, or even Fuller's, which is further up towards the President's house; and, in comparison to other first-rate hotels in the United States, the fare and accommodations in all of them are altogether beneath mediocrity. Gadsby, by the by, keeps an excellent assortment of wines, and he is himself a very gentlemanly and agreeable man.

Among the boarding-houses there is, I believe, a good deal of aristocratic classification, owing to the different sets of senators and representatives who establish their clubs in them. Some also there are whose pretensions to gentility are principally founded on the landladies being descended from some ancient family, or on their being related to some distinguished members of Congress. In short, every boarding-house marks a particular shade of aristocracy; the Southern (those for Southern members) being the most refined, and each of them, in spite of the bad living, the focus of a particular coterie.

There is also a hotel in Pennsylvania Avenue, called "The NATIVE American;" probably for the accommodation of such members of Congress and their friends as think themselves entitled to worse fare than can be obtained at other places, for having the aristocratic preference of birth—no matter where, and of whom, in the United States,—over every unfortunate stranger *directly* descended from Europe. I am not disposed to quarrel with any American for *enjoying his birth;*

though I cannot but think that the American Indians are much more entitled to be called "Native Americans" than any descendant from an English, Scotch, Irish, German, French, Dutch, Swedish, Spanish, or Portuguese family that happens to be born in the Union.

The first thing that struck me in Washington was the unusual number of persons perambulating the streets without any apparent occupation, of which every other American city, with the exception of Philadelphia, seems to be entirely drained. If there be poor and idle persons walking the streets of New York, Boston, or Baltimore, it is, I am sorry to say, generally owing to some late arrival from Europe,— some of the steerage passengers being yet left without employment. Washington, however, is a city of *American* idlers,—a set of gentlemen of such peculiar merit as well to deserve a public comment. They live in what is called "elegant style," rise in the morning at eight or nine, have breakfast in their own rooms, then smoke five or six cigars until twelve, at which time they dress for the Senate; few gentlemen ever honouring the *House of Representatives* with their presence, except just before leaving the Capitol.

The Senate of the United States is, indeed, the finest drawing-room in Washington; for it is there the young women of fashion resort for the purpose of exhibiting their attractions. The Capitol is, in point of fashion, the opera-house of the city; the House of Representatives being the crush-room. In the absence of a decent theatre, the Capitol furnishes a tolerable place of rendezvous, and is on that account frequented during the whole season—from December until April or May—by every lounger in the place, and by every *belle* that wishes to become the fashion.

After speaking and talking is over in the Senate, the idlers commence the regular performance of eating, which is no sort of amusement to any one in America who is obliged to dine at an ordinary. For this reason they club together in numbers from four to six, to dine at their rooms; single dinners being too expensive, and the people who have the means of entertaining in Washington being not sufficiently numerous to secure every dandy a place at a private gentleman's table.

The routs in Washington, in spite of the small rooms and the economy of refreshments, are delightful, lasting generally from nine in the evening until two in the morning; after which the *élégants,* wholly exhausted from the uncommon exertion of being agreeable four or five hours in succession, repair to some cellar or beef-shop, not quite so well furnished as the common resorts of cabmen and omnibus drivers in London, but which the aristocratic taste of the young men elevates into "refectories."

It is in these cellars that a stranger may become acquainted with "real life in Washington." In the best part of the season, when speeches are plenty and cash flush, the idlers' "refectories" keep open the whole night; the regular eating and drinking, and, as I was informed, also the *gambling,* never commencing until twelve o'clock.

One of these establishments,—the best of the kind I believe in the metropolis,—"the Epicure House," as it is termed, was recommended to me as doing canvass-back ducks in the neatest style, and being always the resort of the most fashionable company. This recommendation, joined to the fact that nothing can be obtained at an inn after the hour of eleven,—a practice which adds much to the convenience of the *innkeepers,*—induced me to try the skill of a coloured cook, and to have a peep at the young men that were called "the first" in the law-giving city.

On inquiring the way, I was pointed to a house forming the corner opposite to Gadsby's hotel, to which was attached a lamp which gave exactly as much light as was necessary in order not to break one's neck in descending the staircase which led to the entrance, but left the establishment itself in precisely that sort of obscurity which is always desirable for a place serving as a rendezvous for *comme-il-faut* people. On entering it,—it being only a little after eleven,—I found the room, which was divided into boxes after the manner of a common English eating-house, nearly empty; a few persons only eating scolloped oysters or drinking punch, but a number of black imps slinking about in evident expectation of better business. I hesitated at first whether I should take a seat, the appearance of the table-cloths, cruets, &c. being far from inviting; though the bar was stocked with bottles bearing the inscriptions—"Sillery champaign," "Klause Johannisberger," "Marco-brunner," "Hermitage," &c.

The bar-keeper, perceiving my want of resolution, came forward, and accosted me in the most polite terms.

"You wish, perhaps, for a private room, sir? If you do not want it longer than after midnight, I can give you the one adjoining. At twelve I expect a party who may want it until three or four in the morning."

"Thank you; I do not like to take possession of a room which I am obliged to give up in three quarters of an hour. Have you none other?"

"I have yet another room up stairs; but it is occupied by a dinner-party, which is not likely to break up till two or three in the morning."

"You keep very late hours, then?"

"Why, sir, we commence late. If you stop here till two o'clock, you will see this room crowded. This evening all the gentlemen are at Mrs. ***'s, who gives nothing but tea and cakes; which, as you may imagine, is not precisely the thing for young men that are dancing the whole evening. Many of them are yet *growing*, and, as is usually the case with such gentlemen, have an excellent appetite."

"And so they come here to sup?"

"They do me that honour, sir; and I do my best to accommodate them."

(What a polite publican, thought I, if he were not a mulatto!) "And what have you fit to eat?" demanded I.

"Fine canvass-back ducks, oysters, and venison. Canvass-back ducks are prime; just the season. Shall I show you into the other room?"

"No, I would rather take a duck here; but you must give me a clean table-cloth."

"Certainly, sir. What sort of wine will you take? hock, champaign, claret, madeira, or sherry? I have got some first-rate Johannisberger and some of Lynch's claret."

"Have you champaign in pint bottles?"

"At your service, sir.—John! put a clean table-cloth at No. 3. Do you want the papers in the mean while?"

In less than fifteen minutes one of the best specimens of that inestimable bird, the canvass-back duck, for which the Americans might justly be envied by European princes, was placed before me, "with the usual trimmings," consisting of jelly, butter, beets, and pickles, together with a small bottle of the Napoleon brand champaign. The whole was served in good order; and I could not but wonder that in a place of so mean and unfashionable an appearance a person should find such excellent accommodations. What would Mr. Stuart have said if his good fortune had led him to the Epicure House in Washington? I can assure him that in no other place in the United States could he have eaten canvass-back ducks more deserving of praise and comment.

Hardly had I commenced eating, before a noisy uproarious set of men entered the premises, singing and swaggering, and calling in a stentorian voice for cheese and *crackers*.*

* A small biscuit, not a firework.

"What a d—d shabby party that was!" exclaimed a young man, dressed in the latest New York fashion, with dirty gloves, and his shirt-collar turned down with perspiration; "one of your regular *Boston* ones.* I believe nothing was handed round but lemonade and sponge-cake, and of that there was scarcely enough for the ladies."

"Why did you not go up stairs?" cried another; "there were plenty of sandwiches, besides a large basin of toddy."

"How could he have found time for that; he was all attention to Miss ***; were you not, John?" ejaculated a little creature dressed in boots.

"Ah! are you here?" cried John; "we lost you at the door; how did you get here?"

"On my legs," replied the little fellow. "Did you expect me to pay two dollars to one of those rascally niggers for the pleasure of a *ride?*"†

"But did you wear boots at the ball?"

"Certainly not; I took them off in the entry, and put them on again as I came out. I always carry my shoes in my pocket when I go to a party."

"That's regular Boston fashion!" shouted the company. "How much do you make by it a year?"

"I *save* by it more than a hundred dollars; and 'a dollar saved is a dollar earned,' says Franklin."

"But what do you do with your boots at the party?"

"I *hide* them as well as I can; I have only lost one pair in Boston. They were taken away by mistake; but I advertised them in the papers, and got them back again. But I say, John! how do you stand with Miss ***? All right, hem?"

"For mercy's sake, don't bother me now!" cried John; "I am too dry to talk." (Turning to a bronze-faced mulatto boy, "Why, you cursed little imp, cannot you bring me the whisky punch I ordered?") "To dance a cotillon lasting three hours! Those girls' feet don't seem ever to get tired."

"And a German cotillon, too," rejoined a tall gentlemanly figure, who appeared to be a Southerner; "if it had not been for the mazurka, which some of our ladies still object to, because there is too much

---

* Parties without supper are, in Washington and the Southern States, called "Boston parties;" for what reason it is impossible to say, the Boston parties being generally renowned for their rather ostentatious suppers.

† "Ride" is in America constantly used for "drive."

whirling and dancing on the heels in it, I should not have had a moment's rest. I wonder how the women can stand it!"

"And then the *gallopade!* why, that alone wears out a pair of shoes," cried the Bostonian; "the mazurka only requires *heeling.*"

"They ought to make you president of the savings' bank!" observed the Southerner.

"That is," said John, "if he understands saving other people's money as well as his own."

By this time the waiter returned with the punch, a huge lump of cheese, and a basket of biscuits, which was immediately seized upon and devoured, as if the persons present were the half-starved crew of some American whaler just returned from a three years' cruise round Cape Horn.

"I say, Jim," said John, "did you taste the wine?"

"I did," replied Jim; "but I could not swallow it. It was not worth three dollars a dozen."

"I believe it was Sicily madeira."

"Heaven knows *what* sort of madeira it was; I took to the toddy."

"If these ladies had not kept me going, I should have done so too."

"That's the pleasure of courting," said Jim tauntingly.

"Why, a man has to come to it some time or other," said John.

"Miss *** is certainly a pretty girl; but, if I were in your place, I should not like her flirting in Washington. Washington is the worst place for a young lady in the United States. It is altogether too European."

"I do not like it myself," observed the Southerner; "nor the custom of our fashionable women to bring their daughters here just as they have left the boarding-school, in order to introduce them to the *beau monde.*"

"And to teach them the gallopade and the mazurka, which is setting a premium on *foreigners,*" said John with some bitterness.

"Don't be angry," cried Jim. "You don't expect to be cut out by a German or a Pole, do you?"

"You may go to — with your insinuation," cried John: "what I object to in the society of Washington is, that it teaches women to *amuse* themselves; or, rather, that it obliges *us* to amuse *them.*"

"That is rather bad," interrupted a thin pale-looking gentleman with spectacles; " as it must necessarily interfere with our serious pursuits."

"Such as drinking punch, and playing cards," observed the Southerner.

"I mean *literary* pursuits," said the man with spectacles.

"Oh yes! we forgot that. Mr. *** writes the *on dits* for the New York ***; of course he has no time to throw away upon women. 'Time is money,' says Franklin.—I say, George, did you win or lose at whist?"

"I won twenty dollars."

"Then you neither lost your time nor your money."

"If that's the case, George must pay the punch," shouted the company.

"George is going to do no such thing," replied the littérateur.

"Then let us toss up for it," proposed Jim.

"That would not do," objected John; "he, as a Yankee, would have the advantage in *guessing*."

"I think it best," said George, "for every man to pay his own reckoning." So saying, he called the waiter, paid for his punch, and, without uttering another syllable, left the party to settle their accounts after their own manner.

"What a selfish, unsociable, stingy fellow that is," cried Jim; "would not even toss up for it! and yet—would you believe it?—he is engaged to one of the prettiest girls in New England."

"She probably marries him for his literary reputation. Boston women are sometimes in love with that!" said John. "But let us now toss up for the reckoning."

"It's all paid," observed the waiter, pointing to the Southerner.

"Just like him; always throwing away his money!" muttered John, pocketing his piece. Jim made a bow, and swore he would be revenged: but all finally agreed to go home, visibly contented.

Scarcely had they left, before a large party of about fifteen or twenty young men, among whom there appeared to be some Europeans, entered the room, swearing that they had been done out of a regular meal, and that they were now going to make up for it. "Let us have three or four canvass-back ducks, and some of Lynch's claret," cried one of them; "the devil take the stuff they call toddy! I had as lief swallow prussic acid,—it has given me the cramp in my stomach."

"If you had drunk it here," grinned the waiter, "you would feel all the better for it; we make that article first-rate."

"Hold your tongue!" cried the gentleman, "and do as you are bid."

"All right, sir!" said the negro, and went to speak to the cook.

"Can we go into the other room?" demanded one of the party.

"Gentlemen are dining there," replied the bar-keeper.

"Gambling you mean, don't you?"

"It's no business of mine to inquire *what* they are doing; they have been there ever since dinner."

"Then they must leave soon, and we may have the room."

"I don't think they will," rejoined the bar-keeper. "Whenever they come to dine, they generally stay for breakfast."

"And the room adjoining?"

"Is already engaged. I expect the gentlemen every minute."

The party cast an inquiring look at one another, and then gathered round a small table as well as they could, quietly awaiting the arrival of the supper.

In less than fifteen minutes from this time, it being nearly twelve o'clock, the whole room was filled to overflowing with the most motley assemblage of persons I ever beheld in my life. It was a group worthy of being preserved on canvas. Besides the party already mentioned, there were gathered round the chimney a parcel of Kentuckians, a giant race of men, full of strange oaths and tobacco-juice, discussing politics, and betting heavily on the issue of certain matters then under debate. Their language, surely, was not altogether intelligible to me; but what I *did* understand convinced me that they are justly reputed for their wit and humour. One of them—standing, I should judge, six feet two—was a good-natured punster, who, in spite of the serious turn their conversation had taken, kept the company in a continual roar of laughter.

Round the bar was stationed a more noisy and less original set of men; such as a person might see in any of the larger gin-shops of London on a Saturday evening. They were vulgar and "uproarious," smoked bad cigars and spit promiscuously round the room, while the Kentuckians showed their better breeding by always hitting the same spot. A third party, evidently composed of *young bucks,* dressed in the latest London fashions, with perfumed hair and real French kid gloves, were discussing the merits of women; which they did *con amore,* using all the English slang they had collected from the newspapers, or from fashionable novels, and taking great pains to appear as outlandish as possible. The intervals between these clusters were filled up with single gentlemen, of all ages and descriptions, and in every possible state of consciousness,—from that of a perfect knowledge of "the thousand natural shocks this flesh is heir to," to that of the most total oblivion, and triumph "o'er a' the ills o' life."

What gave a peculiar character to this little pandemonium was the continual apparition and vanishing of the black, brown, and yellow waiters; all shining with perspiration, and leaving, as they passed, something not altogether unlike the odour of brimstone behind them. These exhalations, the steam of the viands, the smell of rum, brandy, and tobacco, independent of the corrupt, sultry air produced by the presence of a large number of persons in a small room, soon obliged me to quit the scene of merriment; and, in half an hour later, I found myself safely in bed at Gadsby's.

CHAPTER XVII

Corps Diplomatique in Washington.—What a Fashionable Lady thinks of an Ambassador.—The Secretary of the Treasury.—Popularity-hunting of American Statesmen.—Its influence on National Politics.—Mr. Woodbury's Hospitality to Literary Men.—Henry Clay.—Thomas H. Benton. —Salis Wright.—James Buchanan.—Extraordinary Dinner-bell.—Office-hunters in Washington.—State of Finance of the City.—Anecdote of General Jackson and the Office-seeker.—General Character of Washington Society compared with that of other American Cities.

> O momentary grace of mortal man,
> Which we more hunt for than the grace of God!
> Who builds his hope in air of your fair looks,
> Lives like a drunken sailor on a mast;
> Ready, with every nod, to tumble down
> Into the fatal bowels of the deep.
>
> *King Richard III.* Act iii. Scene 5.

THE next day I looked over my letters of introduction, which, being principally addressed to members of the cabinet and the *corps diplomatique,* I determined to deliver in person. The influence of the diplomatic agents in Washington on the moral and social habits of the people, is much greater than their effect on the politics of the State; the executive power of the President and Council being not only limited by the Senate, but also indirectly by the House of Representatives, and the manifestation of public opinion at the annual elections. A minister in Washington is, with regard to his diplomatic agency, pretty much confined to official acts, such as may at any time be made public; his influence with a particular member of the cabinet, or with the President himself,—his success with a particular coterie,—his intrigues against any person that may have rendered himself obnoxious to his government, are of little or no avail at the Congress, with which, as yet, no foreign diplomatist has attempted a political relation. But, in point of fashion, their power is unlimited; their decisions being quoted as oracles, and their manners made the standard of society. In Washington, no party is considered fashionable unless graced by some distinguished senator, and

a few members of the *corps diplomatique.* Between the latter and the
senators exists yet this relation, that every senator has a right to introduce a gentleman to a foreign minister, either personally, or by leaving
his card together with that of his friend; a privilege which is denied to
the more vulgar members of the House of Representatives.

As far as I was able to ascertain the influence of foreign residents in
Washington, it was confined, with the representative of the greatest
power in Christendom, to setting the example of genuine hospitality
in the shape of the most prosperous dinner parties given in the metropolis,—his *attachés,* I believe, went *fox*-hunting in the outskirts of the
city; with the representative of the land of chivalry and tigers, to
setting the example of taste in the shape of regular *soirées musicales;* in
the clever and witty envoy extraordinary and minister plenipotentiary
of a northern power, to introducing the fashion of dancing *on the
heels,**—which, by the by, was a pretty little manœuvre on the part of
the old gentleman, who had long ago lost the use of his *toes* by the
gout; in the representative of a literary court, to the privilege of spouting literature and science to a *sober* audience, &c. The ministers of the
Italian courts, who had the longest string of titles printed on their
cards, had no distinct influence, except in setting the fashion of eating
and drinking gracefully—at another man's table.

To understand the humour and good cheer which reign among the
corps diplomatique in Washington, it is sufficient to know that it
consists almost wholly of bachelors, who, according to the *étiquette* of
the place, enjoy the privilege of inviting *ladies* to their parties.† This is
certainly an enviable distinction; and, if anything can reconcile a man
to living in single blessedness, it is, I am sure, an ambassadorship in the
American metropolis. Yet, great as the advantages of such a situation
are to the ministers of England, Russia, and even France, they prove a
source of incessant vexation to the envoys of minor powers. I was told
of several of the ministers who lived in houses of such frail construc-
tion as to make the ladies afraid of walking into them, much less to
attempt a dance; they said that "they regretted extremely that it was
not in their power to give parties, it being useless to send out invitations
when the ladies vowed they would not come."

In what light ambassadors are held *by the ladies* will appear from the
following anecdote:—At a dinner party to which most of the repre-

* The mazurka.
† My friend speaks of the year 1833.

sentatives of the greater powers and some of the smaller ones were invited, one of them, a jolly old bachelor of the English school, attempted a song, which so much gratified the ladies, that it was proposed every gentleman present should, in turn, follow the example. Russia and some other great powers immediately obeyed the summons; but when the turn came to the representative of a new court, he indignantly exclaimed, *"Mon roi ne m'a pas envoyé ici pour chanter."* —"Well," answered a lady, "if *you* will not sing, we shall ask your gallant king to send us somebody else who *will."*

Being made acquainted with the *étiquette* of Washington, I ordered a carriage, and inquired the directions of the persons on whom I wished to call.

"Bless your soul, sir!" cried the landlord, "that is not at all necessary in this city; all you have to do is to tell the name of the person you wish to call on to the 'driver,' and he will carry you there with the greatest possible speed."

"That may be with regard to the President's house and the residences of foreign ministers; but I have also letters to some of the senators, and even representatives of Congress."

"That don't signify," rejoined the landlord. "These black fellows not only know the residences of every senator and distinguished member of Congress, but also those of the higher public officers, clerks, editors of newspapers, &c. Once under the care of a black 'driver,' it is quite needless for you to know the direction of a single gentleman in this city."

With this piece of information I "embarked," as the Americans say, "on board of a Washington hack,"—the usual means of conveyance for gentlemen; and in a short time found myself *tête-à-tête* with the editor of one of the first papers. I found him a plain unassuming gentleman, though he enjoyed the reputation of being a man of extraordinary talents. He regretted that he could not be of more service to me during my short stay in the city; but, notwithstanding, promised to introduce me personally to some of the most distinguished senators of his party. "I have nothing to do with the rest," added he; "but I dare say you have letters to some of them, and one will cheerfully introduce you to all the others." He then unceremoniously excused himself with pressing business, invited me to dine with him *sans cérémonie* on the Sunday following, in company with a select number of *his party,* and almost bowed me out of the room.

"A singular character!" said I to myself, as I again stepped into my carriage and ordered the coachman to proceed to Mr. Woodbury, the secretary of the Treasury. "I have, after all, done wrong to omit the *De*."

I was so fortunate as to find Mr. Woodbury at home, and was at once ushered into the parlour. I found him surrounded by his family, equally distinguished for beauty and accomplishments. Mr. Woodbury is a gentleman very nearly, or quite, fifty years of age, of agreeable address and kind manners; though, probably owing to his being born and brought up in New England, a little ceremonious. It has been the fashion in America for the last eight or ten years to decry "the secretary of the Treasury," and to impeach even his honesty; as if the money withdrawn from the United States' bank had filled his coffers and those of the President.

Mr. Woodbury is a man of great tact for business, and of the most indefatigable application; but the style of his official documents is often laborious and cumbrous, with an occasional attempt at laconism, which renders the fault still more apparent. But, notwithstanding this imperfection, his annual reports contain a vast deal of information, and the most minute statistical details of the progress of agriculture, manufacture, and commerce, not only of America, but of every other country. To judge fairly and impartially of the ability of Mr. Woodbury as a head of department, it is necessary to consider that every question which has agitated the country ever since the elevation of General Jackson, has turned on the subject of finance, and that therefore the secretary of the Treasury was placed in the most difficult and conspicuous position of any public man in the United States, the President himself scarcely excepted.

Mr. Woodbury has been represented, not only in America, but also in England, as a cunning politician and popularity-hunter. This reproach, as far as I have been able to judge,—and I believe I have had as good an opportunity of observing Mr. Woodbury, and the course of public events, as any one who has felt himself called upon to publish his lucubrations to the world,—is altogether malicious and groundless. Mr. Woodbury owes his elevation to his firmness of character and his sincere attachment to republican institutions. So far from courting public favour, he is but too frequently wanting in those trifling attentions and nice observances which insure popularity. I ought yet to observe that Mr. Woodbury has a taste for letters, which he manifests in the best possible manner, by being kind to those who have more leisure than he to cultivate them. Mr. Willis,—the same that dined at the Duke of Gordon's,—Dr. L***, and a number of minor stars, are indebted to his kind hospitality; and I myself can testify to his condescension even to ordinary men.

What I have said on the subject of Mr. Woodbury's popularity naturally induces me to say a few words on the peculiar character of American politicians. The question proposed by a member of that body is generally this:—"What measure can we carry to defeat our antagonists?" neither party appearing to have any fixed political tenets further than refer to the public revenue, which is a home question with every man and every party. On this account we often see in the United States the Democratic party assume the very principles they once denounced in the Federalists; and, on the other hand, the Federalists profess the doctrines which they most abhorred in the Democrats. The fact is, very few senators, representatives, and men in office have a clear understanding of the vast importance of the principles they maintain; nor do they seem to have a correct notion of republicanism, *as contrasted with other forms of government.* But then, how many of them possess an adequate knowledge of history—even of their own country? They all have, indeed, a certain republican instinct, or what the Americans call a correct *feeling,* of what is compatible with the text of their constitution; but not many of them, I believe, take a philosophical view of their government, such as would enable them to reduce the whole to a *system,* and to perceive accurately the bearing of every new question on the principles laid down in the national charter. Nor would such a metaphysical knowledge of the constitution materially benefit a partisan leader, who never asks what is right or wrong in the abstract, but merely "What do *my constituents* consider as right or wrong? What is the opinion of the public on this subject?" When a new question is proposed, he thrusts out his *feelers,* to feel the public pulse; and, having ascertained that, he makes his speeches accordingly, in order that the people may see that he is actively engaged on their side; for on the side that beats he *must* be, or he is "a ruined man."

This sort of moral cowardice, which more or less pervades all classes of society, and of which the example is set in Congress, is certainly one of the worst features of American politics; and would almost make a man doubt the beneficial influence of republican institutions on the developement of mind and character, if their numerous blessings in other respects did not prove them capable of insuring the happiness of a people.

When I thus speak of American politicians, I do not mean to draw envious comparisons between them and European statesmen. I belong neither to that class of Europeans that cannot pronounce the name of America without a grudge, nor to that class of fashionable and travelled Americans that cannot find anything in their own country equal to Europe. On the contrary, I maintain that there is quite as much intelligence, application, and certainly of virtue, in the members of the cabinet at Washington, as can be found in the ministerial council of any European prince. And I say this, fully aware of its producing more sneers among the higher classes in America than in Europe.

If the conduct of every European minister were inquired into, like that of a head of department in Washington,—if his private and public transactions were canvassed with the same unrelenting severity as in America,—if he had to account for every one of his acts, not merely to Parliament, or, in course of time, to a limited number of electors, but to the people at large, speaking annually through the ballot-boxes,— then, I am afraid, few would be found capable of sustaining their position for a single year.

An American statesman has the most difficult position of any one in the world, for he has to solve a great and intricate problem in the presence of a multitude of spectators, who are never to see that he is puzzled, and who never have the patience to wait for the end, but condemn a measure from the first moment its immediate results do not answer their expectations. For this reason few men in America, even if they possess the talent, have the *courage* to propose a radical reform of abuses, or to work some signal good, unless the execution of it is sure to be *step by step* applauded by large majorities. It is this courting of popularity which is the bane of even the best statesmen in the United States; but it is in part forced upon them,—it is the *conditio sine quâ non* of their usefulness.

From the secretary of the Treasury I drove to the lodgings of Mr. Henry Clay, the celebrated senator from Kentucky. I found this extraordinary man, who was then already a little past his prime, the very type of what passes in Europe, ever since the clever caricatures of Mrs. Trollope, as "an American character." Mr. Clay stands upwards of six feet; has a semi-Indian, half-human half-savage countenance, in which, however, the intellectual strongly preponderates over the animal. His manners, at first sight, appear to be extremely vulgar; and yet he is graceful, and even dignified, in his intercourse with strangers. He chews tobacco, drinks whisky punch, gambles, puts his legs on the table or the chimney, and spits, as an American would say, "like a regular Kentucky hog-driver;" and yet he is all gentleness, politeness, and cordiality in the society of ladies. Add to this that his organs of speech are the most melodious; and that, with great imagination and humour, he combines manly eloquence, and the power of sarcasm in the most extraordinary degree; and it will easily be conceived why he should have been able to captivate high and low,—*l'homme du salon,* and the "squatter" in the Western wilderness.

Much as Mr. Clay is esteemed in America, I do not think the people have as yet done justice to his talents. These, to be sure, are, owing to his advanced age, on the decline; but even the *remnants* of a mind like Clay's are great, and entitle him to be ranked among the greatest living statesmen. He was for a long time the advocate of the system of internal improvements, combated with so much success by General Jackson. He advocated successively the establishment of national roads and canals, the continuance of a United States' bank, the tariff, and, in short, every measure conducive to centralization. That this system, while it strengthens the government, and introduces order and uniformity into the administration of the country, diminishes, at the same time, the liberties of the individual States, and, in general, ill agrees with the principles of a pure democracy, such as are laid down in the American constitution, no one, who is not himself interested in the question, can reasonably deny; but it would be equally absurd to suppose every man who is an advocate of a central measure, to be at once an enemy to republican institutions, and a traitor to his country.

Mr. Clay advocated every measure he proposed, not as a mere partisan, but as a statesman who clearly saw its first and ultimate bearings on national politics. His is a mind of vast conceptions, which, if it had not at one time speculated too much in elections,—I allude to the trick he played at the election of Mr. John Quincy Adams,—might have long ago enabled him to fill the station to which his unfortunate ambition a little too early aspired.

From Mr. Clay I called upon Mr. Thomas H. Benton, the democratic senator from Missouri. This gentleman is altogether in a false position; for he is, in my opinion, as much over-rated by his friends as he is under-rated by his enemies. I was the bearer of a letter to him by one of his most intimate friends, and a person of high standing and much influence in the country; and yet the reception I met with was cold and ceremonious,—his manners forced, and almost ludicrously dignified. The truth is, Mr. Benton behaves on most occasions like a man who has not yet found his level in society; being continually on his guard lest he might not be done justice to, and afraid lest his unrestrained familiar manners might derogate from the estimation in which he is held by the public. The first impression that he makes upon a stranger I should judge to be decidedly unfavourable, though he greatly improves upon acquaintance, and, as he drops his dignity, shows his truly estimable points of character. As Mr. Benton's democracy is probably proof against the seductions of Europe,—a thing I would not assert of one American out of ten,—I would recommend to him a trip to Paris, —not to London,—in order that he might learn to carry himself with a little more ease. It would vastly improve his manners and general appearance, and perhaps make him find favour even with *female* philosophers.*

Mr. Benton is perhaps the most unfortunate speaker in the Senate; not, indeed, as regards the substance of his discourses, most of which are clever and full of information; but with regard to his disjointed, broken, sometimes loud, and again sometimes scarcely audible, delivery. This is undoubtedly the reason why his speeches are so much underrated, though they contain more solid matter of statistics and history than can be found in the perhaps more eloquent efforts of his colleagues. Mr. Benton is a most uncommonly laborious man, and is constantly collecting facts, not only in America but also in Europe, in support of his political doctrines; though his partiality for France, and his eternal and irksome comparisons between the republic under the consulate of Bonaparte and the confederation of the United States, rather injure than establish his theories with a considerable portion of the American public. Another fault with which Mr. Benton has been reproached consists in his indelicate allusions to his personal prowess. Every one knows that Mr. Benton is as brave as Cæsar; but it is not necessary that he himself should refer to it. An appeal to arms in a deliberative assembly is always vulgar, if not absolutely savage; and ought to be avoided in the most studious manner, not only by every man of religion and principle, but also by every gentleman of good

---

* The reader will remember with what severity Miss Martineau commented on his talents, though she had only seen him once or twice *en passant*.

taste. There is, as yet, too much bullyism in the legislative assemblies of America; many worthy representatives forgetting that it is easier to fight for, than to establish by argument, the correctness of a political principle. On the whole, Mr. Benton is a clever politician, an industrious collector of statistics, and, with the exception of his delivery, a most skilful debater in Congress. He has, during a certain period, been almost the only and valiant defender of General Jackson's policy in the Senate; and has, by his perseverance, honesty, and good faith, become universally popular among the labouring classes, whose interests he has during his whole life constantly and successfully advocated.

My next visit was to Mr. Salis Wright, senator from the State of New York, the avowed democratic champion of that State, and indeed a man of the most extraordinary talents. He is one of those men whose urbanity and frankness the Americans indicate by saying, "he has not a bit of starch in him." Mr. Wright is a statesman, not a mere politician; and will, if his talents be properly placed before the public, play an important part in the history of his country. He and Mr. Calhoun are almost the only two senators free from the "Congressional" sin of making everlasting speeches. He is always concise, rigorously logical, and, what is very rare in an American politician, singularly free from personal abuse. His mind is of that rigid composition which does not allow him to depart, for one instant, from the point under consideration; and hence, instead of indulging himself in irrelevant rhapsodies, sneers, and side-thrusts at the character of his antagonists, he confines himself strictly to his argument; a method which, if it were imitated by every senator, would enable them to transact the same business in about the one-seventh part of the time now needed, saving annually a sum of not less than a million of dollars.

Mr. Wright's delivery is rapid, but distinct; proving that every thought is digested and arranged, and flowing from a well-stored mind. In his private life he is not a fashionable, but a plain, unassuming, modest gentleman; who, notwithstanding his own brevity, possesses that most extraordinary talent of powerful minds—of listening patiently to the tedious prosings of others. I saw him, in his own room, listen to an endless recital of an Indian campaign given by an officer in the army, without even once heaving a sigh, though the thermometer ranged at 96°; his room being one of the closest in the whole city of Washington. At last, having listened to the hero for more than an

hour, he told him patiently that he found his story exceedingly entertaining; but, having a few words to say to one of his friends waiting
in the parlour, he should be obliged to leave him for a few moments, in
order to afterwards hear the conclusion of so interesting a narrative. I
must yet observe that Mr. Wright is seldom seen at the crack parties in
Washington, and is, therefore, not in the way of being much noticed
by foreign tourists.

My next call was on my old acquaintance, Mr. Buchanan, senator
from Pennsylvania. This is a gentleman of plain common sense, agreeable and dignified manners, and the most resolved unchangeable disposition. As a speaker, he does not attempt to soar on the wings of genius;
but his arguments being always founded on experience and practical
good sense, and his unimpeachable honesty being proverbial, he is
always sure of producing effect. Mr. Buchanan never had the character
of an office-seeker, though he has always been one of the most strenuous
defenders of General Jackson's policy; and is even now rarely seen at
the White-house or the levees of the cabinet ministers. And yet in his
externals he is the most courtier-like senator in Congress; his dress and
manners being always what a master of ceremonies at any European
court could wish them to be in order to usher him into the presence of
his royal master. In addition to this, Mr. Buchanan is a bachelor, and
not yet past the age at which bachelors cease to be interesting; which
accounts sufficiently for his being universally beloved, even by those
who are opposed to him in politics. Indeed, I heard it positively
asserted, more than four years ago, that he was "too much of a gentleman," and "had remained too long in the Senate," to continue much
longer an advocate of democracy. This was evidently among the *on
dits,* which, as far as regards the conclusion, had not the least foundation in it. Mr. Buchanan is, at this moment, as sound a democrat as
ever; proving the vanity and falsehood of Cowper's assertion, that

> "——the age of virtuous liberty is past,
> And we are deep in that of cold pretence;
> Patriots are grown too shrewd to be sincere,
> And we too wise to trust them."

On my return to the inn I found a numerous assemblage of gentlemen waiting on the piazza for the ringing of the dinner-bell; which, at
Gadsby's, owing to the vast extent of the premises, is affixed to a small
steeple on the top of the house, in order that it may warn not only the

gentlemen who may be engaged in politics in their rooms, but also those who may be lounging anywhere within a quarter of a mile from the place of feeding. During the time the table was setting, the dining-room itself was carefully locked, in order "to prevent impatient people from spoiling the looks of it" before it was quite ready. While thus in expectation of the things that were to come, I asked the bar-keeper how many senators and representatives had taken rooms in the house; as, from the number of gentlemen present, it was quite evident his inn was full.

"Only two, sir," replied he.

"And what is the reason you have so few?"

"Because our terms are too high; they can get board cheaper at a boarding-house. We entertain generally but transient people,—lobby-members; gentlemen with their families, who come here to spend the season; now and then a letter-writer, though these are usually stopping at Brown's; and perhaps occasionally a spy."

"And are all these men better able to pay for their board than senators and representatives of Congress?"

"Whether they be better able to pay, I know not; they seem at least to be *more willing* to do so. If they have not got money, they *'hire'* it. Washington is the *'ruination' place* of the United States. Many a man comes here in tolerable circumstances, and leaves the place as a beggar, with his money spent, and his business neglected. So much for politics!"

"That's no very flattering picture of your town."

"Why, sir," said one of the gentlemen near me, "how many persons do you think are solvent in this city?"

"I will hope a great many."

"I do not think," replied he, "there are six persons in town able to pay their debts, if their estates were to be settled to-morrow. The corporation itself has more debts than it can conveniently manage. There is not a city in the Union as badly off as ours."

"And then what a continual influx of paupers!" interrupted the bar-keeper; "all coming here to seek office, to see the President, and to avail themselves of their acquaintance with one or the other member, to obtain a place for themselves or one of their relations. Would you believe that people come here from a distance of from six hundred to a thousand miles, to hunt an appointment of six hundred dollars a year; and that, in order to enable them to get home again, after they have spent their last farthing, the President is often obliged to pay their passage out of his own pocket?"

"I can testify to that," said one of the gentlemen; "General Jackson has done so more than once. When they first come here, they expect nothing less than an appointment of two thousand dollars a year; but by degrees their expectations become more moderate: they would then be satisfied with a clerkship; by and by with a still more subordinate station; and at last they would be glad if any one would pay their bill, and enable them to get home again. I remember a most remarkable story, which was current here shortly after the election of General Jackson, and which is singularly characteristic of the notions of our people as respects the power of the executive.

"One morning, scarcely a fortnight after the General's arrival at the White-house, a shabby-genteel looking man presented himself at his parlour, and, after the usual salutation and shaking of hands, expressed his joy at seeing the venerable old gentleman at last hold the situation of chief magistrate of the country, to which his bravery, his talents, and his unimpeachable rectitude fully entitled him. 'We have had a hard time of it,' said he, 'in our little place; but our exertions were unremitting: I myself went round to stimulate my neighbours, and at last the victory was ours. We beat them by a majority of ten votes, and I now behold the result of that glorious triumph!' The General thanked him in terms of studied politeness, assuring him that he would resign his office in an instant if he did not think his election gave satisfaction to a vast majority of the people; and at last regretted his admirer's zeal for the public weal should have been so severely taxed on his account. 'Oh, no matter for that, sir!' said he; 'I did it with pleasure,—I did it for myself and for my country' (the General bowed); 'and I now come to congratulate you on your success' (the General bowed again). 'I thought, sir,' continued he, 'that, as you are now President of the United States, I might perhaps be useful to you in some official capacity.' (The General looked somewhat embarrassed.) 'Pray, sir, have you already made a choice of your cabinet ministers?'—'I have,' was the reply of the General.—'Well, no matter for that; I shall be satisfied with an embassy to Europe.'—'I am sorry to say there is no vacancy.'—'Then you will perhaps require a head-clerk in the department of State?'—'These are generally appointed by the respective secretaries.'—'I am very sorry for that: then I must be satisfied with some inferior appointment.'—'I never interfere with these: you must address yourself to the heads of departments.'—'But could I not be postmaster in Washington? Only think, General, how I worked for you!'—'I am much obliged to you for the good opinion you entertain of me, and for your kind offices at the last election; but the postmaster for the city of Washington is already appointed.'—'Well, I don't particularly care for that; I should be satisfied with being his clerk.'—'This is a subject you must mention to the postmaster.'—'Why, then, General,' exclaimed the disappointed candidate for office, 'haven't you got an old black coat?' You may well imagine that the General gave him one.

"As extravagant as this story appears, I can assure you that there are at any time in Washington hundreds of persons seeking employment of some sort or other; nine-tenths of whom return home disappointed, cursing the ingratitude of those whom they have elevated by their suffrages, and who are now so monstrously ungrateful as to suffer them to gain a livelihood by common labour. All these men finish by joining the opposition, expecting to be treated with more consideration by the next administration."

Scarcely had he finished, before the bell, or rather the tocsin, sounded for dinner. In an instant the whole company, consisting of more than a hundred persons, were seated at table,—the dinner, including soups and desserts, being served at once,—and in less than ten minutes the greater portion of them began already to disperse. I had seen much fast eating in the United States, especially on board of steam-boats; but nothing to compare to the rapidity with which meals are despatched in Washington. What astonished me most was, that most of the gentlemen, very unlike those of Boston, New York, or Philadelphia, did not leave table in order immediately to attend to business; but merely to walk or stand on the piazza, smoke, read the papers, or talk politics.

Washington, as I observed before, is the only city of idlers in the whole Union; and, for a man that is not a manufacturer or a merchant, quite an agreeable residence. Despite of its ridiculous extent, and the miserable and scattered situation of the dwelling-houses, it is a focus of intellect, and contains more resources for a man of education than any other Transatlantic city. It is in Washington where the national mind is formed; where local prejudices vanish under the influence of more enlarged political views; where, if I may use the expression, the totality of the American people absorbs the provincialism of the different sections of the country. It is the only city in the United States, north of the Potomac, where a man is not bored with the everlasting talk of business,—where the *markets* are not considered the most important topic of conversation.

Literary and professional men, though they are tolerated in other American cities, and, from vanity and ostentation, occasionally shown up, or, as a clever writer on diplomacy has it, "used by the ladies as a pepper-box," find their level only in Washington. Even statesmen like Webster, Clay, Calhoun, Wright, &c. are at home only listened to from complacency, unless they touch upon a subject immediately affecting the interest of their particular State; but, arrived in Washington, they find themselves at once drawn into a circle of attraction, which not only furnishes food for their minds, but, from the nature of its composition, acts as a stimulus on their energies. Washington, in fine, is the only place in America where talent is esteemed on account of itself,— not because it enables the person endowed with it "to get handsome things."

To call a man "visionary," or to consider his talents useless to society, because he cannot immediately reduce them into "shoes and stockings for paupers," marks a low estimate of humanity; and, in spite of the greatest political progress, a backward state of civilization. I have heard gentlemen in the Northern States boast of having worked sixteen hours a day in a manufactory, or in a store, as if they had actually benefited the world with their manual labour. The thought never struck them that they might have been more useful to society by employing poor men to do the same work for them, and reserving their faculties, if such they had, for some occupation that had some relish of intellect in it. As long as the rich men in America think it more creditable to themselves to compete with the wages of the poor by assuming a part of their labour, than by cultivating the higher branches of knowledge to increase the floating intellect, American society may abound in common sense, but it will prove the grave of talent and genius. All this, fortunately, does not apply to Washington, in which the mass of property is really so small in proportion to the intellect that governs it, as to leave a large balance in favour of the latter.

It cannot be doubted but that the vastness of material interests in the Northern States crushes the loftier aspirings of the mind, though it may be favourable to a certain degree of elementary instruction and general information very well compatible with a total neglect of the higher branches of knowledge, and the absence of taste. It is certainly a matter of rejoicing, not only for the Americans, but for every philanthropist, that there should exist at least one country in the world emphatically to be termed "the land of beef and pudding, clean shirts, and whole stockings for all;" but in these things does not yet consist the ultimate happiness of a people, or its capacity for great and generous actions.

That the great mass of the American people are further advanced, not only in politics, but in general civilization, than any nation of Europe, the English themselves not excepted, no one acquainted with the state of society in the United States will venture to deny: the question only is, whether that advanced position contains also the germ of further progress; and whether the direction civilization is taking in America is sure of leading to the developement of the higher faculties. A nation may, like the Germans, be too exclusively engaged in learned and literary pursuits, and thereby neglect to provide for those physical comforts which, after all, contribute so much to men's happiness; but it is also possible to give to the latter more than their full share of attention, to the total neglect of every noble and disinterested pursuit.

The apology one continually hears in the United States, "We are a young people,"—"you cannot expect us to be as far advanced as other nations,"—"we have not yet the means," &c.—are, as regards the Eastern and Atlantic States, nothing but idle cant. The *West* may excuse itself for the want of refinement by the prodigious amount of labour and personal exertion incidental to the settlement of a wilderness; but the Northern and Eastern people have no such excuse for being altogether absorbed in money-making. There is more property accumulated in Boston, New York, and Philadelphia than in any German town of the same extent; the intercourse with Europe is constant; the treasures of science and literature as much unlocked to the Americans as to any other people; and if, notwithstanding all this, these departments remain still neglected, it can only be because there is no real taste for them, and because *other pursuits are more sure of securing the respect of society.* As long as the salary of a head-clerk in a respectable counting-room surpasses that of a professor of mathematics and astronomy in the first and oldest American university, and as long as the company of the latter is hardly considered good enough for a wholesale dealer in dry goods or an auctioneer, it is useless to talk of being "a young people," "of having no time for literary pursuits," &c. The age of the nation has nothing to do with it; it is *the taste of the higher classes,* who rather imitate the follies of fashionable European

254 *Aristocracy in America*

life, than the European student in his closet or the munificence of his patron.

"What a boor that fellow is!" exclaimed a Boston lawyer, half audibly, at a fashionable party in that city, pointing to a young man wearing boots.—"But, sir, they are dress boots," said I; "I have seen them worn by English gentlemen."—"Oh, then I have no objection to them!" The young man who wore them had just returned from England, and was showing off his new fashion. Why do the hundreds and thousands of young Americans that overrun Europe, and put ministers and consuls in requisition to be presented at the different courts, not visit the more humble dwellings of men of letters, or the *ateliers* of artists, and on their return show off something else than their heels?—*Answer.* "Because the heels are most likely to be observed; and a man more easily pardoned for ignorance or stupidity than for unacquaintance with the usages of Europe." The Americans in Europe just float on the surface of society, and it is consequently only the froth of it which they afterwards transplant to their own country.

Washington, as I have said before, is a city to which people come to *spend* money, not to *make* it. The hum and bustle of business nowhere obtrude themselves on one's ears, men's minds are occupied with more enlarged views of society; and conversation, instead of being confined to a narrow circle of common-place observations, spreads over topics of political and historical interest. In addition to these advantages, one can already notice in Washington Southern manners and Southern hospitality. Nothing, indeed, is easier than to be introduced into the best society; a single letter of introduction answering all the purpose. Some of the *habitués* seem to make it their business to procure invitations to parties for strangers. "What party is there to-night?" you hear a gentleman ask in the morning.—"It is Mrs. ***'s. Are you invited?" —"I have not the honour of being introduced."—"Will you give me your card?"—"With pleasure;" and in an hour or so your invitation is left at the bar of your hotel. Many of these parties are indeed supperless, a circumstance much complained of by the dancers: but then the general tone is agreeable; the people having far less pretensions, and being much more natural in their manners, than either the New-Yorkers or the Philadelphians.

CHAPTER XVIII

The Library of Congress.—Conversation with several Members of Congress.—Practice of Public Speakers in Washington.—Mr. Van Buren's Method of parrying an Invective.—Discussion of General Jackson's Character.—Jackson and Wellington's similarity of Character.—Mr. Van Buren's Character.—Instability of American Institutions.—Insecurity of Property the Consequence of it.—Want of Enthusiasm in the Higher Classes.—Their Toad-eating in Europe.—Cooper's last Publication.— Vanity of boasting of the Natural Resources of the Country.—Thinskinnedness of the Americans when attacked by European Critics.— Toad-eating to the People.—Necessity of establishing a Moral Quarantine for all Americans returning from Europe.—Americans ashamed of their Institutions.—Anecdote of a vulgar rich American and the Grand Duke of Tuscany.—Democratic Twaddles.—Advantages of a poor Capital.

*　　*　　*　　*　　*　　*

"Ambition rends, and gaming gains a loss;
But making money, slowly first, then quicker,
　And adding still a little through each cross,
(Which *will* come over things,) beats love or liquor,
　The gamester's counter, or the statesman's *dross*.
O gold! I still prefer thee unto paper,
Which makes bank credit like a bark of vapour."

BYRON's *Don Juan,* Canto xii. 4.

BEING engaged in the evening, I spent the time from four till five in the afternoon in visiting the library of Congress at the Capitol. I was introduced to the librarian by one of the members, and found him exceedingly obliging. The collection of books, manuscripts, newspapers, &c. is of course small, the number of works in any one department being probably insufficient to form a scholar: yet, for the entertainment of the members, and for such current and useful instruction as may be desirable for the purpose of reference, it is probably more than sufficient; and thus it well answers the purpose of its founders. After taking from one of the windows a fine view of the city, which looks more like a newly settled colony than the capital of a powerful country, I took a walk with two senators and a member up and down the macadamised road, called the Pennsylvania Avenue, which leads from

255

the Capitol to the President's house; this being the fashionable prom-
enade, business street, habitable quarter, and sum total of the whole
American metropolis.

The two senators belonged to the democratic party, it being a rare
case for a Whig ever to associate with a Democrat, and *vice versâ;* the
member of the House belonged to the same class of politicians.

"What sort of speech was it Mr.*** made to-day?" demanded one of
the senators of the member.

"Clever enough, I believe; but nobody listened to it. Mr. *** speaks
too much."

"And on all occasions, probably?"

"Precisely so."

"Then I do not wonder no one likes to hear him: it is the worst
possible taste to be always up. A man has to be very careful with that.
The older members do not like the younger ones to speak more on a
question than is absolutely necessary. This privilege is entirely reserved
for the veterans. A young man of talent must be cautious how he
shows off; or they will make a dead set at him, and hunt him down.
The best practice is to speak seldom, and only on great occasions."

"But you know," observed the member, "a man must give some signs
of life, or he will not be re-elected. Most of our speeches are manufactured for home-consumption. We 'let fly' at them in the House, then
print it, and then send a couple of thousand copies of it to our constituents. Uncle Sam, you know, pays the postage"*

"None of us has a right to complain about that," replied the senator:
"speeches are made on both sides; each party possessing the same right,
and making the same use of the privilege of franking."

"But then our party does not make near as long speeches as the
Tories: it is only the higher classes of society will read a discourse filling
more than seventeen columns in a newspaper."

"But how do they get people to listen to them?" demanded I.

"They don't," answered the member. "We just let him speak on, and
employ our time in reading the newspapers, writing letters, conversing with one another, talking to some gentleman in the lobby, or in
reading some interesting book. We always find some useful occupation:

* Every member, as well as every senator in Congress, possesses the "privilege of
franking." "Uncle Sam" is the familiar appellation of "United States," from the initials
U.S. For the same reason, U.S.L.D. (the initials of "United States' Light Dragoons,") are
translated into "Uncle Sam's lazy dogs."

it is only the greenhorns listen to a long speech, with a view to catch an idea."

"Reading is sometimes practised with great success," observed the senator, "while a personal attack is made upon a gentleman. Mr. Van Buren,* for instance, is in the habit of reading a novel as often as a Whig or Tory senator gets up to pour out his abuse against him. In this manner he is not only able to weather the storm without getting angry, but to show at the same time his contempt for the invective."

"That is a capital plan. I presume he occasionally looks over the book?" said the member with a laugh.

"Only when the abuse is very heavy; and then it is done with the most placid countenance, just to let his antagonist know how little he can shake him. It serves in the place of a reply, and keeps his party all the while in countenance."

"But what must a member or a senator do to obtain a hearing from his colleagues?" demanded I.

"Why, he must have friends, either political or personal, and he must know how to keep his audience in good humour; a task which is more difficult than you imagine."

The conversation then turned upon General Jackson, and the prospects of the opposition.

"General Jackson," said one of the senators, "understands the people of the United States twenty times better than his antagonists; and, if his successor have but half the same tact, the Whigs may give up the hope of governing the country for the next half century."

"You ought not to say '*tact*,' " interrupted the other senator, "for that alone will not do it; he must have the same manners as our present President. General Jackson has a peculiar way of addressing himself to the feelings of every man with whom he comes in contact. His simple, unostentatious manners carry into every heart the conviction of his honesty; while the firmness of his character inspires his friends with the hope of success. His motto always was, '*Never sacrifice a friend to an enemy;*' or, '*Make yourself strong with your friends, and you need not fear your foes.*' These things, however, must be *born* with a man; they must be spontaneous, and felt as such by the people, or they lose the best part of their effect. All the tact in the world will not answer the same purpose; for, in exactly the same proportion as we perceive a

---

* The above notes were written in part during the administration of General Jackson, when Mr. Van Buren was President of the Senate.

man is prudent, we become cautious ourselves,—and then farewell to popularity!

"When the people give their suffrages to a man, they never do so on a rigid examination of his political principles; for this task the labouring classes of any country neither have the time nor the disposition, and it is wholly needless to attempt to persuade them to a different course by a long and tedious argument. The large masses act in politics pretty much as they do in religion. Every doctrine is with them, more or less, a matter of *faith;* received, principally, on account of their trust in the apostle. If the latter fail to captivate their hearts, no reasoning in the world is capable of filling the vacancy: and the more natural and uncorrupt the people are, the less are they to be moved by abstract reasoning, whether the form of government be republican, monarchical, or depotic."

"Precisely so," ejaculated the member. "General Jackson is popular, just because he is General Jackson; so much so, that if a man were to say a word against him in the Western States, he would be '*knocked into eternal smash.*'"

"And this sort of popularity," continued the senator, "our Northern people consider as the mere consequence of the battle of New Orleans. The battle, and General Jackson's military character, had undoubtedly a great deal to do with it; but they were not of themselves sufficient to elevate him to the Presidency. In a country in which so large a portion of the people consider the acquiring of a fortune the only rational object of pursuit,—in which so great and so exclusive an importance is attached to money, that, with a few solitary exceptions, it is the only means of arriving at personal distinction,—a character like Jackson's, so perfectly disinterested, and so entirely devoted to what he at least deemed the good of his country, could not but excite astonishment and admiration among the natural, and therefore more susceptible, people of the Western States. The appearance of General Jackson was a phenomenon, and would at the present time have been one in every country. He called himself 'the people's friend,' and gave proofs of his sincerity and firmness in *adhering* to his friends, and of his power to protect them. The people believed in General Jackson as much as the Turks in their prophet, and would have followed him wherever he chose to lead them. With this species of popularity it is in vain to contend; and it betrays little knowledge of the world, and the springs of human action, to believe those who possess it men of ordinary capacity.

"What the French call *'le génie du caractère,'* which is the true talisman of popular favour, is perhaps the highest talent with which mortals can be endowed. It is a pure gift of Heaven, and has accomplished the noblest deeds in history. When Napoleon reproached Voltaire with not having sufficiently appreciated the character of Mahomed, whom the French poet introduced in the drama of the same name as a mere impostor, he felt that none but a great mind could have conceived and executed what to ordinary men would have appeared absurd or chimerical; and that he who had the power to instill a lasting enthusiasm for a new cause into millions, and on that enthusiasm to establish an empire which has spread over half the world, must have been more than a mere charlatan, for he must have been possessed of a thorough knowledge of human character. This is a thing a man cannot acquire by study, if he do not possess it by intuition; and hence it can neither be defined nor understood by men not similarly gifted, who, applying their own scale to what is truly incommensurable, are always astonished at the success of those whom they were all their lives accustomed to look upon as second or third rate men.

"Have we not heard it objected to Napoleon, that he could not write an elegant epistle? Do the French not pity Shakespeare for having been so little of a scholar, and so inelegant in his expressions? And yet wherein consisted the particular genius of these men, so entirely opposite to one another, if it was not, principally, in the perfect knowledge which truly intuitively they possessed of human character?

"In the same manner it has been said of General Jackson that he is incapable of writing a good English sentence, as if this were the standard by which to measure the capacity of a political chief, especially in America, where, out of a hundred senators and representatives, scarcely one has received what in Europe would be called a literary education. If classical learning were to constitute the scale by which to measure the talents of our statesmen, how far would they not rank behind the paltriest Prussian schoolmaster! General Jackson understood the people of the United States better than, perhaps, any President before him, and developed as much energy in his administration as any American statesman. I do not here speak as a partisan, nor do I wish to inquire whether all his measures were beneficial to the people; but they were, at least, all in unison with his political doctrines, and carried through

with an iron consequence, notwithstanding the enormous opposition
that wealth, and, in a great degree, also talent, put in the way of their
execution. And yet they call Jackson a second-rate man, because he is
not a regular *speechifyer,* or has never published a long article in the
newspapers!

"To judge of a man like General Jackson, one must not analyze him
after the manner of a chemist; one must not separate his talents—his
oratory—his style of composition—his generalship, &c.; but take the
tout ensemble of the man, and I venture to say there is not such another
in the United States. It is useless to draw envious comparisons between
him and Washington, Wellington, Napoleon, Jefferson, and so forth.
Great men always wear the imprints of the times and circumstances
which call their talents into action; but history is sure to preserve the
name of any man who has had the strength and genius to stamp his
own character on the people over whose destinies he presided. General
Jackson has many political enemies, and his political doctrines are perhaps only maintained—I will not say maintainable—by his own great
personality. His successor in office may not be able to continue to
make head against the opposition;—another party may get into power,
and introduce different doctrines into the administration of the country;—but the impulse which General Jackson has given to the democracy of America will always continue to be felt, and impel the government in a more or less popular direction."

"You are a great friend of General Jackson," said I, "from the animated defence you make of his character."

"I certainly am, sir," said he; "and I do not know a single man of our
party that is not warmly attached to him. Not that I approve of all his
political principles; but I like the man, and would rather see *him*
President than any other."

"You have spoken my very heart," cried the other senator. "I like
Old Hickory, because he is just the man for the people, and as im-
movable as a rock. One always knows where to find him."

"He is just the man our party wanted," rejoined the first senator, "in
order to take the lead."

"And I like Old Ironhead," said the member, "because he is a man
after my own sort. When he once says he is your friend, he *is* your
friend; but once your enemy, then *look out for breakers.*"

"And, what is more," interrupted the senator, "his hatred is of that pure Saxon kind which is always coupled with moral horror; and, for that reason, irreconcilable."

"And, what is better than all," cried the member, chuckling, "he has a good memory; he never forgets a man who has rendered him a service, nor does he ever cease to remember an injury. The former is sure of being rewarded, the latter will with difficulty escape punishment. Mr. Adams, during his Presidency, was pusillanimous enough to endeavour to reconcile his enemies by all sorts of *douceurs;* he appointed them to office, invited them to dinner, and distinguished them even before his friends. This conduct naturally alienated the latter; while the former, perceiving his drift, did not think themselves bound to be grateful for his attentions. General Jackson introduced the doctrine of reward and punishment, and has *'got along'* with it much better than his warmest friends anticipated. He appointed his friends to office, and dismissed his antagonists the moment they had taken an active part in politics. That principle, sir, is the proper one to go upon. The hope of reward, and the fear of punishment, govern men in politics and religion."

"You have expressed some apprehension," said I, turning to the senator, "that Mr. Van Buren, whom I suppose you mean by the successor of General Jackson, might not be able to retain the reins of government long."

"If I did so," replied the senator, "it was not because Mr. Van Buren's principles are not fully as orthodox as Jackson's; but he will be called on the stage immediately after a great actor will have left it, in order to perform a part not *originally* intended for him. He may be a much greater statesman than General Jackson, and yet fail to satisfy the country. He may not be allowed to act out his own views, and unable to identify himself with the party as General Jackson did,—be reduced to an exceedingly precarious position. Besides, his means of reward, as my friend chooses to call them, will be limited; General Jackson having already distributed the best offices among his friends, and the power of creating new ones being with great reluctance granted by the people. As regards the power of punishment, Mr. Van Buren will be left entirely impotent; General Jackson having already cleared the vineyard of the most noxious weeds, and the dismissal from office of a person appointed by Jackson being sure of raising a hue and cry throughout the country."

"All that may be," observed the second senator; "but Mr. Van Buren is a shrewd man."

"So he is; but all the shrewdness in the world will not change the disagreeable predicament in which he will be placed at the resignation of General Jackson. I am still afraid of the bank question."

"That is long ago knocked on the head."

"I wish it was; but I cannot bring myself to think so. The smallest commercial crisis—and our country is continually exposed to the largest ones—may revive the hopes of the opposition. It is the peculiar curse of our country never to come to a lasting conclusion on any political principle. What is law under one administration is abolished under another, and *vice versâ*, just as the one or the other party happens to command a majority of votes.

"What doctrine may now be considered as settled in the United States?—Not one; except that we are opposed to royalty—principally on account of its expenses. There is the system of internal improvements; have we come to a conclusion with regard to that?—No; the democratic party merely let it fall through, in order that the Whigs on obtaining power may take it up again. There is the American system with the high tariff; how does that question stand?—The parties are precisely in the same position in which they were before the passing of the Compromise Bill in 1832-3; the North calling for a protective system, and the South determined to nullify.* And so it is with the question of a United States' bank, the merit of each principle being every year newly tested by the result of the elections. This state of things is far from being enviable, as it renders the possession of property every day more and more insecure."

"Not only does it render property insecure," rejoined the other senator, "but it undermines the stability of our institutions. Instead of adhering to the text of the *constitution,* our parties are led by different *policies*. There is the tariff policy; as if manufacturing, or getting rich by selling home made cotton and broad-cloth, were the last end proposed by government. Then comes the national improvement policy; people must have large roads and canals in order to force trade into one or the other direction. They cannot wait until the wants of commerce shall have called them into existence; neither will they rely upon private enterprise for their execution: it must be done by the protecting guardianship of the government, and the whole country *en masse* must contribute to benefit particular States. Then comes the question of a

* Mr. Calhoun declared in one of his recent speeches that he was neither for the administration, nor against it; but was merely an honest *nullifier*.

national bank; which has agitated the country before it was quite ushered into the world, and ever after. What great national question has occupied public attention more than the art, science, practice, custom, and expediency of making money? It has employed all the wisdom, all the discretion, and all the energies of our statesmen; clearly indicating what direction the republic of the nineteenth century would take, and wherein consists the greatness of our times.

"All these questions have been so continually agitated that we have found no time for anything else; and yet we wonder Europeans do not take a sufficient interest in the progress of our country. What have we done that is so very marvellous? We have, thanks to the infinite resources of our country, built more railroads and canals than *they* have; we have built and blown up more steamboats; and we have, in proportion to our population, a larger mercantile navy than any other people. But what progress have we made in the arts and sciences, in literature, or in philosophy, to entitle us to be ranked foremost in the scale of nations? There exists now an international literature among the civilized nations of the world. What share do we take in that? The present age is in labour to give birth to a new order of things, to a new era in history; what is America doing to aid the delivery?—she who has had so much to do with the conception, and who is now responsible to the world if the whole prove an abortion. Is not every such sympathy expressed by our people—I mean by the mass of our population—laughed to scorn by our 'respectable' citizens; and are not nine-tenths of all the Americans travelling in Europe a living parody of our republican institutions? Has not even Cooper written half a dozen books on England, Italy, France, &c. as if his main purpose were to teach his countrymen good manners, and to convince them that he is a competent instructor, having himself been admitted into the best society? Why, if the speeches of our fashionable gentlemen were published in Europe, if *their* estimation of our people and of our institutions were taken as a criterion of the justice and strength of our government, then the state of our country might, indeed, be held up *in terrorem* to every nation aspiring to liberty.

"What have we achieved to be proud of, if it be not our national charter? And is not this expounded by every party in a different manner? We do not even seem to know whether we shall really have a republican government, or whether our constitution shall be a mere mock-word, granting to the people in theory what a large and influential portion of our citizens endeavour to deny them in practice. As long as our institutions are looked upon as a mere experiment, not only by a certain class in Europe, but by the *élite* of our *own* people; as long as our fashionable toadies pour out their contempt for popular governments in the ante-chambers of princes and nobles; and as long as our enlightened press finds no better food for the patriotism of our people than to entertain them with the court fashions and the court etiquette of Europe,—we have no right to find fault with the literary and thinking portion of Europeans for not wondering at our progress, or not thinking us the very first nation in the world.

"To boast of the inexhaustible resources of the country God in his infinite mercy has granted us for the noblest experiment; to be proud of our getting rich, of our being well-fed and well-clothed; and to look down with a mixture of pity and contempt on the millions which in less favoured climes are struggling against hunger and despotism,—proves a degree of vulgar egotism against which European writers have a right to use every weapon with which sarcasm and ridicule can furnish them.

"Instead of bawling like little children when we are hurt by some European critic, let us be sufficiently independent to go on fearlessly, and without reference to the fashions of other nations, in the development of those maxims and principles which have led to the establishment of our government. Let every nation develope and improve that to which it is principally indebted for its existence and power, instead of continually borrowing from others, and introducing heterogeneous elements into the state, which can only weaken its cohesion. The peculiar genius of our people is their capacity for self-government. Let them follow the inspiration of that genius, and esteem themselves for their *real* worth, and they will have no need of fearing the sting of European sarcasm."

"That's it—that's it exactly!" shouted the member. "Instead of going on 'gloriously,' 'irresistibly,' and 'triumphantly,' we stop all the time to pick up knowledge in Europe."

"There is enough knowledge to be picked up in Europe for you or me," replied the senator with a significant look on the member; "but, when our people go to Europe, they pick up the weed, and overlook the wholesome plant. We have no discrimination in our choice; and hence most of our countrymen, when they return home from abroad, arrive in a poisoned state, and immediately infect their neighbourhood.

We ought to establish a sort of moral quarantine at the entrance of all our ports, where we ought to retain gentlemen and ladies returning from Europe, until they should have given symptoms of returning reason."

"That's exactly what *I* say," cried the member. "I wish somebody would make such a motion!"

"Is it not strange," continued the senator, "that we, who are descended from the English, should resemble them so little in one respect? The English carry their national customs and manners wherever they go; whereas we, poor unfortunate Yankees! with the sympathy of half the world in our favour, are absolutely ashamed of our own, and embarrassed when asked about the nature of our government."

"If any such there be, I wish I knew their names," interrupted the member; "they ought to be published."

"That would be ungentlemanly," retorted the senator, vexed with the interruption; "you would surely not introduce a reign of terror!"

"I don't know about that," ejaculated the member; "I am the man for the people, and, when any one insults them, my *dander* is up; and then I don't know *what* I am doing."

The senator made no reply.

"There are men in Paris," continued he after a while, "who do more harm to their countrymen than all the books that have been written on America."

"And who are they?" demanded the member eagerly.

"I shall not name them," said the senator; "but they are some of our vulgar rich men, and the very worst hunters after nobility. One of them gives fine parties, and has by his extravagance acquired a sort of notoriety which he is mistaking for reputation. This man, who is much more proud of his intercourse with French noblemen than of his familiarity with his own countrymen, while at Florence actually refused to recognise one of our worthiest citizens whom he well knew, and whom the Grand Duke had received on several occasions.—'Do you know Mr. ***?' asked the Imperial Prince of Austria, the lion of Paris.—'I do not,' replied the latter, somewhat abashed.—'He has certainly a very agreeable family,' observed his Highness, by way of explaining his motive.—'That may be,' answered the wealthy nothing; 'but he is a *merchant,* and I do not associate with these.'—'Indeed!' remarked the Grand Duke naïvely, 'I was always told the merchants composed your best society!'"

"And I dare say," said the member, "he would have been glad, while in America, to be ranked with the society of merchants."

"It is the character of every toad-eater," observed the senator drily, "that he ceases to recognize his friends the moment they can no longer be useful to him. There are toad-eaters in politics as well as in society. A man may be a toad-eater to the mob as well as to those above him; and I do not know which of the two kinds is the worst. We have a set of political sycophants who fawn and cringe before every party that is in power, and who are always the first to desert them at the least *mauvais contretemps*. Our democracy has no greater enemies than those twaddles. They come over to the side of the people when they have no other alternative left, and are the servants of the people just as long as the people have the power to retain them. They are democrats for a share in the loaves and fishes, and injure the party more than its most avowed opponents; just as treachery in your own ranks is worse than an attack from your enemy."

"But I should think people would soon find them out," observed the member.

"They may indeed very easily be detected," said the senator; "only the *people* find them out too late. One of the surest means of detecting them is to watch their animosity against harmless individuals, while they show the greatest delicacy for persons who have the power to injure them. These men are always ready to kill the fly that annoys them, but move quietly out of the way of the elephant; they never show their courage unless they are quite sure of opposing the weak, or, like Falstaff at the battle of Shrewsbury, merely stab the slain."

The conversation here began to flag; and, in a short time after, the honourable member, under pretext of having a pressing engagement with a friend, left us to enjoy the rest of our walk as best we might, without the advantage of his remarks. I seized this opportunity to ask the senator whether what I had heard of the poverty of the city of Washington was true, and whether the town is really deserted during the summer?

"I am glad," replied he, "the people here are poor, and unable to give splendid entertainments. They would otherwise have the power of seducing senators and representatives with the display of fashion, and the numerous attractions and manœuvres of wealthy coteries. It is a fortunate circumstance that the legislative assemblies of the States of New York and Pennsylvania meet in comparatively small towns; because not only the influence of the mob, which Jefferson dreaded, but also the aristocratic seductions of the higher classes, are capable of destroying the independence of legislators. From these evils we are happily exempted by the almost hopeless condition of the inhabitants of this place. Washington is, in this respect, like a German university, in which all the citizens make their living by the students and the professors, and on that account must do what the latter like, instead of holding out inducements for them to desert the path of duty. With the exception of half a dozen people of large estates, and particularly the very generous and hospitable General V—ss, all the parties, entertainments, balls, concerts, &c. are given by the *corps diplomatique,* or by the gentlemen holding office, among whom some of the secretaries are particularly remarkable for their unostentatious civility to strangers. The company, again, is principally composed of persons connected with the government, of senators, members of the House, and foreign diplomatic agents; so that the rich visitors from the Atlantic towns are incapable of making a sensation, and are only admitted on even terms."

"That's a very flattering account of Washington society," said I, delighted with the prospect.

"If you are this evening invited to Mrs. ***'s, you may probably have an opportunity of verifying all I have said. The meagre salaries of our public functionaries do not enable them to pamper their guests with hot suppers, as is the custom among the nabobs of New York; but if agreeable and affable manners, and the *réunion* of the first talents of our country, can compensate you for a leg of a turkey or an oyster-pie, you will not regret staying a few days in the American metropolis."

So saying, he bid me good-b'ye; begged me to make use of him in any manner I pleased, especially if I wished to be introduced to the President and Vice-president, or to any of his colleagues on *his* side of the question. I thanked him cordially for his kindness; and, intending to pay my respects to the President and Vice-president, told him frankly that I should be under great obligations to him for a personal introduction to General Jackson and Mr. Van Buren. This declaration had the desired effect, and it was agreed between us that he should call on me early on the morning of the following day in order to present me to the chief magistrate.

CHAPTER XIX

"The greatest problem of the human race, to the solution of which men are forced by the peculiarity of their nature, is the establishment of a society for the maintenance of their rights."—*Kant's Idea of a Universal History in a Cosmopolitical Sense.*

ON my return to the hotel I found the people at tea, which was served with beefsteaks, chops, ham, &c. and answered the purpose of a regular meal. It being too early for me to join them, I quietly sneaked off to my room, or rather to the third part of a room, which was granted me by the kindness of the innkeeper; the other two-thirds, with the corresponding beds, &c. being occupied by a lieutenant in the navy, and a young man of fashion just returned from Europe, who, in proof of his foreign civilization, was constantly singing French songs without reference to melody or metre. One of these, which he usually sang in the morning, when owing to our late rising we got a cold breakfast, I yet remember had this singular *refrain:*—

> "Je suis content, je suis heureux;
> Tout homme doit l'être dans ces lieux."

Being afraid lest the songster should enter the room, and dispute with me the use of the only looking-glass, I dressed as quickly as I could; and then went down to the reading-room, to drag out the time from six till eight with the newspapers. The appointed hour finally arrived, and with it the carriage I had previously engaged; and in less than three-quarters of an hour,—the house of Mrs. *** being situated on the confines of the ideal town,—my "negro driver" halted before a small building with a wooden staircase in front, which looked as though it might be blown off by the first gale, or washed away by the rain, considering that it was exposed to the unmitigated fury of both, and evidently placed there for no other purpose but to save room for the kitchen. The house, which was so uncommonly snug as to have but three windows in front, was brilliantly illumined by the aid of a single chandelier; and the door left open, in order that the invited guests might see their way up stairs into the parlour.

Arrived at the place, my coachman sprung off the box, opened the door of the carriage, and assisted me in alighting amidst a group of dark faces that were only rendered visible by the reflection from the whites of their eyes. I passed the review of the servants without loss of time, and scrambled up the wooden staircase in order to force my entrance into the parlour. This, however, was in vain; the gentlemen, who, much against their own inclination, were placed with their faces in the room and the more vulgar part of their composition outside, being unable to move forward, in order to admit the ingress of a new-comer, without interfering with the dancers. I tried to look *into* the room, in order to have at least a peep at the ladies; but, measuring but five feet ten, and the two gentlemen who guarded the entrance being probably Kentuckians, I could not manage to look over their shoulders. I endeavoured to have a glance between their bodies, or between their shoulders and arms. Vain attempt! they were too compact to suffer a beam of light to go through them.

In despair I went up another pair of stairs, which led into a sort of refectory, to which the entrance, though difficult, was not impossible. The room was furnished in a befitting style of simplicity. There was no display of overgrown wealth; a few painted chairs and tables, a small ebony-framed looking-glass, and a few settees,—the bed having been previously ejected in order to make room for the company,—constituting the sum total of the *ameublement*. On a small side-table, neatly covered with a white table-cloth, were placed several large plates of sandwiches, bread and ham; and in the middle of the room stood a large basin, which at first I took for a Roman bathing-tub, placed there for the accommodation of such guests as came from a distance, but, on drawing near, discovered to be full of that exquisite beverage called "apple toddy," which differs very little from Mr. Price's gin punch at the Garrick, so much approved of by Mr. Theodore Hook. Indeed, I rather think the advantage, if any, on the side of the toddy, the apples imparting to the gin a much more simple and delicate flavour than the Maraschino; and the thing would be better still if iced soda-water were added to the compound.

The gentlemen formed a very interesting group round this tub; and, perceiving a stranger step amongst them, immediately made room; while one of them, probably the president *pro tem.* seized a huge ladle, and immersing it first into the liquid, and holding it up again in triumph as high as he could, filled a more than double-sized glass to the very brim without spilling one drop of the liquid. This feat, which convinced me at once of his being an *habitué*, was scarcely accomplished, before, in the most graceful manner possible, he offered me the glass with the amicable greeting of—

"Every stranger is welcome in Washington!"

I of course pledged him in due politeness, and in less than five minutes felt perfectly acquainted with the whole company. I then made a second attempt at forcing an entrance into the ball-room, which, the Kentuckians being gone, and their places filled by two spindle-shanked heroes of New York, succeeded beyond my most sanguine expectations; admitting me not only into the room, but into the presence of the lady of the house. Having been invited only through the kind intercession of a friend, without knowing mine hostess, and the custom of announcing by servants being not yet introduced into the United States, a gentleman who acted as usher immediately offered me his arm, and led me into the presence of an elderly lady, dressed rather in the English matron style than *à la française,* and whose countenance betokened a life passed in domestic peace and comfort.

The gentleman introduced me as *Monsieur* DE ***, much against my own inclination, and I could clearly perceive the consequence that little word *de* gave me; not so much with the lady of the house, as with a number of fashionable misses, strangers in the metropolis, "who had just come out that season." I do not know whether *vanity* had something to do with it, but I thought I heard one of them ask whether I was a bachelor; which question being answered in the affirmative, I am quite sure I heard another one say, "Hem! I dare say he is as poor as that Polish Count ***, who flirted with every young lady, and, when it came to the scratch, had hardly money enough to pay the parson."

This common-sense remark of an American belle, which proved in a most satisfactory manner her preferring the useful to the agreeable, did not much affect me; neither did I ascribe it to the want of liberality towards strangers, having seen *native Americans* victimized in the same manner. I therefore pretended not to have heard the remark, and asked the gentleman who acted as master of the ceremonies to have the kindness to introduce me to the lady who, I thought, had inquired whether I was married.

I found her well-educated, *spirituelle,*—full of imagination. I even think she gave me to understand that she once wrote poetry—as an exercise at the boarding-school, and that she always had a secret attachment to men of letters. Among the various English writers, she was most in love with Scott, who completely transported her to the times of chivalry and knight-errantry; while her own countryman Cooper was to her "an object of perfect horror," though she had no particular objection to his last works, "which contain a great deal of information about the state of society in Europe." She *"longed* to see Europe; and was very much indebted to mamma for bringing her to Washington, where she could already have a foretaste of it." On hearing this, her mother, who stood near her, said that she was a child, and that I must not listen to her. Being really not disposed for a flirtation, and seeing the same senator with whom I had taken a walk in the afternoon enter the room, I was glad to find an opportunity of leaving my sentimental fair one to the care of her tender parent, who had instilled into her such delicate tastes.

When the senator saw that I was disengaging myself, he came up to me without ceremony, shook me by the hand, and asked me how I liked the party. I related to him my adventure in the upper room, which made him smile. "You may depend upon it," said he, "that if ever you meet with any of those gentlemen in the neighbourhood of his estate, you will not be able to get off with less than a month's stay at his house,—such would be his hospitality, and the pleasure of meeting you again. I must now lead you round a little, in order to show you some of our most remarkable characters.

"That man there, with white hair and dark keen eyes, who so violently gesticulates, is Mr. Wise, a member from Virginia. He is a paragon of American speakers,—always up, always ready, always determined to speak, on every occasion, the modicum of two or three hours, were it but to show his friends and constituents that he is 'up and doing.' He is a member of the Whig opposition; fighting against the government as against a hydra with many heads, all which *he* has to sever from the trunk. His contempt for the present administration knows neither bounds nor reason; and he is opposed to every one of its measures, to every member or senator that ever seconded or defended one of these, and to every man that ever voted for any such member or senator. He goes, in fact, 'the whole hog t'other way,' and, as such, is the very type of an American Whig. He carries his opposition almost to madness, though amongst his numerous speeches there are a good many clever ones."

"I could never tell the object of your Whig party," said I; "pray, what *are* its peculiar principles?"

"Our appellation of *Whigs* or *Conservatives,* and *Tories, Democrats,* or *Destructives,*" replied he, "must really puzzle the English. I would ask, what have *our* Conservatives to preserve? What our Destructives to destroy? Our Conservatives possess no exclusive rights, no privileges beyond those enjoyed by the people at large; their names are not associated with the history of the country; their ancestors, if they were known, had nothing to do with establishing the government,—for the *mania* for aristocracy is least to be found among those families whose forefathers distinguished themselves in the revolutionary war; they hold no property which the first commercial crisis may not destroy; and hold, in fact, the very *reverse* position of the Conservatives in England. They do not endeavour to *preserve* what they *possess,* but strive *to acquire more;* they are not associated with the *past,* but entertain bright hopes of the *future;* they do not stand on the broad basis of the history of their own country, but seek for precedent in Europe. This, sir, is the character of *our* Conservatives, Whigs, or Aristocrats, who bear no more resemblance to the English Tories, than a poor man, who tries to become rich by shaving his neighbour, does to a millionnaire who defends his own property.

"You must not be misled by the idle declamations of those who incessantly talk of the levelling system, and its consequences on the people of this country. The levelling system commenced at the very settlement of the country, and was most active during the revolution. It was then that the Conservatives, with some show of logic, might have declaimed against the levelling principle; not now. There are

some who will gravely tell you that the most eminent American statesmen, during the revolution and immediately after, were Conservatives,
or moderate Tories; but what does this prove, if it be true? Simply, that
a great number of those whom an overruling Providence used as instruments in bestowing liberty and happiness on our people, did not
understand what they were doing: which, after all, does not make so
very much against them; there being at all times, and in all countries,
but few politicians capable of foreseeing the ultimate result of an
innovation. And what, I would ask, have nine-tenths of these Tories
to lose by this levelling system, that makes them so tenacious of their
doctrines? Where is the elevation from which they are afraid to
descend? What noble principles which they cherish, will thereby be
trodden in the dust? What protection which they give to arts and
sciences, will thereby suffer? Echo must answer, 'What?'—Daniel
Webster, the gentleman there with the hawk-eyes, told us that the war
between the democrats and the aristocracy is a war of the poor against
the rich; and I am inclined to think he is half right,—as far, namely,
as concerns his own party. But if wealth form the only distinction, the
only claim to supremacy in our country, the sooner we get rid of its
influence the better. It is the most degrading of all, and must be equally
spurned by the labourer and the man of genius."

"But a great number of your literary men belong likewise to the
opposition."

"Pray, don't talk to me of our literary men! We have as yet, for the
most part, but literary imitators, who follow the beaten track of the
English or French; and the organization of our society is admirably
calculated to retain them in this state of imbecility. It is the want of
nationality, the absence of generous and expanded feelings, which are
crushed by the vulgar inordinate desire after money, and the little love
which our upper classes in general bear to the institutions of our
country, which are the cause of our poets singing the praise of the lark
and the nightingale, with whose melodious strains they are only acquainted through the medium of some English annual. What is there
in our country to inspire poetic sentiments, if it be not the love of
liberty and of nature, the great sources of all poetry?

"We are told that our political principles are bad, because they do not
meet with the approbation of some two or three score of vain scribblers
calling themselves *literati,* but being in fact pettifogging lawyers, that
have not wit enough to make a living by their profession. Now, in

order to prove such an assertion to be correct, it would first be necessary to show that these representatives of the wisdom, intelligence, and patriotism of the country are capable of forming a correct judgment of the position and wants of our people; and, secondly, that they are capable of forming an *independent* judgment. When our *literati* shall be known otherwise than by writing for the newspapers, or occasionally for an album, I shall believe the first; when I shall see a paper without advertisements, I shall trust in the second.

"We talk of an independent press, and our editors are more easily bought and sold than any writer in France! They are, indeed, not bought by so much money down, simply because there is none to give it them; but by contributions of twenty-five dollars a-piece for *annual advertisements,* paid at the end of the year,—if the subscriber does not fail in the mean time. Our *literati* want to make a living with their pen, and are in this respect just like other trades-people.

"There," said he, pointing to a young man dressed in the latest London fashion, "is a gentleman, the son of a respectable merchant in New York, who may serve as an illustration of what *we* mean by a Tory. He is just turned twenty-one, and has already been in France, England, and Italy. His father is rich; that is, he associates with fashionable people, keeps a carriage, and will, if he do not meet with great reverses, leave to his six children from fifteen to twenty thousand dollars a head. This modicum the young man will have to improve, or he will die a beggar; so that, if he does not marry a rich woman, he will be unavoidably condemned to personal labour and exertion. Yet this young man is *an aristocrat!* His father, knowing his inability to provide for him in such a manner as to render him independent, thought fit to give him a *practical* rather than a literary education. The young man accordingly *learned* reading, writing, and spelling; writes a tolerably fair hand, and has studied mathematics—as far as the rule of three! When he had acquired so much of a practical education, he was sent to Europe to *perfect* himself.

"He first went to England, where he saw all the great actors and actresses, went up St. Paul's to take a view of the city of London, made the round of the principal gambling-houses and other public establishments worth the attention of a traveller, dined with every gentleman to whom he brought a letter of introduction, and then wrote home, that, being perfectly acquainted with English society, he was now desirous of seeing France. His father accordingly sent the money, and the young man set out in a stage-coach from London to Dover. From Dover to Boulogne he went in a steamer; and at Boulogne he took the *malle-poste* for Paris, making observations all the way on the manners of the French people.

"Arrived in Paris, his first care was to secure comfortable lodgings; then he delivered his letter of introduction, which was a letter of credit on Messrs. *** and Co.; then dined with his banker; after which he dined again at a *restaurant,* and then set out to prepare for his daily avocation, which consisted in strolling from his lodgings in the Rue Rivoli, through the Rue St. Honoré, to the Palais Royal; from the Palais Royal, through the Rue Vivienne, to the Place de la Bourse; thence through the Passage du Panorama to the Boulevards; and over the Boulevards, through the Rue de la Paix and the Place Vendôme, into the garden of the Tuileries, which, together with the principal theatres and other places of amusement, contained his circle of acquaintance in the French metropolis.

"Society in France being a little easier of access than in England, he obtained, by dint of perseverance,—one of our cardinal virtues,—access to one or two respectable families, and left his card with our minister in order to be presented at court. Whether he was actually admitted into 'the presence of royalty,' after which his heart panted ever since he was a boy, I know not; but I rather think he *was,* since, immediately on his return, he cut most of his old friends and acquaintances, and was, in fact, quite another man.

"The time of his embarkation at Havre being fixed upon, he employed the remaining six or seven weeks to see Italy; not forgetting to buy in Milan some *black lace* for his sister, in Genoa some *velvet* for his mother, and in Rome one or two pieces of *mosaïque,* in order to show his taste in the fine arts. The reason he did not purchase a *hat* at Leghorn was, that he did not know how to dispose of it in his portmanteau. I forgot to say, that, during all the time the young gentleman was in Europe 'improving himself,' he wrote home 'the most touching letters,' which were shown to all the acquaintance of the family; and, it being thought a pity that such talents should remain hidden under a bushel, and not enlighten other Americans that did not enjoy the same advantages, some of them actually appeared in the papers, superscribed *'Correspondence of an American Gentleman now travelling in Europe.'* What was particularly remarkable in his correspondence was the great number of Gallicisms; showing his acquaintance with a foreign idiom, which he had already mastered to such a degree as to forget his own language. At last he came back from his tour, and has ever since been a lion in our fashionable society. Such, sir, is the usual type of our aristocrats, who are constantly railing against the levelling system, which would confound them with the industrious mechanic, the honest farmer, and the enterprising and thriving backwoodsman. But we have already lost too much time with a *puppy;* I must now show you some of our *men.*

"That gentleman there, whose animated conversation has brought together a circle of hearers, is Mr. Rives, senator from Virginia. He is one of the best specimens of our Southern gentlemen, uniting great vigour of mind, and the eye of a statesman, with those agreeable and affable manners which throw off restraint without diminishing respect; a gift which nature seldom bestows on those born under more Northern latitudes. He will be a prominent candidate for the Vice-presidency, and a great support to the democratic party. Mr. Rives is an agreeable speaker, clear and precise in his arguments, and an enemy to the rhetorical or flowery style. He has no notion of sinking the bathos, or of shaking the Senate with the thunder of his voice.

"Next to him stands a gentleman with a red wig and a laughing countenance; his eyes sparkle, though he has not yet had any champaign, and the spirits confined within his brain seem to celebrate one continual Lord Mayor's day. This is Mr. Preston, senator from South Carolina. What a pity it is he is on the side of the opposition! He is full of fun; mixes up repartee, sarcasm, irony, and *persiflage* in one continual strain of humorous eloquence; and is, in fact, the prince of wags in Congress. His manners, of course, are those of a gentleman,—which indeed he cannot help, being a South-Carolinian; and his wit, though it sometimes touches to the quick, is accompanied by so much good-nature that it is impossible to be angry with him. These qualities, of course, do not make him a *leader,* but rather the cavalry of the opposition; and his spirited attacks sometimes make greater havoc than the artillery of Clay or Webster.

"Mr. Webster you know already. He sits at yon table, playing at whist. This is trifling away his time, for he is the last man to spend his hours in innocent amusements. Mr. Webster is, according to *my* opinion, a gentleman without imagination or extensive reading; but of immense natural talents, and severe application to his profession. He is considered one of the best, and there are those who consider him *the* best, constitutional lawyer; and, certes, his judgment, discrimination, and logic are not surpassed by any member or senator in Congress. Yet, with all these qualities, he is better calculated for a debater than for a leader; his mind being more of that analytic order which succeeds in dissecting and destroying, than of that synthetic character which combines simple elements to an harmonious whole. The latter requires a creative genius, and a certain intuitive knowledge of things; whereas the process of dissection presupposes but a careful examination of facts, and the application of sound logic.

"To understand where Mr. Webster's talents lie, it is only necessary to study his parliamentary tactics, and to read his speeches. He never rises from his seat, except to repel an attack, or to take advantage of an overture given by one of his enemies. When an important question—of which he is hardly ever the originator—is proposed, his practice is to wait until every one has given his opinion; he then compares them, dissects them, analyses them, and (wonderful!) pronounces upon them like a judge after hearing the argument of each counsel. Every flaw in the reasoning, in the expression,—every logical imperfection is sure to be detected; and his speech, which in truth is a critical abstract of all the speeches delivered in Congress, passes then, with his friends at least, for an *original* production. But I would ask, what particular measure has he originated that produced either good or evil to the country? The tariff?—That was Mr. Calhoun's measure. Internal improvements, or a bank?—That honour(!) belongs to Henry Clay. When, at the session of Congress in 1832–3, the country was threatened with civil war, was it *he* that averted the calamity by the proposition of a measure calculated to satisfy all parties?—No; this honour belongs again to Henry Clay. What, then, I ask, has he done that is so wonderful?—He is a great constitutional lawyer! That may be; but he has not yet delivered his ideas in a scientific form, and the commentaries of Mr. Justice Story will perhaps outlive the fame of Daniel Webster.

"Mr. Webster's great tact in repelling an enemy consists in personal satire and irony. Thus he succeeded against Mr. Haines, and against a number of minor opponents, who all went to swell his renown. His speeches are clear and argumentative; but, which they occupy your understanding, they leave you cold and cheerless. He cannot excite your imagination; he cannot touch your feelings; and he does not stimulate your enthusiasm. Neither is he capable of supplying this deficiency by his personality; for, though respected and admired throughout the country, he is not beloved,—no, not even by his own partisans. Mr. Webster knows the laws of his country; but he is less acquainted with the men that are to be governed by them, and possesses none of those conciliating and engaging qualities which insure personal popularity. This accounts for his position in Congress, where, notwithstanding the powerful aid he lends to the opposition, he stands alone—*the terrible senator from Massachusetts.*

"Neither is Mr. Webster as a speaker entirely without faults. He sometimes tries to sink the bathos by being flowery and rhetorical; and he seems to labour under the singular impression that a public speaker must commence and leave off with a flourish, and on this account violates his imagination with the composition of regular beginnings and ends, which are but too frequently wholly irrelevant to the text of his discourses. He had, in this respect, better follow the example of certain landscape painters, who, being perfectly equal to the *inanimate,* leave the *figures* to be done by somebody else."

———

N. B.—It is now three years since I noted down the conversation of the democratic senator. I have since heard so much of Daniel Webster, —European writers, and especially Miss Martineau,* having actually made his apotheosis,—that, as a *pendant* to the Old Bailey speech recorded in her last work on America, I cannot refrain here from laying before the British reader some elegant extracts from one of his speeches (called the *Great* Speech), in reply to the remarks of John C. Calhoun, delivered in the Senate on the 12th of March 1838. This speech, one of the most elaborate of which he was ever delivered, fills, in the "New

* Miss Martineau, I understood of my American friends, was, like many English reformers, a great enthusiast for democracy in the abstract; only that in her private intercourse she preferred the society of distinguished persons belonging to the opposite coterie. This probably accounts for her partiality with regard to Daniel Webster and Henry Clay, and her antipathy to the administration. The Quarterly Review, in an excellent article on that useful and instructive work of Mr. Walker, entitled "The Original," ascribes to the influence of the generous and brilliant hospitality of the noble Lords Lansdowne, Holland, Sefton,—and the clever writer might have added his Grace the Duke of Devonshire,—"a magic power, which, in the intoxication of the moment, throws many an author off his guard, until he finds or thinks himself irrecoverably committed, and, suppressing any lurking inclination towards Toryism, becomes deeply and definitely a Whig." The administration party in America are unfortunately not much in the habit of entertaining people; but if the number of dishes—no matter how cooked —constituting an American dinner can be put into the scale against the rank, beauty, wit, eloquence, accomplishment, and agreeableness which congregate at the noble houses just named, an *American Whig* dinner, too, is not without its attraction.

York American," seventeen and a quarter columns, and was intended to demolish his antagonist. It is on that account full of personal attacks, occasionally interspersed with a modest praise of himself.

Mr. Calhoun had been defending an independent Treasury, such as exists, and has always existed, in every country, whether the Government was monarchical or republican; while Mr. Webster, the advocate of a union between the Government and the Bank, tried to ridicule the idea; endeavouring to show that his adversary had been *previously wrong* on a question relating to the *tariff*. Mr. Calhoun, in his opening remarks, pointed to the evils of the irresponsible American banking system; to its "self-sustaining principle, which poised and impelled the system, self-balanced in the midst of the heavens like some celestial body, with scarcely a perceptible deviation from its path from the concussion it had received;" and at last took the following philosophic ground:—

"But its most fatal effects (the effects of the American banking system) originate in its bearing on the moral and intellectual developement of the community. The great principles of demand and supply govern the moral and intellectual world no less than the business and commercial. If a community be so organized as to cause a demand for high mental attainments, they are sure to be developed. If its honours and rewards are allotted to pursuits that require their developement by creating a demand for intelligence, knowledge, wisdom, justice, firmness, courage, patriotism, and the like, they are sure to be produced. But if allotted to pursuits that require inferior qualities, the higher are sure to decay and perish. I object to the banking system, because it allots the honours and rewards of the community in a very undue proportion to a pursuit the least of all others favourable to the developement of the higher mental qualities, intellectual or moral,—to the decay of the learned professions, and the more noble pursuits of science, literature, philosophy, and statesmanship, and the great and more useful pursuits of business and industry. With the vast increase of its profits and influence it is gradually concentrating in itself most of the prizes of life, —wealth, honour, and influence,—to the great disparagement and degradation of all the liberal, useful, and generous pursuits of society. The rising generation cannot but feel its deadening influence. The youth who crowd our colleges, and behold the road to honour and distinction terminating in a banking-house, will feel the spirit of emulation decay within them, and will no longer be pressed forward by generous ardour to mount up the rugged steep of science as the road to honour and distinction, when, perhaps, the highest point they could attain in what was once the most honourable and influential of learned professions would be the place of attorney to a bank."

The force and truth of these remarks are amply illustrated by the actual composition of American society, and would be equally felt in England, if, with a system of banking similar to that now in use in the United States, the people were at any time to be *deprived* (I use that word on purpose) of the influence of the nobility and clergy. It is the absence of high dignitaries, and of men placed by their birth and education above the level of ordinary men, which renders the presence of a moneyed aristocracy in the United States truly odious and degrading; and forces every man of sound sense, who is capable of understanding the true position of the country by comparing it to that of others, naturally over to the democratic party. In proportion as science and literature will be cultivated in America, democracy will become more and more powerful; for it is only vulgar and inferior minds Whiggism can purchase with money.

To the short and pithy speech of Mr. Calhoun, then, Mr. Webster made, as I said before, a seventeen and a quarter column answer. This I surely have no intention of inflicting upon the innocent reader;* but, in order to verify the criticism of the democratic senator, I shall quote a few of those passages in which Mr. Webster gives into the poetical,— that is, those passages in which his imagination seems to be sufficiently excited to *quote* poetry, exhibiting his taste in the selection,—and the grand *finale,* which will demonstrate his art of sinking the bathos.

At the head of the ninth column, after expatiating at some length *on the inconvenience* of counting money, which would ensue in case of a Treasury, he says,

"But this is not all: once a quarter the naval officer is to count the collector's money, and the register in the land-office is to count the receiver's money. And, moreover, sir! every now and then the secretary of the Treasury is to authorize unexpected and impromptu countings in his discretion, and just to satisfy his own mind. What a money-counting, tinkling, jingling, generation we shall be! All the money-changers in Solomon's temple will be as nothing to us. Our sound *will*

---

* One of the arguments of Mr. Webster has already been mentioned in another chapter.

go forth into all lands. We shall be like the king in the ditty of the nursery,

> 'There sat the king a-counting of his money.' "

What mighty reasons these for not having a Treasury! And what glorious quotation of poetry! What a beautiful association of ideas! To think of the nursery ditty in the Senate of the United States! How well Mr. Webster remembers the days of his innocence! and what a talent he must have had, even as a boy, for finance, to remember just the verse which relates to the "king *a*-counting of his money!"

The next quotation of poetry occurs on the fourteenth column, where Mr. Webster speaks of the issue of Treasury notes, which, as the orator assures us, might be given out by the Government so as to *flood the country.**

"And now I pray you to consider, Mr. President," says Mr. Webster, "what an admirable contrivance this would be to secure that economy in the expenses of Government which the gentleman has so much at heart. Relaxed from all necessity of taxation, and from the consequent responsibility to the people,—(this is a wilful misrepresentation of the fact,)—not called upon to regard at all the amount of annual income,— having an authority to cause Treasury notes to be issued, whenever it pleases,

> 'In multitudes, like which the *populous* North
> *Poured* never from her *frozen* loins to pass
> Rhine or the Danau,'—

what admirable restraint would be on Government!" &c.

Now mark how well those three lines of blank verse are brought in! What a beautiful simile, to compare the issue of Treasury notes to the *populous* North *pouring* from her *frozen* loins hordes of barbarians to cross the Rhine or the *Danau!* How applicable! Just the thing for America! What a terrible sensation those children of the North would make among the Yankees, just as they are crossing the Rhine or the Danube!

---

* Mr. Webster does not enter on that part of Mr. Calhoun's speech in which the latter observes, that the Government, issuing Treasury notes only to the amount of the anticipated revenue, and for the necessary expenses of the State, could not abuse its privilege half so much as the United States' Bank, dependent as the latter is on commercial fluctuations, and on the peculiar system of credit established in America.

But the conclusion of Mr. Webster's speech is a perfect *chef d'œuvre*. He there apostrophises Calhoun in the following manner:—

"Let him go! I remain! I remain where I ever have been, and ever mean to be. Here, standing on the platform of the General Constitution,—a platform broad enough and firm enough to uphold *every* interest of the *whole* country,—I shall still be found!"

The words, "Let him go! I remain!" produce a sort of dramatic effect; and are, I believe, a happy imitation of those ancient soliloquies which commence thus: *"He is gone, and I am alone."* And then how natural that the platform of the General Constitution, which is broad enough "to uphold *every* interest of the *whole* country," should also support *him!* Nothing could be more *à propos.*

"Intrusted," continues Mr. Webster, "with some part in the administration of that constitution, I intend to act in its spirit, and in the spirit of those who framed it. Yes, sir; I would act as if our fathers who formed it for us, and who bequeathed it to us, were looking on us,—as if I would see their venerable forms bending down to behold us from the abodes above! I would act too, sir, as if that long line of posterity were also viewing us, whose eye is hereafter to scrutinise our conduct."

What a thorough view and review that is! and what can be more pathetic than to see the fathers of the constitution first *looking* upon them, and then bending down their venerable forms to *behold* them!

Mr. Webster continues the same beautiful figure still farther.

"Standing thus as in the full gaze of our *ancestors* and our *posterity,* having received this inheritance from the former to be transmitted to the latter, and feeling that, if I am born for any good in my day and generation, it is for the good of the whole country, (what a modest way this of recommending himself to the Presidency!) no local policy or local feelings, no temporary impulse shall induce me to yield my *foothold*(!) on the constitution and the Union. I move off under no banner not known to the whole American people, and to their constitution and laws. No, sir; these walls, these columns,

————————————————'fly
From their firm base as soon as I.' "

This is the third and last quotation of poetry, and a direct challenge of the nullifier, *defeated by General Jackson*. The selection is beautiful! Mr. Webster's bravery needs no comment!

Then comes the real *last end* of the speech,—a perfect *bijou* of rhetorical amplification.

"I came into public life, sir, *in the service* of the United States." (Mr. Webster probably means *to serve* the United States.) "On that broad *altar* my earliest and all my public vows have been made. I propose to serve no other *master*. So far as depends on any agency of mine, they shall continue United States, united in interest and affection, united in every thing in regard to which the constitution has decreed their union; united in war, for the common defence, the common *renown,* and the common glory; and *united, compacted, knit firmly together* in peace, for the common prosperity and happiness of ourselves and our children."

Who does not here remember the wholesome piece of advice Napoleon gave to his brother Lucien when the latter had sent him a proclamation intended for the public? "I have read the proclamation," observed Napoleon; "it is good for nothing. There are too many words and too few ideas in it. You struggle after pathos. This is not the way to speak to the people. They possess more tact and judgment than you are aware of. Your *prose* will do more harm than good."

I am not disposed to undervalue Mr. Webster's talent as a judge and critic,—except as regards poetry and the arts. The bench is the proper place for him; but as a statesman, or party leader, he can only succeed by the blunders of his antagonists.

The next gentleman to whom my democratic friend directed my attention was a short stout figure, with a bald head, and a cold, displeasing, repulsive countenance, which, notwithstanding, beamed with an almost supernatural intelligence. "This is Mr. John Quincy Adams," observed my friend, "formerly President of the United States, and now a member of Congress. Next to General Jackson, he is perhaps the most remarkable man in the country, though he is his perfect antipode. If anything shows the superiority of character over abstract knowledge, it is the triumph of the honest, straightforward soldier over this hairsplitter. Were there yet twenty Jacksons in the country, they would yet twenty times succeed against such a man. This is a law of nature.

"Mr. Adams, if you consider his acquirements, is probably the best informed man in America, though his knowledge is somewhat rhapsodical, like his character. He has the most astonishing memory, and possesses great conversational powers. Yet, with all these eminent qualities, he has not one true friend! With almost universal talent, and, I might add, universal application, he possesses no genius, no great personality, like Jackson, born to wield the destinies of a country. He is full of information, understands most perfectly the routine of business, reads everything, examines everything, and remembers everything; and yet, when he comes to act, is sure of committing some blunder which will expose him and his friends. He is, in fact, a living illustration of Voltaire's motto:

> 'Nous tromper dans nos entreprises,
>   C'est à quoi nous sommes sujets;
> Le matin je fais des projets,
>   Et le long du jour des sottises.'

The reason is, he knows Europe better than he does America;—he is a stranger in his own country. He fights his battles on paper; calculating the number of men, their position, and the kind of arms, but making no allowance for their moral character. Many of his plans are well conceived, but all are badly executed; and he has the weakness of most bad generals, to account for his lost battles by the faults of his inferior officers.

"The *gaucheries* which distinguish his political life also mark his private intercourse; he talks better than any man in the United States, and yet is sure to be embarrassed when addressed, unless previously prepared for it. This want of social talent I have frequently noticed among the most eminent men of New England, and it accounts for their little popularity. Mr. Adams belongs, of course, to the opposition; but, like the independent Yankee militia-man, fights his battles '*on his own book*.'* He will not suffer any one near him, and attacks indiscriminately friend or foe that opposes his progress. Of late, few of his own party have dared to come within his reach; for, though his political principles are somewhat *rococo,* his wit and sarcasm are as unimpaired as ever, and his capacity to scratch those who tread upon his toe as good as in the best days of his manhood.

Mr. Adams's peculiar manners have, with the exception of too much panegyric, been well described in an article entitled "Glances at Con-

* This was the answer of a citizen, who, being called upon to join a company during the last war, wished to express his determination to fight independently, *on his own account.*

gress," inserted in the first number of the United States' Magazine and Democratic Review, published at Washington. "Our attention," says the reporter who furnished the article, "is now attracted to a ray of light that glitters on the apex of a bald and noble head, 'located' on the left of the House, in the neighbourhood of the Speaker's chair. It proceeds from that wonderful man, who in his person combines the agitator, philosopher, poet, statesman, critic, and orator,—John Quincy Adams. Who that has seen him sitting beneath the cupola of the hall, with the rays of light gathering and glancing about his singularly polished head, but has likened him to one of the luminaries of the age, shining and glittering in the political firmament of the Union. There he sits hour after hour, day after day, with untiring patience; never absent from his seat, never voting for an adjournment, vigilant as the most jealous member of the House; his ear always on the alert, himself always prepared to go at once into the profoundest question of state, to the minutest point of order. What must be his thoughts as he ponders on the past, in which he has played a part so conspicuous! We look at him, and mark his cold and tearful eye, his stern and abstracted gaze, and conjure up phantoms of other scenes. We see him amid his festive and splendid halls ten years back, standing stiff and awkward, and shaking a tall, military-looking man by the hand, in whose honour the gala was given, to commemorate the most splendid of America's victories. We see him again, years afterwards, the bitter foe of that same military chieftain, and the competitor with him for the highest gift of a free people. We look upon a more than king (!?), who has filled every department of honour in his native land, still at his post; he who was the President of millions, now the representative of forty odd thousand, quarrelling about trifles or advocating high principles. To-day growling and sneering at the House, with an abolition petition in his trembling hand; and anon lording it over the passions, and lashing the members into the wildest state of enthusiasm by his in-dignant and emphatic eloquence. Alone, unspoken to, unconsulted, never consulting with others, he sits apart, wrapped in his reveries; and, with his finger resting on his nose, he permits his mind to move like a gigantic pendulum, stirring up the hours of the past and disturb-ing those of the hidden future. Or probably he is writing,—his almost perpetual employment;—but what?—who can guess?—perhaps some poetry in a young girl's album! He looks enfeebled, but yet he is never tired; worn out, but ever ready for combat; melancholy, but let a witty thing fall from any member, and that old man's face is wreathed in smiles. He appears passive, but woe to the unfortunate member that hazards an arrow at him; the eagle is not swifter in his flight than Mr. Adams; with his agitated finger quivering in sarcastic gesticulation, he seizes upon his foe; and, amid the amusement of the House, rarely fails to take a signal vengeance.

"His mode of speaking is peculiar. He rises abruptly, his face reddens, and, in a moment throwing himself into the attitude of a veteran gladiator, he prepares for the attack. Then he becomes full of gesticulation, his body sways to and fro, self-command seems lost; his head is bent forward in his earnestness till it sometimes nearly touches the desk; his voice frequently breaks, but he pursues his object throughout its bearings. Nothing daunts him; the House may ring with the cries of 'Order, order!'—unmoved, contemptuous, he stands amid the tempest, and, like an oak that knows his gnarled and knotted strength, stretches his arms forth, and defies the blast."

———

Leaning against the wall, his hands folded on his back, a contemplative spectator of the busy scene before him, stood a gentleman with venerable white hair, and a pale placid countenance, which at once bespoke reserve and affability, firmness of purpose and urbanity, in an extraordinary degree. This, as my friend acquainted me, was Mr. Forsyth, formerly senator from Georgia, but now Secretary of State. He was one of the most strenuous defenders of General Jackson's policy at a time when the latter had a large majority against him in the Senate, and was shortly after called into the cabinet. There he distinguished himself by his tact, moderation, and sound statesmanlike policy. The part he took in the recent difficulties with France is known, though it is believed he principally acted under General Jackson's direction.

Mr. Forsyth is one of those few members of the cabinet who have escaped the ferocious attacks of the opposition. Though a strong partisan of democracy, neither his private nor his public life furnished a text for the abuses of party. Some ignorant and uncultivated persons have *accused* (!) him of too great a devotion to the ladies; but this reproach, so far from injuring him in the estimation of sensible persons, only goes to elevate his character as a man.

It is high time for the Americans to leave off the barbarous and ridiculous notion that a man, in order to be a statesman, a lawyer, an orator, or a man of business, must necessarily be a bore in society. I was once present when an American, who was in the habit of delivering gratuitous lectures on morality, was asked by a Frenchman what sort of impression the sight of a beautiful and lovely woman made upon him? "Precisely the same as that of a fine *horse,*" replied he, by way of showing the utter subjection in which he kept his passions.—"*Dieu merci!*" cried the Frenchman; "I vill not invite you to see my darters." Nothing, certainly, marks the irredeemable vulgarity of a person more strongly than his indifference to beauty and accomplishment.

"There are yet three gentlemen," continued my friend, "whom I would gladly show you, as amongst those who have the greatest influence on the destinies of our country; but unfortunately they are not here, and, with the exception of Mr. Van Buren, who is one of them, are seldom seen at parties. To-morrow, however, after our call on General Jackson, I shall introduce you to them personally. At present you must excuse me; I have to see some of my colleagues in order to prepare them for a question which I know will to-morrow come up in the Senate. The opposition want to steal a march upon us; but I am determined they shall find us prepared."

Shortly after the senator disappeared, and with him a number of his colleagues. Scarcely one member remained after twelve, though the dance continued till half-past two. On this occasion I saw the first *mazurka* danced in the United States; four fashionable ladies consenting to be partners to three Russian gentlemen and a Polish count, who was something of a lion in Washington. The three Russians were none other than the amiable and witty Baron K—r, the Russian minister; the clever and kind-hearted Mr. K—r, the secretary of legation; and Mr. G—, the *attaché.* The partners could not have been better selected: and, though I could observe not a few sneers in the countenances of the elderly portion of the fair, the younger was evidently delighted; and, as I understood afterwards, practised the steps and the "turnabouts" more than a week, to the exclusion of everything else. I remained until two; at which time I took another glass of apple-toddy, which enabled me to return home without stopping on the way at the "Epicure House."

CHAPTER XX

Drive to the White-house.—Anecdote of Mr. Jefferson and the British Ambassador.—Reception at General Jackson's.—The General's Conversation and Character.—The President's Prayer.—Anecdotes of General Jackson.—Reception by Mr. Van Buren.—Anecdote illustrative of Mr. Van Buren's Tact—his Character.—Character of the American Opposition.—Political Hypocrisy.—Mr. Calhoun.—Mr. Kendall.—Conclusion.

"There is no terror, Cassius, in your threats;
For I am arm'd so strong in honesty,
That they pass by me, as the idle wind
Which I respect not."

Julius Cæsar, Act iv. Scene 4.

THE next day, at precisely ten o'clock, my friend called on me in a carriage; and, twenty minutes later, we arrived at the White-house. On the way thither he told me an anecdote of Mr. Jefferson, "the father of American democracy," which I have since heard corroborated in a higher quarter, and which I thought sufficiently amusing to write in my note-book.

Shortly after the commencement of the French revolution, when the general war threatened to involve America as one of the belligerent parties, the noble Lord E—ne, then the Honourable Mr. E—ne, was sent out as envoy extraordinary and minister plenipotentiary of his British Majesty, in order probably to maintain the friendly relations existing between the cabinets of St. James's and Washington. The noble lord was then a young man, full of ardour and ambition, and devoted to the service of his country. He was, therefore, particularly anxious to make the best possible impression on Mr. Jefferson, whose party was then in the ascendant; and accordingly determined on a splendid *début* of his diplomatic functions. A rich court uniform, beautifully embroidered with gold, was selected for the purpose, together with a most costly carriage of state; and the servants of the ambassador shone in the richest and gayest livery ever beheld by Democrat or Tory in the Western world.

In this carriage, early on a fine morning, sat the envoy extraordinary and minister plenipotentiary, dressed in his rich court uniform, with his credentials in his hand, conning over his harangue on his drive to the American President. Having but a short distance to go, the carriage stopped at the White-house just as he had finished the rehearsal; and, immediately after, one of his footmen jumped off, and made the usual English *tapage* at the door, which, being a novelty in America, did not fail to produce alarm and confusion among the inmates. Instead of one negro servant, two rushed forthwith to the door; but, dreading a popular tumult, did not dare open it, until a second rap, more dreadful than the first, proved the urgency of the case, and the necessity of performing their duty. One of them at last summoned courage, and, thrusting out his head without exposing his body, accosted the ambassador's footman in these terms:—

"Hallo! wat row are dat?"

The footman then explained that the Honourable Mr. E—ne, envoy extraordinary and minister plenipotentiary of his British Majesty, wished to wait upon his Excellency the President of the United States. This explanation made, *Bacchus* so far recover from his fright as to induce him to open the door and admit the ambassador. *Jupiter,* the second servant, drew also near; and, gazing upon the rich uniform of the stranger,

"Bacchus," said he, "wat are dat man so dun up for?"

Scarcely had the ambassador time to recover from his astonishment when he was ushered into a small room, containing the President's library; the negroes going before him. There he waited some time, amusing himself with looking out of the window; one of the black imps having assured him that he would call "massa" immediately. At last Mr. Jefferson made his appearance, in his *robe de chambre* and slippers without heels. The Honourable Mr. E—ne was more perplexed than ever; but still trusting to his speech, and throwing himself into the most graceful attitude, he commenced.

"Mr. President!"

"Sit down, sir!" said Mr. Jefferson, pointing to a seat.

The ambassador continued unmoved.

"Sit down, sir! I pray you," reiterated Mr. Jefferson, throwing himself into a large black leathern arm-chair; and the ambassador had to follow his example.

The effect of the harangue being thus wholly destroyed, the British envoy made the best of his hands and lungs. Vain effort! Mr. Jefferson remained impassible; crossing his legs, and from time to time throwing up his slipper, which with wonderful dexterity he always caught again at the point of his toe. At last, when the ambassador came to the end of his speech, in which he expressed the wish that the friendly relations which had heretofore existed between his Majesty's Cabinet and the Government of the United States might continue without interruption, up goes the slipper nearly to the ceiling of the room, and down again on the President's toe, without the latter contracting a muscle.

"I hope," said my friend, as we were alighting from the carriage, "we shall not be received in this manner by General Jackson, who possesses, without exception, the most dignified manners of any man in the country.* He is a soldier, free from artifice and disguise; one of nature's noblemen, possessing more genuine politeness than nine-tenths of our fashionable people, who import their good-breeding from Europe. He is, in fact, a phenomenon in our country, which the present money-making generation cannot understand,—a living paradox in the eyes of our capitalists; aiming at the happiness of the people by destroying the National Bank,—a monster 'who would rather see commerce and credit perish than the constitution of the country!' "

"Is General Jackson at home?" asked the senator of the Irish servant that opened the door.

"He is, sir."

"Here is my card," said I, "if you wish to announce me."

"That is not necessary," replied my friend; "every one can see the President."

We walked up one pair of stairs, and, the General happening to be alone, were immediately admitted into his presence. On our entering the room, the General rose, and shook us both by the hand. He then asked us to sit down, and in a few minutes I felt more at my ease than I ever did in the house of an American broker. Understanding that I was a German, he told us, that while in North Carolina, not far from a number of "Dutch" settlements, he applied himself assiduously to the study of the German language; but, "moving" soon afterwards to the State of Tennessee, was obliged to give it up. "It is a fine language," added he, "spoken by an honest people." He then drew a picture of the German settlements, and of the Germans in general, which betrayed a

---

* It is hardly necessary to remark, that Mr. Jefferson, who during his stay in Europe had ample opportunities of becoming acquainted with court fashion, affected this *nonchalance* for a political purpose.

knowledge of character I have not yet had the good fortune to discover in any of his political antagonists. From the Germans the conversation turned to the Irish, whose leading features he traced with the same accuracy; and so he went on discussing every set of emigrants, and at last the people of his own country. The sketch he gave of the last was excellent, and proved him to be thoroughly *master of his subject.*

After this, the senator, in order to draw him out, introduced various political topics, on which the General expressed himself without a moment's hesitation with the utmost determination and precision. It was as if every thought and principle he uttered had been fixed in his mind ever since he was born, and had never undergone a change up to the present period. Politics with him do not consist in a mere series of cold rules and maxims, in order to obtain a particular object; he is an enthusiast, full of faith in the people and in the perfectibility of human nature, and deeply imbued with the purest religious sentiments. No abstract argument can drive him from his position, for he is nothing separate. He is a politician, a soldier, an enthusiast for the rights of the people, and a Christian at the same time. If the politician is convinced, there remain still the soldier, the enthusiast, and the Christian to be satisfied; if the soldier is captured, there remains still the enthusiast; and so on. He is always a whole; head, heart, and hand,—conception, determination, and action—being one and inseparable. Such men are always a riddle to the world, accustomed as the vulgar are to ascribe every signal success to a particular talent, or to this or that capacity, without ever considering the connection between mind and character.

Of General Jackson's enthusiasm I soon had an opportunity of satisfying myself. Miss Martineau being at that time in Washington, and having been overheard to make a remark at her boarding-house to this effect, "that it was really a wonder General Jackson succeeded against the United States' bank, considering that all the talent and the genius of the country were against him," my friend seized the opportunity to direct the General's attention to the peculiar manner in which British writers were accustomed to view his government. Upon this he rose from his chair, drew himself up to his full height, and, with his eyes flashing fire, remarked to the senator:—"You might have told her, sir, that all the *honesty* and *integrity* of the country were on *my* side." Then, without uttering another syllable, he resumed his seat, and was as friendly and agreeable as before.

Shortly after, an old man of the "far West" entered the room. Jackson rose to salute him, but was told, almost in a sulky manner, "not to disturb himself, it being evident that he was engaged;" and that the stranger, who wore boots, and a cloak with three capes, "would amuse himself, in the mean while, with looking on the pictures."

"Do so," said the General; but following him with his eyes, and perceiving him standing still before an engraving representing a battle fought in the revolutionary war, the thought seemed to strike him that the man, who was very old, might have been a revolutionary soldier.

"You are perhaps acquainted with the details of that battle?" said General Jackson, drawing near him.

"Indeed I am, sir," said the veteran; "I was myself engaged in it, and carried off a nice keepsake here on my left arm."

I do not remember what dialogue now ensued between the soldier and the General,—it was, indeed, too rapid for me to follow it; but I saw the old man, who at first answered the General sulkily, grow warmer and warmer, until at last he was actually moved to tears. He sternly gazed on the President's face; then, as if a sudden revolution had taken place in his mind, he turned round, wished the General a good morning, and left the room. This man may have been an enemy to General Jackson's administration, who had come to see the President for no other purpose but to satisfy his curiosity; but I am quite sure he left him with the determination to vote for him at the next election.

Our visit was soon again interrupted by the arrival of three gentlemen from the Northern States. They came to Washington to pay their respects to the President, who almost instantaneously recognised them as belonging to the opposition. His expressions and manners were remarkably guarded; and, in a short time, he introduced the subject of manufactures. He inquired particularly into the method of cotton-spinning, and at least managed to keep them in good-humour. Soon after we all left together, and, in going down stairs, I heard one of the company say, "He would not be so bad a President after all, if he were not so d—d obstinate!"

"Well, sir," said the senator, as we were again seated in our carriage, "how do you like the President?"

"He is, indeed, an extraordinary man!"

"And have you observed his talent in making himself beloved by all who come near him? You have probably seen him with his enemies; but you ought to see him when he is without restraint among his friends,—how, from pure benevolence, he just says to every man what is most agreeable to him!—how delicately he alludes to every little service rendered him!—how he remembers every act of kindness, every opinion expressed in favour of his measures,—and you would at once perceive the reason of his unparalleled popularity.

"And then see him again in his cabinet,—explaining his political principles, and providing for the means of carrying them into effect,— always determined, never wavering on account of the doubts raised by his friends, and inspiring his own council with confidence in his measures,—and you would be convinced that General Jackson, so far from being influenced by his advisers, is himself the director of his cabinet, in which, perhaps, he rules with as much absolute power as any potentate in Europe. And yet, with all this *penchant* towards absolutism, what a staunch defender of democracy! the Wellington of our Liberals! and who knows but that Wellington, had he been born in America, would not have acted like Jackson; finding the democratic form of government the most legitimate, the most natural, and that which is sure to develope all the resources of the country? Minds of the same tenor sometimes act very differently under different circumstances; and *he who in England is a strong Conservative, may in America, for very analogous reasons, be a sound Democrat.*

It was not long after my presentation at General Jackson's that I had the honour of taking tea with him; which gave me an opportunity of seeing him in his private circle. The invitation was given unceremoniously, just at the moment I was going to take leave of him. We passed into another room, where the company, consisting of his private secretary, his adopted son and his lady, and a gentleman who has since had an important influence on public affairs, were assembled round a small table,—Mrs. Jackson (the wife of his adopted son) doing the honours of the house. After each of us had taken the place assigned him by the lady, General Jackson rose, and with a loud and solemn voice, which bore the imprint of sincerity, thanked the Giver of all for His infinite mercy. The prayer was short, but impressive; and the example of his devotion had a visible effect on every individual present. Add to this, that General Jackson is a tall majestic-looking man, with a stern countenance, grey piercing eyes, and bushy white hair, that stands almost perpendicularly on his head, leaving his large high forehead entirely free, and you will easily conceive the solemnity of the thanks'-offering of the American President.

One of the most characteristic anecdotes of General Jackson relates to the late difficulties between the Governments of the United States and France, when the King of the French seemed to insist on an apology from the President. This, as is well known, General Jackson peremptorily refused; and accordingly a cabinet council was convened in Washington, in which every member delivered his opinion according to his own manner, General Jackson listening to all with the utmost patience. There was the Secretary of State, not knowing how far a war with France would be supported by the people of the different States; the Secretary of the Treasury was already computing the deficit in the budget; the Secretary of the Navy thought it his duty to observe that the naval force of the United States was hardly capable of coping with that of the French; and at last came the Secretary of War, who alluded to the state of the army, a great portion of which was absorbed by the Indian campaign. General Jackson remained immoveable. At last, when every one had finished, he rose; and, placing his hand with some violence on the table, said in a solemn and firm voice: "We have obtained judgment against the French King; and, by the Eternal! we must sue out the execution!"—"But what if we meet with reverses? The French will cut off our commerce; they will arm privateers against our merchantmen; and what if they attempt a landing?"—"That's precisely the thing they will attempt," observed General Jackson calmly; "and you may depend upon it we will give them a good drubbing." This anecdote gave rise to a caricature, representing a French army, led by the Gallic cock, swimming across the Atlantic; and General Jackson standing on the American shore with his cane drawn, and a numerous staff behind him, expecting their arrival. Another caricature, drawn after the settlement, representing General Jackson holding in his left hand a bag of money, with the figures 25,000,000 written on it, and in his right hand a cane, which he is shaking at Louis Philippe, with the words to his mouth, " 'Tis well that you paid me, or by the Eternal!" to which the King is represented bowing, and saying, "Not another word of apology, my dear General!" has already been mentioned in another work.

The following fact, which was related to me by Mr. Power, an American sculptor of much merit, now at Florence, is yet deserving a place in my note-book. When Mr. Power was last in Washington to take a bust of General Jackson, a friend observed to the artist that it would be impossible for him to give the right expression to the mouth, the General having lost his front teeth, which destroyed the expression of firmness about his lips; and that he had therefore better try to persuade the General to wear false teeth for one or two sittings. The artist, grateful for the hint, did not omit to ask General Jackson in a truly Western manner (Mr. Power was born and brought up in Cincinnati) whether he had ever worn false teeth? "I have," said the General; "but I am sorry for it."—"But had you not better put them in once more, to give me an opportunity of modelling the mouth; it would greatly enhance the effect."—"The *truth,* sir! the whole truth, and nothing but the truth!" exclaimed the General with a stern voice; "you have no right to represent me otherwise than I am."

What simplicity of character! and yet what energy and perseverance!

We drove from the White-house towards Georgetown; stopping at one of the houses, called "The Seven Buildings." This was the dwelling of the Vice-President. My friend gave both our names, and in a moment after we were admitted into the presence of Mr. Van Buren. He received us in the same manner as General Jackson, only with less solemnity. His conversation was rapid, but concise and logical; his voice calm and steady, and his manners those of a perfect courtier. Understanding that I was a German, he introduced the subject of travelling, which gave him an opportunity of comparing the scenery on the Rhine with that of the Hudson, and pointing out the distinct beauties of each; which he did with more taste and less affectation than I had yet heard from an American when speaking of foreign countries. He gave the preference to his native river, and supported his opinion with such forcible arguments that he converted me to his doctrine. He then drew a parallel between the state of Europe and that of the United States; pointing to the advantages of the latter, to their government, the manners and customs of the people, and to their happiness. All this he did with so much gentleness, with such an entire absence of conceit, and such admirable management of terms, that it was impossible either to resist his eloquence or to be offended with his conclusions.

Our visit was interrupted by the arrival of several Western members, who, being alarmed at General Jackson's message in relation to the differences with France, desired to know whether it was the Vice-President's opinion that France would pay "without having a tug for it." Mr. Van Buren, without being for one moment embarrassed by this abrupt question, instead of an answer, took up a British periodical, the name of which I do not now recollect, but which treated the French-American question in a very sensible manner. From this he read to the

members several passages, which expressed themselves favourably to
General Jackson's policy; and at last the conclusion, which ran thus,
"Jonathan has claimed the money, and Jonathan will have it." The
members were delighted; and the conversation then passed to other
topics. I mention this as an instance of Mr. Van Buren's tact, a quality
full as indispensable to a statesman as a sound knowledge of politics.

———

"Well, and what do you think of our Vice-President?" asked my
friend, as we were driving towards the lodgings of Mr. John C.
Calhoun.

"I have certainly left him with the highest respect for his mind and
character."

"And yet, sir! there are those who call him an *intrigant,* a 'little
magician,' a 'non-committal man,' &c. though there is not one man in
the country whose attachment to the democratic cause is better known
or understood. The firmness of a man's political principles is, in this
country at least, always commensurate with the degree of abuse heaped
upon him by the opposite party. Our people, I mean 'the higher and
better informed classes,' are seldom inexorable with regard to a politician holding out some chances of conversion; but let a man's character be established, and there is no end to their vituperation. This has
happened to Mr. Van Buren, and ought to be considered by every
democrat as a pledge of his fidelity.

"What act of Mr. Van Buren has ever had any other than democratic
tendency? What principle did he ever advocate that was not strictly
conformable to that doctrine? If he be a non-committal man, it must
be that he never committed himself *to his enemies.*

"The reason why in America, more than in every other country,
political controversies are personal, is, that the opposition, which in
consequence of universal suffrage can only triumph by popular majorities, is obliged to apparently uphold the principles maintained by the
democracy; so that, while it cannot make war upon the general doctrines of the administration, it is concentrating all its venom in its attacks on particular measures, and the men who support them. Let any
Whig, either in or out of Congress, deny the correctness of this proposition, and, I say, he either does not understand our institutions, or he
is wilfully disguising the truth. There is no other real distinction of
parties in the United States, except that one really does or means to do
what it says; while the other is saying one thing, and preparing or hop-

ing to be able to do another. There is more political hypocrisy in this country than perhaps anywhere else,—not among the people, but among 'the upper classes;' owing to the basis of our society being purely democratic, and the superstructure a lamentable imitation of the usages of Europe.

"I know," continued he after a pause, "that no administration or set of men is without its political misconceptions and mistakes; but have the opposition calculated how many of these are to be charged to their own account? Into how many errors they force the administration by their reckless and indiscriminate resistance against all measures emanating from the executive? And do they not thus force the government to avail itself continually of 'the party' in carrying measures which ought to originate in calm reflection and sound statesmanship, and be applied in a generous spirit to all classes of society? The spirit of party is, indeed, at the basis of our institutions; an opposition we *must* have, and the peculiar nature of our government requires a powerful one; but most unfortunately our demagogues—Whigs and Democrats—oppose men, not principles. If there be a man in the country capable of acting as mediator between the two hostile parties,—appeasing the one without sacrificing the principles of the other,—that man is Mr. Van Buren; and future events will prove it."

We now halted before a small house in Pennsylvania Avenue, situated not far from the Capitol. This was the temporary residence of Mr. John C. Calhoun, senator from South Carolina. If the South, in general, have a right to be proud of the great number of eminent statesmen and orators who represent its interests in Congress, South Carolina in particular may glory in Mr. Calhoun. He is a statesman, not a lawyer; and perhaps the only senator in Congress whose course of reading was strictly adapted to the high functions he was to assume. When my friend and I entered the room, he was stretched on a couch, from which he rose to offer us a warm Southern welcome. He almost immediately introduced the subject of politics, in which his superiority over my friend soon reduced the latter to the situation of a mere listener.

As he was explaining his views and theories, which, contrary to the usual American practice, he did in the most concise manner, and with a degree of rapidity which required our utmost attention to follow him, his face assumed an almost supernatural expression; his dark brows were knit together, his eyes shot fire, his black hair stood on end, while on his quivering lips there hung an almost Mephistophelean scorn at the absurdity of the opposite doctrine. Then, at once, he became again all calmness, gentleness, and good-nature, laughing at the blunders of his friends and foes, and commencing a highly comical review of their absurdities.

Mr. Calhoun is, without contradiction, the greatest genius in Congress, and secretly acknowledged as such even by his most declared political enemies. His speeches are the shortest, his political views the most elevated, his delivery the most impressive of any one of his colleagues; and he adds to all these qualities the most unsparing irony. He was Vice-President at the commencement of General Jackson's administration; but subsequently joined the Whigs in order to oppose the tariff, *nullified* by his native State. Without this step, which destroyed his popularity in the North, he would, with very little opposition, have become General Jackson's successor in office. This alone proves the absurdity of the charge of unlawful ambition repeatedly brought against him. The Presidential chair of *the United States,* once within his reach, was assuredly a higher mark than the Presidency of "the *Southern* Union," the *bête noire* of the enlightened opposition. Mr. Calhoun has lately again joined the administration in its endeavour to separate itself from the banks; a short extract from his speech I have already presented in a previous note.

"You must yet see one of our most remarkable men," said my friend; "but I cannot take you to his house. You must see him at his office, where he is from five o'clock in the morning till late at night, always 'up and doing.' I mean the fifth auditor, Mr. Amos Kendall, who, according to the account of the opposition, has governed the country for the last six or eight years, and against whose genius their united talents were unable to prevail. Mr. Kendall is a native of Massachusetts, and a graduate of Dartmouth College. He emigrated to Kentucky, where, like many New-Englanders, he was for a time employed as an instructor, and for a short time engaged as private tutor in Mr. Clay's family. He subsequently became editor of a paper, which is said to have revolutionised *the State,* and, inasmuch as the leading articles of one journal are copied into the others, *the whole country.*"

"No man knows like Mr. Kendall how to address the people: his language is always popular, and yet concise; he never destroys the effect of a strong thought by spinning it out into a long sentence; and, above all, he avoids declamation. His style is forcible; because it convinces the people in their own way, instead of fatiguing them with laborious researches, or overwhelming them with the unfathomable pathos of a regular orator. He has shown to his political opponents that the various principles of democracy may be united into a system, and that that system may be maintained in practice by a government strong within and without."

At this moment our coach stopped at the entrance of the war department, and the next minute we were ushered into the audience-chamber of the fifth auditor. He was at that moment talking to several people that besieged his office, without leaving off writing. When I was introduced to him, he made a slight motion forward, seizing me by the hand; but immediately sank back again into his chair with a seeming intention to recommence his labours. He spoke but a few words, principally by way of asking questions; and having ascertained who I was, what I sought, and what my opinions were, was evidently forming an estimate of my mind and character. While he was thus conversing with my friend and me, filling up the intervals with writing, I observed that he was equally watching the rest of the company; among whom I recognised an individual who I knew did not in his native place enjoy a very high reputation for industry, and who, to judge from Mr. Kendall's glances at him, had no particular chance of success in Washington.

Mr. Kendall's person is one of the most striking I ever beheld. He is of a spare frame, of rather less than middle stature, and, when walking or standing, inclines his body slightly forward. His face is pale, wearing the imprint of over-exertion; but his large eyes are full of animation, and his forehead, the highest and broadest I ever saw, bespeaks the greatest intellectual power. His head, which indeed is one of the most extraordinary phrenological specimens, is of the most unusual size when compared to his body; and it seems as if, by continual exertion of his intellectual faculties, his whole body had been made tributary to his brain. A man with Mr. Kendall's extraordinary powers of mind, and such indefatigable habits of industry,—calm, passionless, and endowed with the most unerring judgment,—must naturally be hated by his political antagonists; though not even the most obstinate members of the opposition have as yet ventured to dispute his talents.

We did not remain long at the office; but, on our way home, my friend finished the picture. "You ought to see him in the centre of his family," said he: "what an excellent husband and father! in his private intercourse how remarkably modest and unassuming! He has indeed but one fault, which, however, is sufficient to damn him with our fashionable people: he is not fond of the dissipations of society, and does not give sumptuous entertainments."

N. B. Mr. Kendall is now Postmaster-general, and as such a member of Mr. Van Buren's cabinet. Though in rank the last, he is known by friend and foe to be the first in activity; and his counsel is decisive with the most experienced men in Washington. Mr. Kendall commenced his political career not more than ten years ago with editing a small paper in the Western country; and stands now foremost in the ranks of the most eminent statesmen of America. If he were a *parvenu* merchant or broker, he would be cited by the aristocracy as an example worthy of imitation; but, having risen merely by his *talents* and his *pen,* the very mention of his name is offensive to the high-minded stock-jobbers in Wall and State streets.

————

In order to form a correct idea of the American government, it is absolutely necessary one should stay some time in Washington; and frequent, not merely the fashionable society, but the company of those sturdy members of Congress, who, deputed from every part of the Union, actually represent the opinions, habits, and sentiments of the different sections of the country. During the session of Congress, Washington is the miniature picture of the United States; enabling a stranger to form a better estimate of the character of the American people than many years' residence in different parts of the Union. The picture is always complete, not a mere fragment, as is necessarily the case in any other city east or west of the Alleghanies. It is there one can take a correct view of the state of parties; of the magnitude of the different interests, whether commercial, manufacturing, or agricultural; and of the political prospects of the country.

One of the most amusing and instructive occupations is to contrast the representatives from the "New States" (the men that have not yet learned how to bow, and do not yet know what P. P. C. on a card means,) with the supple members from New York or Massachusetts, with their French and English civilization hanging loosely about them, like a garment not made for their use; how the latter are striving for ascendency, and how they are daily losing influence with those vigorous sons of the West, that reflect the genius and enterprise of a new world! The West—not the East continually troubled with European visions—is ultimately destined to sway the country. The sea does not separate America from Europe; but behind the Alleghanies is springing up a new life, and a people more nearly allied to the soil that nourishes them, than the more refined and polished population of the seaboard.

To sum up the whole: what is termed "the aristocracy of America"— that is, a considerable portion of all people worth from fifty to an hundred thousand dollars,—are, *owing to the growing power of the West,* a most harmless, though I cannot say "inoffensive," part of the population. They live in houses a little larger than those inhabited by respectable mechanics, cover the floors of their parlours with Brussels carpets instead of Kidderminster, pay nine pence for beef which the labourer purchases for eight, pay a shilling more for a pound of tea, and keep a man-servant. Some of them keep a carriage, but by far the greater part are content with hackney-coaches. In point of accomplishment they are only inferior to the middle classes of Europe; but in pride and conceit they surpass the ancient nobility of the Holy Roman Empire and the thirty-four princes of the actual Germanic Confederation. This circumstance does not much add to their amiability, and does not in particular grace the boys and girls composing "the first society." Some of them lay a great stress on family when it is joined to money; but, without this most indispensable requisite, *la vertu sans argent n'est qu'un meuble inutile.* It is, however, to be observed that property not only produces respectability, but also acts backwards on a man's ancestry; there being not one rich man in the United States,— foreigners excepted,—who is not descended from a respectable father and grandfather.

In politics they are the most implacable enemies to democracy; which, with them, is synonymous with mob-government and anarchy. They are for a *strong* administration, made out of their own party; and would hardly object to royalty, if the King would support himself out of his private chest. A court in Upper Canada, such as Lord Durham established there for a short time, would be a great attraction, and would undoubtedly cause many emigrations to Quebec. In all other respects their political opinions do not seriously differ from those of the mass of the people, except that they are for two trifling reforms in the *status quo,*—the introduction of an electoral census, and the re-establishment of the law of primogeniture. It is true that, had this reform been carried ten years ago, they would themselves be in the situation of those against whom these measures are now intended to be effectual; but this is a matter of no consideration when compared to the good which would accrue from it to "society."

But it is not so much in America as in *Europe* that the true character of the American aristocracy can be successfully studied. At home the vulgar clamour of the mob, and a few silly editors setting up for the representatives of public opinion, interfere too much with the display of their true sentiments. It is but in Europe—where they are relieved from these trammels—that they show the natural man, their *penchant* for the elegancies of society, their contempt for the poor, and their toad-eating to the higher classes, in which they even "beat the English." It is there they sink the "American citizen," in order to become noblemen without pedigrees, and courtiers without manners. I would therefore recommend to the next English tourist that is going to publish a work on "American Society," to visit the courts of Italy and France rather than the United States. He will there find richer materials for a satire on American institutions than he would be able to discover from the State of Maine to Louisiana, and from the broad Atlantic to the Rocky Mountains. I am only able thus to throw out the hint, and leave the execution of the plan to a pen abler than my own.